Solutions to

Physics
for the
Life Sciences

Fourth Edition

ISBN 0-17-610145-4

PREFACE

This text provides detailed solutions to all problems in "Physics for the Life Sciences" (Fourth edition). Many of the solutions are written in a tutorial style. This allows for the use of the text in two ways: (I) as preparation material for tutors instructing students in smaller groups parallel to the lectures, or (II) as self–study material for students who prefer individual studying or where an insufficient number of tutorial sessions are offered.

The current text contains morew than 220 problems, spread over 22 chapters. This means that a typical chapter is accompanied by about 10 problems. These have been chosen with two objectives in mind: (I) to provide a manageable selection for weekly assignments for full–time students, and (II) to provide a diverse range of problems to cover as many as possible of the issues discussed in the textbook. It is, therefore, recommended to work on the problems at a steady rate throughout the course.

The textbook is also intended for students who review the subject for examinations in physics, including the Medical College Admission Test (MCAT). Such students may use the solutions text as an enrichment of their studies as many of the problems carry the topics of each chapter slightly further than the main text.

The author wishes to acknowledge the support of those who have helped with the preparation of this manuscript: M. Rasche for her extensive artwork, J. Mansfield, D. Fraser, S. Chadi, A. Vandenbogaard and A. Young for carefully editing the text.

London, Ontario, May 2005

M. Zinke–Allmang
Professor of Physics
e–mail: mzinke@uwo.ca

TABLE OF CONTENTS

Titlepage:

The four images on the cover illustrate the electric fields experienced by a human subject during magnetic resonance imaging (MRI). During MRI a person lies within a very strong magnetic field and the nuclei of the hydrogen atoms in the water molecules (such as those in human tissue) are excited by radio frequency (RF) radiation. The excited protons then rotate at a frequency that is proportional to the strength of the magnet. In order to influence the frequency of the signals received from the body a second magnetic field, called a *gradient* is applied, on top of the main magnetic field. The gradient coil can be switched on and off, and makes the frequency of the received signal dependant on position. Like on the cover of the textbook, the patient is situated with his head and neck inside the magnet, but is shown this time from the side. As the gradient coil is switched on and off to obtain the image, the rapidly changing magnetic field induces an electric field. This electric field can cause charges to accumulate on the boundary between tissue and air and results in electric field patterns such as those illustrated.

Fundamental aspects of the medical use of MRI are discussed in Chapter 23. Image and data courtesy of Rebecca Feldman, Department of Physics and Astronomy, The University of Western Ontario. Rebecca is part of an MRI research group working on MRI related issues in the Department. The group is headed by Blaine Chronik. He can be reached at bchronik@uwo.ca.

Backcover:

Three illustrations of optical illusions caused by our color vision (see Volume II, p. 187):
(I) Pudding on a dish: Dim the light in the room. Hold the book at arm's length and move it slowly sideways back and forth. You should see the pudding wobble back and forth on the dish.
(II) Thunderbolt striking a tree: Dim the light in the room. Focus on the blue sky to the left of the thunderbolt. Let your eyes jump back and forth between the blue sky to the right and to the left of the thunderbolt, about once or twice a second. You should see the thunderbolt flashing up brightly every time you move your eyes.
(III) Fish in the fish-bowl: In bright light, focus on the red fish for about a minute (this requires patience). Then, suddenly, look at the black dot in the empty fish–bowl. For a short moment, you should see a red fish and then a greenish–blue background in the bowl.
How do these illusions work? You find out in Chapter 19.

CHAPTER I

Physics and Biology: An introduction

Problem 1.1

Fig. 1.2 shows a double–logarithmic plot of the brain mass in unit [g] versus body mass in unit [kg] for several mammals. The line is a fit to the data. In the formula:

$$m_{brain} = a \cdot M_{body}^{b} \qquad (1)$$

(a) determine the exponent b,
(b) determine the prefactor a.
(c) The statement, "we are smarter than chimpanzees because we have a bigger brain" better be wrong, because otherwise Fig. 1.2 would imply that we are dumber than porpoises, elephants and blue whales. Based on Fig. 1.2, how would you formulate a similar comparative statement about the human brain mass which would address our perception that we are also smarter than the three species with the heavier brains?

Solution parts (a, b): Note that Fig. 1.2 shows the brain mass in unit [g] but we want to determine the coefficients a and b in Eq. (1) with the standard mass units [kg]. The best approach is to convert the ordinate in Fig. 1.2 right away to unit [kg], i.e., rewrite the tick marks to run from 10^{-4} kg to 10^{0} kg. Note that 10^{0} kg is the same as 1 kg.

Table 1.1: Data set for analysis from Fig. 1.2.

Set	ln(m)	ln(M)
#1	− 7.900	− 4.605
#2	+ 0.810	+ 9.210

Next we rewrite Eq. (1) in linearized form, i.e., after taking the natural logarithm on both sides:

$$\ln(m_{brain}) = \ln(a) + b\,\ln(M_{body}) \qquad (2)$$

If you are not familiar with this approach, read the section on graph analysis in the General Appendix of the textbook (Chapter 24). We will analyze Eq. (2) in the same fashion as discussed in the General Appendix.

A pair of data sets is read off the solid line in Fig. 1.2. These data are shown in Table 1.1. The data in Table 1.1 are substituted into Eq. (2):

(I)	− 7.90 =	ln(a) + b (− 4.605)
(II)	+ 0.81 =	ln(a) + b (+ 9.210)

$$+ 8.71 = \qquad b\,(13.815)$$

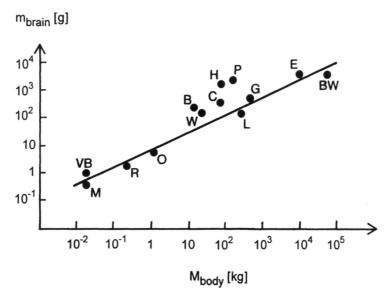

m$_{brain}$ [g]

M$_{body}$ [kg]

Fig. 1.2 for problem P–1.1.

1

This leads to b = 0.63 ≈ 2/3. Substituting this value for b in either one of the two equations, (I) or (II) given above, yields ln(a) = – 5.0, i.e., a = 6.74 × 10^{-3}.

Solution part (c): Brain size alone has no direct link to intelligence but scales simply with body size (solid line in Fig. 1.2). What appears to be linked to intelligence is the distance above the solid line in Fig. 1.2, i.e., the excess brain mass. This excess brain mass reflects a larger cerebrum, which is the part of the brain associated with intelligence. The mammal closest to humans in this respect is the porpoise.

CHAPTER II

Locomotion: the strength of forces

Problem 2.1

A standard man rests on a bathroom scale. What are
(a) the standard man's weight, and
(b) the normal force acting on the standard man?
(c) What is the reading on the scale assuming it is calibrated in weight units? Can you suggest a reason why that reading may deviate from the actual value?

Solution part (a): The mass of the standard man is given in Table 2.2 as M_{tot} = 70 kg. We use Eq. (2.5) to calculate the weight, which is the gravitational force at the surface of the Earth:

$$F_{gravity} = m \cdot g \qquad (1)$$

Relabelling $F_{gravity}$ = W, substituting the standard man's mass and the gravitational acceleration (e.g. from Table 24.7) we find:

$$W = 70 \; [kg] \; 9.8 \left[\frac{m}{s^2} \right] = 686 \, N \qquad (2)$$

Solution part (b): We identify the standard man as our object of interest. Two forces act on the standard man: his weight (W) downwards and the normal force upwards. The normal force (N) is due to the contact with the bathroom scale and is directed upwards. These forces are shown in the free–body–diagram of the standard man (dot) in Fig. 2.24.

The standard man in this problem rests on the scale, i.e., he does not accelerate. We apply Newton's first law when no acceleration occurs. We choose the upwards direction as the positive axis in Fig. 2.24 and write for the net force acting on the standard man:

$$N - W = 0 \qquad (3)$$

in which the negative sign indicates that the weight acts downwards. Using the result from part (a) we find:

$$N = W = 686 \, N \qquad (4)$$

Solution part (c): The reading is 686 N, representing the force the scale has to generate; this force is the normal force introduced in part (b).

But should we trust the scale to show the real weight (or mass) of the person? Even a properly calibrated bathroom scale may show different results depending on the floor material below the scale: a person's measured weight may vary by as much as 10 % when the scale is moved from hardwood flooring onto a soft carpet.

Why is that so? The bottom plate of a mechanical scale bends when a person steps on the scale. This changes the various mechanical distances within the scale, but is taken into account during calibration. However, when the scale is used on a soft surface, the bottom plate of the scale may bend less due to the elasticity of the carpet. If you use a mechanical scale, use it always on the same (hard) surface.

Fig. 2.24: Free–body–diagram for a person on a bathroom scale.

Problem 2.2

Fig. 2.17 shows a standard man intending to do reverse curls in a gym. He holds his arms straight, using an overhand grip to hold the bar. If the mass of the bar is given as 100 kg, what is the tension in each of his shoulders? Consider the weight of the arm (see Table 2.2) and the weight of the bar.

Solution: We treat the arm, not the entire person, as the object of interest. For a body part, forces acting across the interface to the rest of the body may have to be included as contact forces. In the particular case, focusing on the shown arm, three forces are included: the

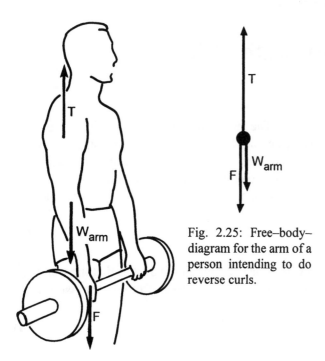

Fig. 2.25: Free–body–diagram for the arm of a person intending to do reverse curls.

Fig. 2.17 for problem P–2.2.

weight of the bar, the weight of the arm and the tension force in the shoulder. For these three forces, Fig. 2.25 shows the free–body–diagram. The two weight–related forces are acting downwards and the tension is pulling the arm upwards.

We choose the vertical axis as positive in the upwards direction. We also note that the problem text implies that the arm does not accelerate at the instant for which we solve the problem. Thus, the problem is an application of Newton's first law. Using the free–body–diagram in Fig. 2.25, we write:

$$T - W_{arm} - F = 0 \qquad (5)$$

We use Eq. (5) to solve for the tension T. The two other forces are quantified with the information given in the problem text, Table 2.2 and Fig. 2.17. The force F is one–half of the weight of the bar. This is due to the fact that the person holds the bar with two hands evenly, i.e., each arm must support 50 % of its weight. The weight of the arm is calculated from Table 2.2. The mass of the arm is 7 % of 70 kg, which is the total mass of the standard man: M_{arm} = 4.9 kg. Thus, Eq. (5) reads:

$$T = W_{arm} + F = \left(4.9[kg] + \frac{1}{2} 100[kg] \right) g \qquad (6)$$

$$\Rightarrow \quad T = 538 \; N$$

Problem 2.3

Fig. 2.18 shows a standard man intending to do close–grip lat pulldowns in a gym. In this exercise, the person pulls the weight of the upper body (arms, trunk and head) upwards using a handle while the legs are wedged under a restraint pad. What is the magnitude of the force exerted by the handle on each of the person's hands?

Solution: Only a part of the person's body is the object of interest in this problem: we consider the combination of head, trunk and both arms, while the legs are excluded as they are wedged under the restraint pad. This means that the person tries to lift the upper body, not the entire body by pulling on the handle. We consider four forces in this case: the weight of the upper body, the two forces exerted by the handle on the hands (called F in Fig. 2.18) and a contact force between the upper and the lower body of the person. This latter force is neglected because we consider a person who intends to pull but at the instant discussed in the problem only hangs on the handles. We combine the remaining forces in the free–body–diagram shown in Fig. 2.26.

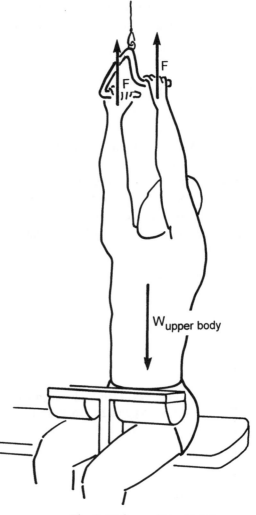

Fig. 2.18 for problem P–2.3.

4

We choose the direction upwards as the positive axis and assume that the same force F acts at each hand. We further note that the upper body remains at rest and, thus, that the problem is an application of Newton's first law. Using Fig. 2.26, we write:

$$2F - W_{upper\ body} = 0 \qquad (7)$$

We use Eq. (7) to solve for the force F. The weight of the upper body is obtained from the problem text and Table 2.2. The mass of the trunk, head and two arms is given as 70 % of the total mass of 70 kg in the table, i.e., $M_{upper\ body}$ = 49 kg. Thus, Eq. (7) yields:

$$F = \frac{1}{2} W_{upper\ body} = \frac{1}{2} 49[kg]\ g \qquad (8)$$

$$\Rightarrow \quad F = 240\ N$$

Problem 2.4
Large hawks, eagles, vultures, storks, the White Pelican and gulls are Canadian birds sailing on rising columns of warm air. This static soaring requires only 5 % of the energy of flapping flight. The birds are essentially in a level flight, holding their wings steadily stretched. The weight of the bird is balanced by a vertical lift force, which is a force exerted by the air on the bird's wings. How large is the lift force for
(a) a Franklin's Gull (which lives in Alberta, Saskatchewan and Manitoba) with an average mass of 280 g, and
(b) an American White Pelican (which lives in Western Canada) with an average mass of 7.0 kg?

Solution part (a): The object of interest is the bird while sailing without flapping its wings. Four forces are involved in flight: thrust and drag in the horizontal direction, lift and weight in the vertical direction. To achieve flight at constant speed, the thrust must compensate the drag force. In the current problem, we are interested in levelled flight, which requires that the lift force compensates the weight. The free–body–diagram in Fig. 2.27 shows the two forces acting in the vertical direction. Levelled flight implies that no vertical acceleration occurs, thus:

$$F_{lift} - W = 0 \qquad (9)$$

in which we have chosen the upwards direction as the positive axis. The weight is entered as a negative value as it is directed downwards. Substituting the weight as

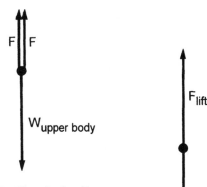

Fig. 2.26: Free–body–diagram for the upper body of a person intending to do close–grip lat pulldowns.

Fig. 2.27: Free–body–diagram for a bird sailing in level flight.

W = mg with m the given mass of a Franklin's Gull, we find:

$$F_{lift} = m\ g = 0.28\ [kg]\ 9.8 \left[\frac{m}{s^2}\right] \qquad (10)$$

$$\Rightarrow \quad F_{lift} = 2.74\ N$$

Note that the mass of the bird has been entered in standard unit [kg]. This is necessary because the standard unit of the resulting force, [N], contains the unit [kg] not [g].

Solution part (b): The only difference in part (b) is the much larger mass of the American White Pelican. Rewriting Eq. (10) with the mass of the pelican, we find:

$$F_{lift} = m\ g = 7.0\ [kg]\ 9.8 \left[\frac{m}{s^2}\right] \qquad (11)$$

$$\Rightarrow \quad F_{lift} = 68.6\ N$$

Thus, a pelican needs a 25 fold higher lift force to sail than the small gull. The economic benefit of sailing in warm updrifts is essential for the large birds and a matter of convenience for the smaller species.

Problem 2.5
Mantis shrimp (stomatopods) possess some of the most lethal weaponry in the animal kingdom. They either spear or smash their prey to death. Smashers literally

5

pulverize the shells of crabs or lobsters with calcified clubs. The spearers use lance–like appendages to strike soft–bodied prey such as shrimp, fishes and squid. The prey has no chance in these encounters: a spearer can accelerate its weapon from rest to 10 m/s in just 4 milli-seconds. Taking into account that an F16 fighter jet has a maximum acceleration of 10 g where g is the gravita-tional acceleration constant, by what factor beats the mantis shrimp the F16 technology?

Solution: We first calculate the acceleration of the shrimp's club. Then, we find the ratio of the shrimp's acceleration to the maximum acceleration of the fighter jet.

The acceleration of the shrimp's club is calcu-lated using the definition of the instantaneous accelera-tion in Eq. (2.9). This formula can be simplified for the case where the acceleration is constant, $a = \text{const}$:

$$a = \frac{\Delta v}{\Delta t} \qquad (12)$$

in which Δv is the change in velocity obtained in the time interval Δt. We use Eq. (12) because we assume that the shrimp operates with a constant acceleration. From the data given in the problem text we obtain:

$$a_{shrimp} = \frac{\Delta v}{\Delta t} = \frac{10 \, [m/s]}{4 \times 10^{-3} \, [s]} \qquad (13)$$

$$\Rightarrow \quad a_{shrimp} = 2,500 \, \frac{m}{s^2}$$

Note that we rewrote the 4 millisecond time interval by using the standard time unit [s] without the prefix. The prefix represents a multiple of 10 and must be entered as such into the calculation. You find a table of these pre-fixes in the General Appendix (Chapter 24). The result in Eq. (13) is equal to $a_{shrimp} = 255.1$ g. This value is ob-tained by extracting $g = 9.8$ m/s² from Eq. (13).

Thus, we calculate the ratio of the two ac-celerations, with the value for the fighter jet given in the problem text:

$$\frac{a_{shrimp}}{a_{F16}} = \frac{255.1 \, g}{10 \, g} = 25.5 \qquad (14)$$

i.e., the shrimp accelerates its bodypart more than 25 times stronger than a fighter jet. It is worthwhile to note though that the acceleration of the fighter jet does not represent an engineering limit but the physical limit for

the pilot. After all, you need the pilot still alive after take–off.

Problem 2.6

There are two horizontal forces acting on an object of mass M = 1.5 kg. In Fig. 2.19 only one of these forces, $F_1 = 25$ N, is shown. The object moves strictly along the shown axis which we choose as positive to the right. Find the magnitude of the second force for each of the following accelerations observed for the object:
(a) a = 10 m/s²
(b) a = 0 m/s²
(c) a = – 10 m/s²

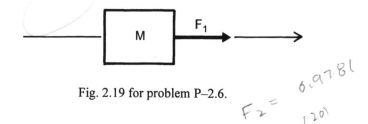

Fig. 2.19 for problem P–2.6.

$F_2 = \frac{0.9781}{(20)}$

Solution part (a): The problem text implies that there are two forces acting on the object of interest along the shown axis. These we label F_1 and F_2, with only F_1 shown in Fig. 2.19. In part (a), the shown object accel-erates toward the right along the positive axis because the acceleration is given as + 10 m/s². We may draw one of two possible free–body–diagrams for the object based on our assumption for the direction of the unknown force. These two choices are shown in Fig. 2.28: sketch (a) applies when the unknown force is parallel to F_1, and sketch (b) applies if F_2 is anti–parallel to the given force. Note that you may choose either one of these two free–body–diagrams. Even if the actual force acts in the op-posite direction, you will recover a correct result; however, you have to carefully study the sign of force F_2. If the result is a negative value, then the actual force acts in the direction opposite to the direction you have chosen in the free–body–diagram. The only way to make a mistake in this context is to choose one free–body–diagram in Fig. 2.28 and then pretend that your results apply to the other one.

a)   b)

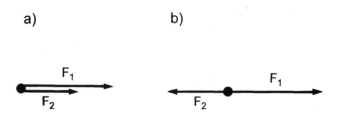

Fig. 2.28: Free–body–diagrams for the two possible ar-rangements of the forces acting on the object in Fig. 2.19.

I choose for part (a) the free–body–diagram shown in Fig. 2.28(a). With this choice I write Newton's second law in the form:

$$F_1 + F_2 = m\,a$$
$$\Rightarrow \quad F_2 = m\,a - F_1 \tag{15}$$

The given values are now substituted into Eq. (15):

$$F_2 = 1.5\,[kg]\,10\left[\frac{m}{s^2}\right] - 25\,[N]$$
$$\Rightarrow \quad F_2 = -10\,N \tag{16}$$

0.978(20) - 3

What does the negative sign imply? When choosing the free–body–diagram in Fig. 2.28(a) I made the assumption that the unknown force acts in the same direction as the given force. This assumption was wrong. The given force F_1 alone would cause an acceleration of

$$a_{F1} = \frac{F_1}{m} = \frac{25\,[N]}{1.5\,[kg]} = 16.7\,\frac{m}{s^2} \tag{17}$$

i.e., the unknown force must act in the opposite direction to reduce this value to the observed value.

Solution part (b): We can apply the same approach as used in part (a) with one exception: for part (b) only the free–body–diagram in Fig. 2.28(b) makes sense. We need a zero net force since a zero acceleration requires that Newton's first law applies. Two forces can only give us a zero net force if they act in opposite directions on the object. Using Fig. 2.28(b) we write:

$$F_1 - F_2 = 0$$
$$\Rightarrow \quad F_2 = F_1 \tag{18}$$

Thus, the unknown force acts toward the left in Fig. 2.19 and has a magnitude of $F_2 = 25$ N.

Solution part (c): This part is again solved in the same fashion as part (a). Either choice of free–body–diagram in Fig. 2.28 is valid and would lead to a negative or positive result in the same fashion as discussed for part (a). However, intuitively we know that the free–body–diagram in Fig. 2.28(b) must apply because we need a large force toward the left to obtain a resulting acceleration in that direction.

Choosing the free–body–diagram in Fig. 2.28(b) we write:

$$F_1 - F_2 = m\,a$$
$$\Rightarrow \quad F_2 = F_1 - m\,a \tag{19}$$

Substituting the numerical values given, we find:

$$F_2 = 25\,[N] - 1.5\,[kg]\left(-10\left[\frac{m}{s^2}\right]\right)$$
$$\Rightarrow \quad F_2 = +40\,N \tag{20}$$

Thus, the unknown force is in magnitude larger than the given force to over–compensate that force's effect.

Problem 2.7
Two objects are in contact on a frictionless surface. A horizontal force is applied to one object as shown in Fig. 2.20.
(a) Use $m_1 = 2.0$ kg, $m_2 = 1.0$ kg and $F = 3.0$ N to find the force between the two objects.
(b) Find the force between the two objects if the force F is instead applied to the object of mass m_2 but in the opposite direction. Explain the difference between the results in (a) and (b).

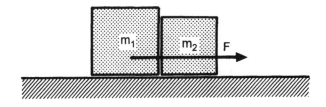

Fig. 2.20 for problem P–2.7.

Solution part (a): The frictionless surface is a part of the environment. Object 1 is the body of (primary) interest as all forces named in the problem act on it. Thus, we choose it as the system. This leaves open what role object 2 plays. It could either be part of the environment or it could be a second system. The difference is that we need to develop a free–body–diagram for a system but not for a component of the environment. It is fair at this point to choose either role for object 2. However, if you choose to consider object 2 to be part of the environment you may have to come back and change that choice. If you choose object 2 to be a second system and this is not

7

necessary, you invest some superfluous effort, however without adversely affecting your ability to solve the problem.

As it turns out, in the current case we have to identify object 2 as a second system, because we need some formulas derived from its free–body–diagram to solve the problem. Consequently, several of the following steps have to be done twice, once for object 1 and once for object 2.

There are four forces acting on object 1, its weight, a normal force upwards due to the contact with the frictionless surface, the external contact force F toward the right, and the interaction force (also a contact force) between the two objects, f_1. This force is directed toward the left as it is exerted by object 2 on object 1. Only the two anti–parallel forces F and f_1 are considered further because we are exclusively interested in effects along the horizontal surface.

Three forces act on object 2. These are its weight, the normal force due to the frictionless surface and the interaction force between the two objects, f_2. Newton's third law relates the two forces, f_1 and f_2 to each other in the form: ＼

$$f_1 = f_2 \qquad (21)$$

in which the two forces point in opposite directions.

The free–body–diagrams for objects 1 and 2 are shown in Fig. 2.29. We choose in both cases the positive axis towards the right. An acceleration is observed along this axis. Thus, Newton's second law applies. We use Fig. 2.29 to apply Newton's law to each system. For simplicity, we drop the indices of forces f_1 and f_2, rewriting Eq. (21) in the form $f_1 = f_2 = f$. This yields:

$$\text{system 1:} \quad F - f = m_1 a$$
$$\qquad (22)$$
$$\text{system 2:} \quad f = m_2 a$$

Note that the same acceleration a is assumed. This is justified because the two blocks always move together. Using the second formula in Eq. (22) to eliminate the acceleration a in the first formula, we find:

$$a = \frac{f}{m_2} \quad \Rightarrow \quad F - f = \frac{m_1}{m_2} f$$
$$\qquad (23)$$
$$f = F \frac{m_2}{m_1 + m_2} = \frac{3.0[N]\ 1.0[kg]}{(1.0 + 2.0)[kg]}$$

Thus, f = 1.0 N.

Fig. 2.29: Free–body–diagrams for the two objects pushed together on a frictionless surface.

Solution part (b): In this part the same reasoning applies, except that the force F is this time applied to object 2 (i.e., objects 1 and 2 change places in the free–body–diagrams of Fig. 2.29). When following through with this approach, we find instead of Eq. (23):

and in terms of F

$$f = F \frac{m_1}{m_1 + m_2} \qquad (24)$$
$$\Rightarrow \quad f = 2.0\ N$$

Why is the force in part (b) different in spite of the fact that the two bodies have the same acceleration a? The force f is the origin for the acceleration of the object on which the external force F does not act. In the second case the force f must accelerate a more massive object, and therefore, must be larger.

Problem 2.8
Fig. 2.21 shows an object of mass M = 3 kg. It is free to move along a horizontal, frictionless surface. This object is further connected to a second object with a mass m = 2 kg by means of a massless string that extends around a massless, frictionless pulley.

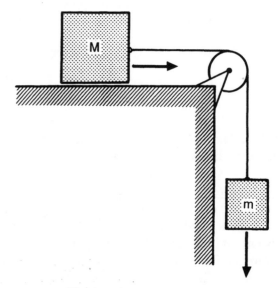

Fig. 2.21 for problem P–2.8.

(a) What resulting motion of the two objects do you predict?
(b) Find the acceleration of the sliding object,
(c) find the acceleration of the hanging object, and
(d) find the tension in the massless string.

Solution part (a): We start with the identification of the systems and the environment in this problem. Clearly, both objects of masses m and M are of interest, as questions (b) and (c) relate to them. Thus, we study each as a system. The pulley, the massless string and the horizontal surface form the environment.

The forces acting on the object with mass M are its weight ($W_M = Mg$) and the normal force (N) in the vertical direction, as well as the tension (T_M) in the horizontal direction. The forces acting on the object with mass m are its weight ($W_m = mg$) and the tension (T_m), both acting in the vertical direction.

To solve the three parts of the problem, we note that the weight of the object of mass M and the normal force acting on that object can be neglected. These two forces must be equal to each other, but they do not contribute to the accelerations or the tensions. Choosing as the axis the direction along the string, we construct two free–body–diagrams shown in Fig. 2.30: Fig. 2.30(a) applies to the object with mass M and Fig. 2.30(b) applies to the object with mass m.

We chose the positive axis in Fig. 2.30(a) toward the right and in Fig. 2.30(b) upwards. Note that separate choices for each free–body–diagram are sometimes beneficial. We further simplify the notation for the tension force, recognizing that $T_M = T_m = T$ which means that we choose a common variable T because both tensions in a massless string are the same, as shown in section 2.3.4. Using T instead of T_M and T_m is the result of a massless string, as outlined in Example 2.5.

The two free–body–diagrams in Fig. 2.30 allow us to answer question part (a). Remember that for any object with balanced forces, the first law applies and the state of motion does not change. This cannot be the case for the object with mass M, because there is no force which balances the tension. Thus, Newton's second law applies, i.e., the object accelerates in the direction of the unbalanced force (non–zero net force).

On the basis of our everyday experience, we guess what happens to the object with mass m when the object with mass M accelerates toward the right: since the length of the string remains unchanged, the object with mass m accelerates downwards.

Solution part (b) and (c): Using the free–body–diagrams of Fig. 2.30, the following two formulas are written for Newton's second law:

$$object\ M: \qquad T = M a_M$$
$$object\ m: \quad T - mg = m a_m \qquad (25)$$

We use the fact that the string does not change its length further to comment on the anticipated accelerations: both objects must accelerate with the same magnitude of acceleration in the same direction along the string. If this were not the case, the length of the string between the two objects would change. Note that this does not necessarily mean, however, that the two accelerations are the same; the two values may carry different signs. Based on our choice of axes for the current problem and assuming that a is a positive value, the accelerations are $a_m = -a$ and $a_M = +a$. With this taken into account, Eq. (25) is rewritten in the form:

$$object\ M: \qquad T = M a$$
$$object\ m: \quad T - mg = -m a \qquad (26)$$

With Eq. (26), we answer problem parts (b) – (d). Parts (b) and (c) are answered together since we already know that the absolute value of both accelerations, a, is the same. Eliminating the tension T between the two formulas in Eq. (26) yields:

$$mg = Ma + ma \qquad (27)$$

which yields:

$$a = \frac{m}{M+m} g = 9.8 \left[\frac{m}{s^2}\right] \frac{2[kg]}{3[kg]+2[kg]} \qquad (28)$$

$$\Rightarrow \quad a = 3.9\ m/s^2$$

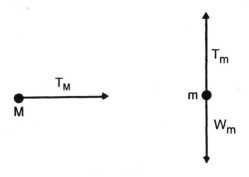

Fig. 2.30: Free–body–diagrams for two objects connected with a string across a pulley at the edge of a horizontal table.

9

The acceleration of both objects has a magnitude of a = 3.9 m/s².

Solution part (d): Next we substitute the result of Eq. (28) in the first formula of Eq. (26):

$$T = \frac{Mm}{M+m} g = \frac{3[kg]\,2[kg]}{3[kg]+2[kg]} 9.8\left[\frac{m}{s^2}\right] \quad (29)$$

$$\Rightarrow \quad T = 11.8\ N$$

The tension in the string has a magnitude T = 11.8 N.

Problem 2.9

Three objects are connected as shown in Fig. 2.22. They move along a horizontal, frictionless surface, and are pulled to the right with a force F_{ext} = 50 N. With the three mass values given as m_1 = 10 kg, m_2 = 20 kg and m_3 = 30 kg, calculate

(a) the magnitude of the acceleration of the three objects, and

(b) the magnitude of the tensions T_1 and T_2 in the massless, interconnecting strings.

Solution: Even if there are several distinct bodies present in a problem, it is not always necessary to treat them as separate systems. This problem is an example of this: we initially choose to treat all three connected objects together as a single system, and only in the later parts choose as systems one or two of the objects.

Solution part (a): Since the three objects are connected with taut, massless strings, they must move and accelerate together, which enables us to treat all three objects together as a single system. The external force is the only horizontal force acting on this system. We don't study forces in the vertical direction because the problem is confined to the horizontal direction. For a single force we do not need to draw a free–body–diagram. We define the positive direction of the horizontal axis in the direction of the external force.

As an acceleration is explicitly mentioned in the problem, this problem must be an application of Newton's second law:

$$F_{ext} = \left(m_1 + m_2 + m_3\right) a \quad (30)$$

which yields for the acceleration a:

$$a = \frac{50\ [N]}{10[kg]+20[kg]+30[kg]} \quad (31)$$

$$\Rightarrow \quad a = 0.83\ \frac{m}{s^2}$$

Solution part (b): We obtained in part (a) no information regarding the tensions in the strings between the three objects. Therefore, the definition of the system must be modified to answer parts (b) and (c).

The tension T_1 is a force acting between the first and second object. We consider object 1 as a separate system and objects 2 and 3 as part of the environment to solve for the force T_1. This case leads again to a simple free–body–diagram as again only one horizontal force acts on the system (object 1): T_1. Keeping the same definition of the positive direction of the horizontal axis, Newton's second law is written in the form:

$$T_1 = m_1\, a \quad (32)$$

which yields:

$$T_1 = 10[kg]\ 0.83\left[\frac{m}{s^2}\right] = 8.3\ N \quad (33)$$

Solution part (c): To obtain T_2, we choose object 2 as the system and the other objects as part of the environment. Since there are two forces acting on object 2, its free–body–diagram is shown in Fig. 2.31. Note that the two forces act in opposite directions since object 1, which causes the tension T_1, is positioned to the left of the system and object 3 and the external force, together causing tension T_2, are located to the right of the system.

We apply Newton's second law because the system is accelerating. It reads:

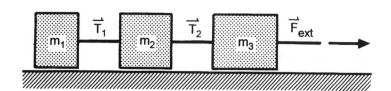

Fig. 2.22 for problem P–2.9.

Fig. 2.31: Free–body–diagram for the center object of three objects connected with strings.

Fig. 2.32: Free–body–diagram for the first vertebra of a person with a traction device as shown in Fig. 2.23.

$$T_2 - T_1 = m_2\, a \qquad (34)$$

Eq. (34) is solved for the tension T_2:

$$T_2 = T_1 + m_2 a = 8.3[N] + 20[kg]0.83\left[\frac{m}{s^2}\right] \qquad (35)$$

$$\Rightarrow \quad T_2 = 24.9\ N$$

Problem 2.10

When patients suffer from a neck injury their cervical vertebrae are kept under tension with a traction device, as shown in Fig. 2.23. The traction device creates tension in the vertebrae by pulling on the head with a force T. This force is in effect applied to the first vertebra at the top of the spine. This vertebra remains in mechanical equilibrium because it is simultaneously pulled in the opposite direction by a force F_{ext} that is supplied by the next vertebra in line. If the physician has prescribed that a force $F_{ext} = 40$ N should act on the vertebra, what mass m should the object suspended from the rope have?

Solution: The object of interest is the first vertebra. Of the many forces which act within our body on a vertebra, we select the two main horizontal forces in this case: the force T due to the traction device and the force F_{ext} due to the second vertebra. This latter force is due to New-

ton's third law as the second vertebra pulls on the first vertebra with an equal but opposite force exerted by the first vertebra on the second vertebra.

Fig. 2.32 shows the free–body–diagram for the first vertebra. We choose the direction toward the right as the positive axis. The problem is an application of Newton's first law because the first vertebra remains at rest:

$$T - F_{ext} = 0 \qquad (36)$$

Thus, the tension must be equal to the prescribed force. The tension, in turn, is caused by the weight of the object suspended from the string at the right side of Fig. 2.23:

$$T = m\, g \quad \Rightarrow \quad m = \frac{T}{g} \qquad (37)$$

which yields:

$$m = \frac{F_{ext}}{g} = \frac{40\ [N]}{9.8\left[\frac{m}{s^2}\right]} = 4.1\ kg \qquad (38)$$

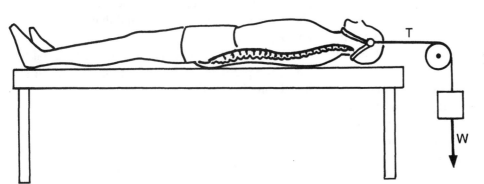

Fig. 2.23 for problem P–2.10.

CHAPTER III

Biomechanics: the direction of forces

Problem 3.1

We study once more Example 3.2, except that the direction of the external force is changed to act tangentially to the circular path of the object of mass m = 1.0 kg, as shown in Fig. 3.28. We assume again that the object is held at a position where the string forms an angle of θ = 30° with the vertical.

(a) What is the magnitude of the tension **T** in the string?

(b) What is the magnitude of the force $\mathbf{F}_{ext}$?

(c) Why is it not possible to repeat the problem with the external force $\mathbf{F}_{ext}$ acting vertically upwards?

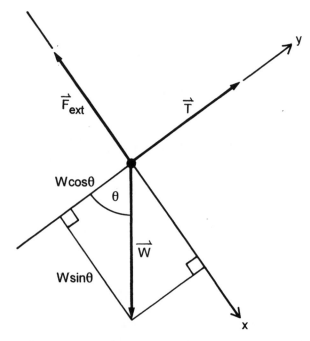

Fig. 3.37: Free–body–diagram for an object on a string.

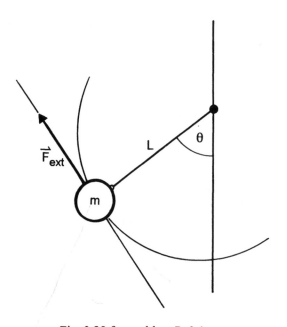

Fig. 3.28 for problem P–3.1.

Solution part (a): The object of mass m attached to the string is the system; the string and the ceiling with the pivot point of the string are part of the environment. Three forces act on the object: its weight and two contact forces, the tension in the string and the external force.

Fig. 3.37 shows the free–body–diagram for the object. The external force and the tension are perpendicular to each other because the tension is directed along the radius of the path of the object and the external force is directed tangential to that path. As a rule of thumb, we want to maximize the number of the forces which act along the fundamental axes; thus, we choose

the y–axis in the radial direction of the path and the x–axis in the tangential direction. With this choice, the tension in Fig. 3.37 has no x–component and its y–component is $T_y = +|\mathbf{T}|$, in which $|\mathbf{T}|$ indicates the magnitude of the vector **T**. In an analogous fashion, the external force in Fig. 3.37 has a zero y–component while its x–component is $F_{ext,x} = -|\mathbf{F}_{ext}|$. This component is negative since the external force is directed opposite to the positive x–direction.

The weight **W** points vertically down and is therefore not parallel to either of the fundamental axes. We need to apply trigonometry to identify its two components: using the angle θ as given in Fig. 3.28, and as shown again in Fig. 3.37, we find that $W_x = +W\sin\theta$ and $W_y = -W\cos\theta$.

The object is held at rest by the external force. Thus, the problem is an application of Newton's first law. Using Fig. 3.37, we write:

$$x-dir.: \quad -F_{ext} + W\sin\theta = 0$$

$$y-dir.: \quad +T - W\cos\theta = 0 \tag{1}$$

in which the first formula shows that the sum of the x–components of all forces is zero, and the second formula shows the same for the force components in the y–direction. We use the second formula in Eq. (1) to solve for the magnitude of the tension:

$$T = W\cos\theta = 1.0[kg]\, 9.8\left[\frac{m}{s^2}\right]\cos30^0 \quad (2)$$

$$\Rightarrow \quad T = 8.5\ N$$

Solution part (b): We use the first formula in Eq. (1) to solve for the magnitude of the external force:

$$F_{ext} = W\sin\theta = 1.0[kg]\, 9.8\left[\frac{m}{s^2}\right]\sin30^0 \quad (3)$$

$$\Rightarrow \quad F_{ext} = 4.9\ N$$

Solution part (c): Consider the consequences a changed direction of the external force would cause in the free–body–diagram of Fig. 3.37: the tension would be the only force with a non–vertical component. As a result, only one horizontal force component would act on the object; based on Newton's laws this cannot lead to a mechanical equilibrium. Thus, the object would have to accelerate, contrary to the implication in the problem text.

Problem 3.2
An object of mass M = 75 kg is pushed at a constant speed up a frictionless inclined surface which forms an angle $\theta = 40^0$ with the horizontal as shown in Fig. 3.29.

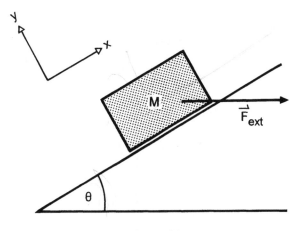

Fig. 3.29 for problem P–3.2.

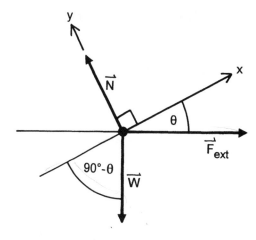

Fig. 3.38: Free–body–diagram for an object on an inclined plane.

(a) What is the magnitude of the horizontal force $\mathbf{F}_{ext}$?
(b) What force is exerted by the inclined surface on the object?

Solution part (a): The object shown as a rectangular box on the inclined plane in Fig. 3.29 is the system; the inclined plane is part of the environment. Three forces act on the system: its weight, the external force and the normal force due to the contact with the inclined surface. Note that the normal force (as its name implies) acts perpendicularly to the underlying surface, i.e., in this problem the normal force is not opposite to the weight!

The free–body–diagram is shown in Fig. 3.38. The angle between the weight **W** and the negative x–axis is labelled $90^0 - \theta$. Make sure you understand why that angle is correct. We choose the coordinate system as shown in Fig. 3.38. Remember, when an inclined plane is part of a problem, it is advisable to choose one axis to be directed along the inclined plane.

This problem is an application of Newton's first law since the object does not accelerate along the inclined surface. Using Fig. 3.38, the following equations are found for the x– and y–components of the net force:

$$(I) \quad F_{ext}\cos\theta - W\cos(90^0 - \theta) = 0$$

$$(II) \quad N - F_{ext}\sin\theta - W\sin(90^0 - \theta) = 0 \quad (4)$$

The magnitude of the external force is obtained from the first formula in Eq. (4):

$$F_{ext} = \frac{W\cos50^0}{\cos40^0} = 617\ N \quad (5)$$

13

in which $\theta = 40^0$, $90^0 - \theta = 50^0$ and the weight of the object is $W = Mg = 75[kg]\ 9.8[m/s^2] = 735$ N.

Solution part (b): The force exerted by the inclined plane is the normal force. Substituting the result of Eq. (5) into the second formula in Eq. (4), we find:

$$N = F_{ext} \sin 40^0 + W \sin 50^0 = 960\ N \quad (6)$$

Problem 3.3

Fig. 3.30 shows the human leg (a) when it is stretched and (b) when it is bent. Note that the kneecap (3) is embedded in the quadriceps tendon (6) and is needed to protect the quadriceps tendon against wear and tear due to the femur (1) in the bent position.

Assume that the magnitude of the tension in the quadriceps tendon of a bent knee is T = 1500 N. Use an angle of 30^0 between the horizontal and the direction of

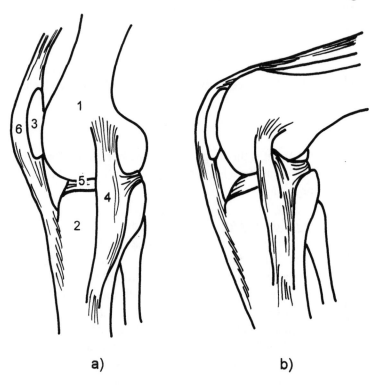

a)   b)

Fig. 3.30 for problem P–3.3. (1) femur, (2) tibia, (3) patella (kneecap), (4) collateral ligaments, (5) meniscus, (6) tendon of quadriceps femoris muscle.

Fig. 3.31 for problem P–3.3.

a)   b)

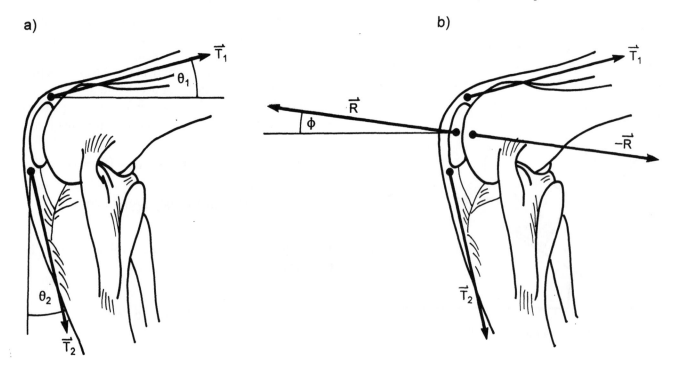

the tension above the kneecap, and use an angle of 70^0 between the horizontal and the direction of the tension below the kneecap, as shown in Fig. 3.31(a). What are the magnitude and the direction of the resultant force exerted on the femur, as shown in Fig. 3.31(b)?

Solution: Even though we are asked to calculate a force acting on the femur, it is not possible to choose the femur as the system. To do so, we would need to include in the discussion several other major forces acting on the femur, such as forces acting at the hip joint. On the other side, we know most of the forces which act on the kneecap. We choose therefore the kneecap as the system. This leads towards an answer, because one of the forces acting on the kneecap is due to the femur; using later Newton's third law, we will be able to relate this force to the force we are asked to calculate.

Three forces act on the kneecap: two tension forces due to the quadriceps tendon, and the contact force exerted by the femur. Note that the two tensions are not the same as they have different directions. Thus, we follow the notation in Fig. 3.31(a) and label these two forces $\mathbf{T}_1$ and $\mathbf{T}_2$.

Fig. 3.38 shows the free–body–diagram for the kneecap. Note that the angle θ_2 is the angle between the vertical and the tendon below the kneecap; this angle is $\theta_2 = 90^0 - 70^0 = 20^0$. The figure further shows the force $\mathbf{R}$, which is the contact force due to the femur. It is important to not draw this force in the wrong direction. We know that $\mathbf{R}$ is directed somehow toward the left to balance the components of the two tension forces which point toward the right. But we cannot judge whether $\mathbf{R}$ is horizontal. Thus, the force $\mathbf{R}$ is chosen toward the left, forming a variable angle ϕ with the horizontal. If $\mathbf{R}$ turns

out to be horizontal, the calculation will yield a value of $\phi = 0^0$. However, if $\phi \neq 0^0$, drawing $\mathbf{R}$ horizontally in Fig. 3.39 cannot be corrected in the later calculations.

Fig. 3.39 also shows our choice of coordinate system: the x–axis horizontally toward the right and the y–axis vertically upwards. The problem is an application of Newton's first law in both directions because the kneecap does not accelerate either upwards nor forward when the knee is bent.

We use Fig. 3.39 for the kneecap:

$$(I) \quad T\cos\theta_1 + T\sin\theta_2 - R\cos\phi = 0$$
$$(II) \quad T\sin\theta_1 - T\cos\theta_2 + R\sin\phi = 0 \qquad (7)$$

Note that we wrote T, and neither T_1 and T_2 in Eq. (7), for the magnitude of the tension as both magnitudes are the same. Eq. (7) contains two unknown parameters: R and ϕ. Calculating both provides us with the force $\mathbf{R}$.

To solve Eq. (7), we isolate the unknown parameter ϕ on the right hand side of each formula:

$$(I) \quad T\cos\theta_1 + T\sin\theta_2 = R\cos\phi$$
$$(II) \quad -T\sin\theta_1 + T\cos\theta_2 = R\sin\phi \qquad (8)$$

Now we divide the two formulas:

$$\frac{(II)}{(I)} \quad \tan\phi = \frac{-\sin\theta_1 + \cos\theta_2}{\cos\theta_1 + \sin\theta_2} \qquad (9)$$

Next we substitute the given angles in Eq. (9):

$$\tan\phi = \frac{-\sin30^0 + \cos20^0}{\cos30^0 + \sin20^0} = 0.364 \qquad (10)$$
$$\Rightarrow \quad \phi = 20^0$$

The magnitude of the force R is obtained by substituting the result in Eq. (10) in either one of the two formulas in Eq. (8). Choosing the first formula, we find:

$$R = \frac{T(\cos\theta_1 + \sin\theta_2)}{\cos\phi} = \frac{1500[N](\cos30^0 + \sin20^0)}{\cos20^0} \qquad (11)$$

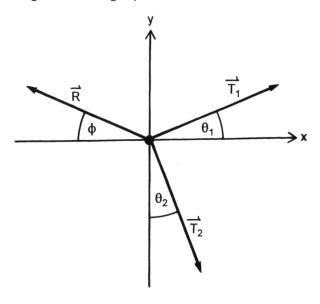

Fig. 3.39: Free–body–diagram: kneecap of a bent knee.

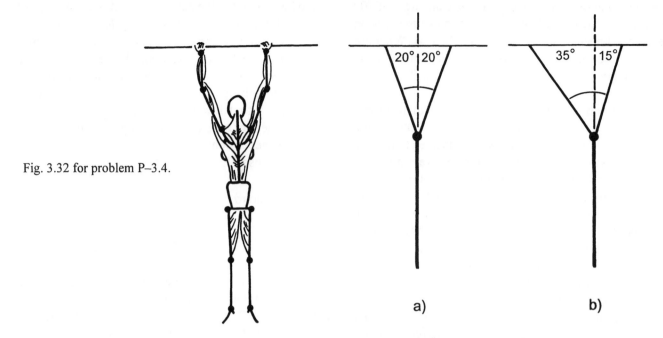

Fig. 3.32 for problem P–3.4.

a)   b)

which yields R = 1930 N.

Two closing comments: first, it is useful to note that R is a very large force. You need such a force to lift an object of a mass of about 200 kg. While bending our knees is done routinely, one can easily imagine how such forces lead to injury or wear and tear.

Secondly, note that Eqs. (10) and (11) are not the answer to the problem. In a last step, Newton's third law must be applied. This is illustrated in Fig. 3.31(b): we determined the force **R** acting on the kneecap, but we sought the force – **R** acting on the femur. Thus, the answer is that a force of magnitude of 1930 N acts on the femur at an angle 20^0 below the horizontal.

Problem 3.4

Fig. 3.32 shows a person of mass m = 70 kg hanging at rest on a horizontal bar.

(a) Assume that the arms are stretched at an angle of 20^0 to the vertical to either side, as shown in the middle sketch. Find the force acting on each arm.

(b) Assume that the arms are held at two different angles as shown in the right sketch. What are the forces acting in each arm in this case?

Solution part (a): The system is the human body hanging from the bar. The bar is part of the environment which interacts with the system. Three forces act on the system: the weight and two contact forces caused by the bar. If you aren't sure, imagine that one of these forces is eliminated. If the weight weren't there the body would float and the person would not hang from the bar rather hold on to the bar. If either one of the contact forces weren't

there the body of the person would swing underneath the hand which still holds on to the bar. Either one of these events would alter the problem. Thus, all three forces are needed.

If you want further to make sure that you didn't miss a fourth force (always a good idea before proceeding!), check for any other physical contact between the system and the environment. Other than the weight (which we included already) all mechanical forces must be contact forces. Since there are no further contact points between the system and the environment in Fig. 3.32, it is safe to proceed.

The free–body–diagram for the sketch in Fig. 3.32(a) is shown in Fig. 3.40. The weight **W** is drawn straight down because that is the direction toward the center of the Earth. The two contact forces are labelled **T₁** for the arm shown at the left and **T₂** for the arm as shown at the right. Next we choose the coordinate system. Since the forces in the current problem are neither parallel nor perpendicular to each other, we choose the

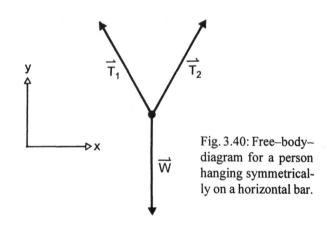

Fig. 3.40: Free–body–diagram for a person hanging symmetrically on a horizontal bar.

16

negative y–axis to coincide with the weight. This coordinate system is shown in Fig. 3.40. We use Fig. 3.40 to quantify the mechanical equilibrium. Newton's first law is applied to the x– and y–components of the net force:

$$(I) \quad -T_{1,x} + T_{2,x} = 0$$

$$(II) \quad T_{1,y} + T_{2,y} - W = 0$$

(12)

in which we have entered components which run in the negative direction with a negative sign. Both right sides are zero since the body is in mechanical equilibrium.

Eq. (12) contains four unknown variables, which are the four components of the two tension forces. Note that the weight is known since we know the mass of the person. To solve for four unknown variables with just two formulas is impossible. However, we have not yet used all the information we are given in the problem. Using the angle $\theta = 20^0$ between each arm and the vertical, we rewrite Eq. (12) in the form:

$$(I) \quad -T_1 \sin 20^0 + T_2 \sin 20^0 = 0$$

$$(II) \quad T_1 \cos 20^0 + T_2 \cos 20^0 - W = 0$$

(13)

In this form, the equation contains two formulas with two unknown variables, which are the magnitudes of $\mathbf{T_1}$ and $\mathbf{T_2}$. Thus, we can solve the problem. From the first formula in Eq. (13) we find that the magnitudes of both tension forces are the same, i.e., $T_1 = T_2 = T$. Entering this result in the second formula in Eq. (13), we find:

$$2T\cos 20^0 = W = mg$$

$$\Rightarrow \quad T = \frac{mg}{2\cos 20^0} = 365 \ N$$

(14)

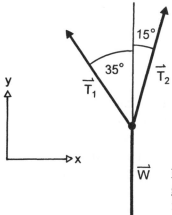

Fig. 3.41: Free–body–diagram for a person hanging asymmetrically on a horizontal bar.

Table 3.3: Force components for Fig. 3.32(b) and the free–body–diagram in Fig. 3.41.

Force	x–component	y–component
$\mathbf{T_1}$	$-T_1 \sin 35^0$	$T_1 \cos 35^0$
$\mathbf{T_2}$	$T_2 \sin 15^0$	$T_2 \cos 15^0$
$\mathbf{W}$	0	$-W$

Solution part (b): This part follows the same scheme as part (a). The same forces with different directions act on the system. The modified free–body–diagram is shown in Fig. 3.41. Due to the change in the directions of two forces, the solution differs from the solution in part (a). Eq. (12) continues to apply; however, the various force components are now as listed in Table 3.3.

Using Table 3.3, we find instead of Eq. (13):

$$(I) \quad -T_1 \sin 35^0 + T_2 \sin 15^0 = 0$$

$$(II) \quad T_1 \cos 35^0 + T_2 \cos 15^0 - W = 0$$

(15)

The first formula in Eq. (15) relates the magnitudes of the forces $\mathbf{T_1}$ and $\mathbf{T_2}$:

$$T_1 = T_2 \frac{\sin 15^0}{\sin 35^0} = 0.45 \ T_2$$

(16)

Substituting Eq. (16) into the second formula of Eq. (15) yields:

$$0.45 \ T_2 \cos 35^0 + T_2 \cos 15^0 = 686 \ N$$

$$\Rightarrow \quad T_2 = \frac{686 \ [N]}{0.45\cos 35^0 + \cos 15^0} = 514 \ N$$

(17)

Substituting Eq. (17) into Eq. (16) then yields:

$$T_1 = 0.45 \ T_2 = 0.45 \cdot 514[N] = 231 \ N \quad (18)$$

Problem 3.5
Leg traction is applied to a patient's leg as shown in Fig. 3.33. If the physician has requested a 50 N force to be applied to the leg and the object hanging from the massless cable has a mass of m = 10 kg, what angle θ must be used?

17

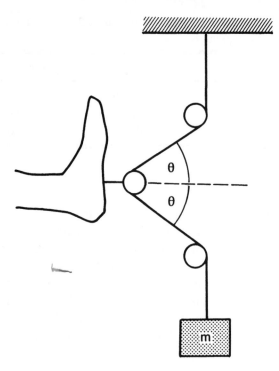

Fig. 3.33 for problem P–3.5.

Solution: We choose the pulley attached to the foot as the system. Three forces act on this pulley: the force **F** toward the left due to the foot, and two tension forces along the cable, **T**₁ and **T**₂. We do not include the weight of the pulley because its mass is negligible.

Fig. 3.42 shows the free–body–diagram for the pulley. We use Newton's first law for the net force component in the horizontal direction because the pulley does not accelerate in this problem:

$$-F + T_1 \cos\theta + T_2 \cos\theta = 0 \qquad (19)$$

From Example 2.5, we know the magnitude of each of the tension forces in a massless cable: the two tensions are equal to the weight of the mass m hanging downwards: $W_m = T_1 = T_2$. Thus, Eq. (19) simplifies to:

$$-F + 2W\cos\theta = 0 \qquad (20)$$

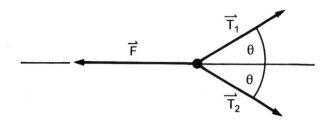

Fig. 3.42: Free–body–diagram: pulley of a traction device.

Eq. (20) is solved for the angle θ:

$$\cos\theta = \frac{F}{2W} = \frac{50\,[N]}{2 \cdot 10[kg]\,9.8\left[\dfrac{m}{s^2}\right]} \qquad (21)$$

$$\cos\theta = 0.255 \quad \Rightarrow \quad \theta = 75^0$$

Problem 3.6
We consider the standard man shown in Fig. 3.34 using crutches. The crutches each make an angle of θ = 22⁰ with the vertical. Half of the person's weight is supported by the crutches, the other half is supported by the normal forces acting on the soles of the feet. Assuming that the person is at rest, find the magnitude of the force supported by each crutch.

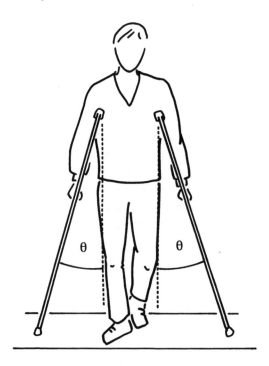

Fig. 3.34 for problem P–3.6.

Solution: The object of interest is the person. Four forces act on the person: his weight **W**, the normal force of the ground at the feet **N**, and two contact forces each along the crutches. We label these **F**₁ and **F**₂. The free–body–diagram is shown in Fig. 3.43. Note the direction of **F**₁ and **F**₂: these forces are shown in the direction in which they act on the person, i.e.,**F**₁ is due to the crutch shown in Fig. 3.34 at the right.

Fig. 3.43 shows also the chosen coordinate system with a horizontal x– and a vertical y–axis. The problem is an application of Newton's first law because the

18

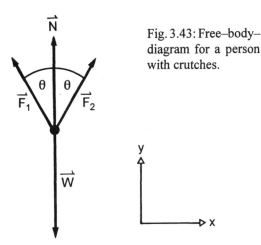

Fig. 3.43: Free–body–diagram for a person with crutches.

cond force $\mathbf{F_2}$
(a) in component notation, and
(b) as a magnitude and direction.

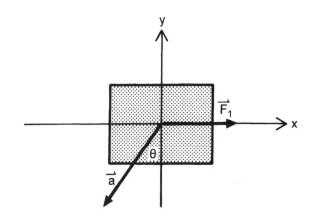

Fig. 3.35 for problem P–3.7.

person does not accelerate in any direction. This leads to the following two formulas for the x– and y–components of the net force:

$$(I) \quad -F_1 \sin\theta + F_2 \sin\theta = 0$$

$$(II) \quad F_1 \cos\theta + F_2 \cos\theta + N - W = 0 \tag{22}$$

From the first formula in Eq. (22) we conclude that $F_1 = F_2 = F$, where we dropped the index because the two magnitudes are the same. We further know that $N = \frac{1}{2}W$ because half the weight of the person is supported by the normal force. Substituting these two results in the second formula of Eq. (22) yields:

$$2\,F\cos\theta - \frac{W}{2} = 0 \tag{23}$$

Substituting the given values in Eq. (23) yields for the unknown force F:

$$F = \frac{W}{4\,\cos\theta} = \frac{70[kg]\,9.8\left[\dfrac{m}{s^2}\right]}{4\,\cos 22^0} \tag{24}$$

$$\Rightarrow \quad F = 185\ N$$

Problem 3.7

There are two forces acting on an object of mass 1.5 kg. Fig. 3.35 shows a top–view of the object. One of the forces is shown and has a magnitude of $|\mathbf{F_1}| = 10$ N. The figure also shows the direction of the acceleration of the object with the magnitude of $|\mathbf{a}| = 10$ m/s² and the angle $\theta = 30^0$ with the negative y–axis. Find the missing se-

Solution part (a): The rectangular box in Fig. 3.35 is the system. None of the components in the environment are shown, although they must be present because they are the origins of the forces referred to in the problem. The text identifies two forces acting on the object. We label these $\mathbf{F_1}$ and $\mathbf{F_2}$. Of these, $\mathbf{F_1}$ is shown in Fig. 3.35 and $\mathbf{F_2}$ is unknown. We do not include the weight in this problem because it acts in the direction perpendicular to the plane shown in the top–view in Fig. 3.35.

The free–body–diagram for this problem, which is not shown, contains only forces $\mathbf{F_1}$ and $\mathbf{F_2}$. The second force is directed in any arbitrary direction, but do not assume that it is perpendicular or parallel to $\mathbf{F_1}$ since we have no evidence that that is the case. The coordinate system has already been defined in Fig. 3.35.

The system is not in mechanical equilibrium since an acceleration has been identified. Thus, we use Newton's second law in component form:

$$(I) \quad F_{1,\,x} + F_{2,\,x} = ma_x$$

$$(II) \quad F_{1,\,y} + F_{2,\,y} = ma_y \tag{25}$$

The two formulas in Eq. (25) are rewritten to determine the two components of the unknown force $\mathbf{F_2}$:

$$F_{2,\,x} = ma_x - F_{1,\,x}$$

$$F_{2,\,y} = ma_y - F_{1,\,y} \tag{26}$$

in which $\mathbf{F_1} = (10.0\ [N], 0)$ and

19

$$ma_x = -1.5[kg] \; 10\left[\frac{m}{s^2}\right] \sin 30^0$$

$$\quad (27)$$

$$ma_y = -1.5[kg] \; 10\left[\frac{m}{s^2}\right] \cos 30^0$$

Both sides of Eq. (27) carry the unit [kg m/s²] which is the same as the unit [N]. Substituting the components of the force F_1 and Eq. (27) in Eq. (26), we find:

$$F_{2,\,x} = -17.5 \; N$$

$$\quad (28)$$

$$F_{2,\,y} = -13.0 \; N$$

Solution part (b): Fig. 3.44 illustrates how the two components of force F_2 in Eq. (28) are related to its magnitude and direction. The magnitude is obtained with the Pythagorean theorem from Eq. (28):

$$F_2 = \sqrt{(-17.5)^2 + (-13.0)^2} \; [N]$$

$$\quad (29)$$

$$\Rightarrow \quad F_2 = 21.8 \; N$$

The direction of a vector is usually expressed by its angle with the positive x–axis, measured in the counter–clockwise direction. This angle is shown in Fig. 3.44 as angle ϕ. To obtain ϕ, we first calculate the angle ψ between the vector F_2 and the x–axis. Using Eq. (28) and the trigonometric definition of the angle ψ, we get:

$$\tan\psi = \frac{F_{2,\,y}}{F_{2,\,x}} = \frac{-13.0 \; N}{-17.5 \; N} = +0.743 \quad (30)$$

This corresponds to either $\phi = 36.6^0$ or $\phi = 216.6^0$. We choose $\phi = 216.6^0$ because the vector lies in the third quadrant.

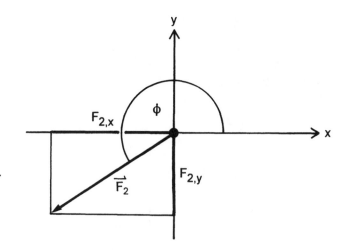

Fig. 3.44: Relation between the component form, the magnitude and the angle with the x–axis for a force directed in the third quadrant.

Problem 3.8

Fig. 3.36 shows an object of mass $m_1 = 1.0$ kg on an inclined surface. The angle of the inclined surface is $\theta = 30^0$ with the horizontal. The object m_1 is connected to a second object of mass $m_2 = 2.5$ kg on the adjacent horizontal surface. Further, an external force of magnitude $|F_{ext}| = 10$ N is exerted on the object of mass m_1. We observe both objects to accelerate. Assuming that the surfaces and the pulley are frictionless, and the pulley and the connecting string are massless, what is the tension in the string connecting the two objects?

Solution: Two separate objects are present and their motions (or their ability to move) are linked. Thus, we identify each as a system, the object with mass m_1 as system 1 and the object with mass m_2 as system 2. The frictionless surfaces, the frictionless and massless pulley and the massless string are parts of the environment. Three forces act on both objects: their respective weights, the normal forces due to the contact with the underlying surfaces and the tension due to the contact with the string. In addition, an external force acts on system 1: the force which pulls the object upwards along the inclined surface.

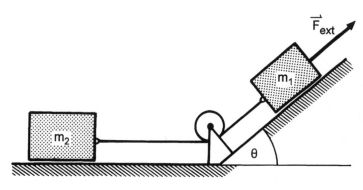

Fig. 3.36 for problem P–3.8.

20

The two free–body–diagrams are shown in Fig. 3.45. To stay consistent, the free–body–diagram at the left refers to system 2 (which is also located at the left in Fig. 3.36). The free–body–diagram at the right refers to system 1. A choice of coordinate system is included with each free–body–diagram in the figure. Note that the x– and y–directions are chosen independently for each system.

We take the following simplifications into account before writing equations based on the free–body–diagrams in Fig. 3.45:
(I) the string is massless and remains taut. This means that:

$$a_{1,\,x} = a_{2,\,x} = a$$

$$T_{1,\,x} = T \quad and \quad T_{2,\,x} = -T \tag{31}$$

in which both accelerations along the direction of the surface are the same and are set equal to a, and the two tensions are the same in magnitude (set equal T) but differ in their direction relative to the respective x–axes.
(II) Nothing interesting happens in the y–direction for either object, i.e., in the y–direction each object is initially at rest and remains at rest throughout the experiment. We are also not asked to solve for anything which would require the normal forces. Thus, the y–component formulas for both systems need not to be considered.

Since both objects accelerate, we use Newton's second law for the x–components. Using Fig. 3.45, we get:

system 1: $F_{ext} - m_1 g \sin\theta - T = m_1 a$

system 2: $\qquad\qquad T = m_2 a$ $\tag{32}$

We solve Eq. (32) for T by using the second formula to eliminate the acceleration a in the first formula:

$$F_{ext} - m_1 g \sin\theta - T = m_1 \left(\frac{T}{m_2} \right) \tag{33}$$

sorting the terms with the variable T on the right hand side of the equation yields:

$$F_{ext} - m_1 g \sin\theta = T \left(1 + \frac{m_1}{m_2} \right) \tag{34}$$

The tension follows from Eq. (34) in the form:

$$T = \frac{m_2 \left(F_{ext} - m_1 g \sin\theta \right)}{m_1 + m_2} \tag{35}$$

Substituting the given values in Eq. (35) finally yields:

$$T = \frac{2.5[kg]\left[10[N] - 1.0[kg]9.8\left[\frac{m}{s^2} \right] \sin30^0 \right]}{1.0[kg] + 2.5[kg]} \tag{36}$$

$$\Rightarrow \quad T = 3.64 \; N$$

$$\frac{0,421(3,2 - 0,182 \cdot 9,8 \sin 40)}{0,421 + 0,182}$$

$$1,44$$

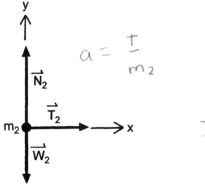

$a = \dfrac{t}{m_2}$

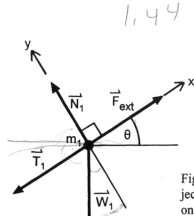

Fig. 3.45: Free–body–diagrams for two objects connected with a string. One object is on a horizontal surface, the other is on an inclined plane.

CHAPTER IV

Kinesiology: the action of forces at joints

Problem 4.1
In the ammonia molecule NH₃ the three hydrogen atoms are located in a plane forming an equilateral triangle with side length a as shown in Fig. 4.43. The nitrogen atom oscillates 24 billion times per second up and down along a line which intersects with the plane of the hydrogen atoms at the center–of–mass of the three hydrogen atoms.

(a) Calculate the length a in Fig. 4.43, using for the N–H bond length $l = 0.1014$ nm and for the HNH–bond angle

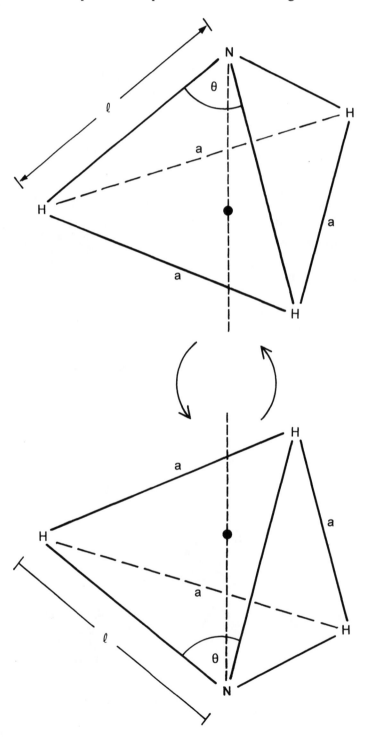

Fig. 4.43 for problem P–4.1.

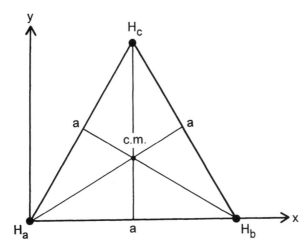

Fig. 4.58: The plane of three hydrogen atoms in the ammonia molecule. A Cartesian coordinate system is used with one hydrogen atom at the origin and the second hydrogen atom located along the x–axis.

$\theta = 106.8^0$.

(b) Calculate the distance between the center–of–mass of the three hydrogen atoms and any one of the hydrogen atoms.

Solution part (a): Fig. 4.57 shows the nitrogen atom and two of the hydrogen atoms of the ammonia molecule drawn in a plane. The symmetry of the molecule allows us to construct a right triangle by enclosing a line dividing the molecule in two equal halves. The angle at the nitrogen atom is $\theta/2 = 53.4^0$ and the length of the side opposite to the nitrogen atom is a/2. From trigonometry we know:

$$\sin\left(\frac{\theta}{2}\right) = \frac{a/2}{l} \tag{1}$$

$$\Rightarrow \quad a = 2 \cdot 0.1014[nm] \sin(53.4^0)$$

which yields a = 0.163 nm.

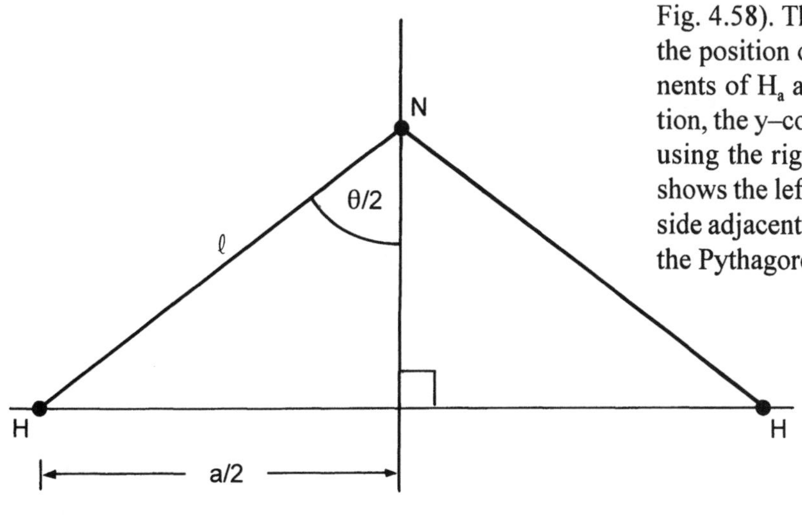

Solution part (b): The center–of–mass position of the three hydrogen atoms in the ammonia molecule is indicated as a dot in Fig. 4.43. Fig. 4.58 shows the position of the hydrogen atoms in their common plane. We identify this plane as the _xy_–plane and choose the two axes as shown in the figure.

Using Fig. 4.58, the Cartesian coordinates of the hydrogen atoms are determined. For this purpose, the three atoms are distinguished by indices a, b, and c. Note that the indices do not imply any chemical difference between the three hydrogen atoms.

The coordinate system in Fig. 4.58 has been chosen such that H_a lies at the origin. Therefore, we know that $H_a = (0,0)$. We further chose the x–axis such that it coincides with the line connecting points H_a and H_b. With the distance a calculated in part (a), the position of H_b is established as $H_b = (a,0)$. Thus, only the position of H_c requires some reasoning.

We know that the symmetry of the molecule requires that the three hydrogen atoms form an equilateral triangle (all three side lengths are equal to a as shown in Fig. 4.58). Thus, due to symmetry, the x–component of the position of H_c lies half–way between the x–components of H_a and H_b, i.e., $H_{c,x} = a/2$. With this information, the y–component of the position of H_c is calculated using the right triangle shown in Fig. 4.59. The figure shows the left half of the triangle in Fig. 4.58, with h the side adjacent to the right angle and H_c. To find h, we use the Pythagorean theorem:

$$a^2 = \left(\frac{a}{2}\right)^2 + h^2 \tag{2}$$

$$\Rightarrow \quad h = \frac{\sqrt{3}}{2} a$$

Fig. 4.57: Geometry of the HNH binding angle in the ammonia molecule.

Thus, the position of the hydrogen atom H_c is given as

23

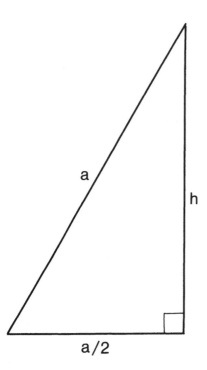

Fig. 4.59: Right triangle used to construct the length h.

$$|H_a\ cm| = \sqrt{\left(\frac{a}{2}\right)^2 + \left(\frac{a}{2\sqrt{3}}\right)^2} = \frac{a}{\sqrt{3}} \quad (4)$$

Substituting the value for a from the problem part (a), we find for the distance from each hydrogen atom to the center–of–mass position a length of 0.094 nm.

Problem 4.2
A person of mass m = 70 kg is doing push–ups as shown in Fig. 4.44. The distances are l_1 = 90 cm and l_2 = 55 cm.
(a) Calculate the vertical component of the normal force exerted by the floor on both hands, and
(b) calculate the normal force exerted by the floor on both feet.

Fig. 4.44 for problem P–4.2.

$H_c = (a/2, a\sqrt{3}/2)$.
    With the coordinates of the three hydrogen atoms established, the coordinates of the center–of–mass position are determined. We use Eq. (4.25) for the x–component of the center–of–mass position, and an analogous equation for its y–component. The mass of the three hydrogen atoms is the same and is labelled m:

$$x_{cm} = \frac{0\,m + a\,m + \frac{a}{2}\,m}{m + m + m} = \frac{\frac{3}{2}a\,m}{3\,m} = \frac{a}{2}$$

$$ (3)$$

$$y_{cm} = \frac{0\,m + 0\,m + \frac{\sqrt{3}}{2}a\,m}{m + m + m} = \frac{a}{2\sqrt{3}}$$

    In the last step, the distance between one of the hydrogen atoms and the center–of–mass position is calculated. The symmetry of the molecule allows us to pick any one of the hydrogen atoms as their distances to the cm–position are equal. For convenience, we pick H_a because that reduces the calculation to determining the distance of the cm–position from the origin. Using the data in Eq. (3), we find for the distance from H_a to the cm–position:

Solution part (a): We identify the human body in this problem as an extended rigid object. This rigid object is in mechanical equilibrium because no accelerations occur. We identify the conditions under which neither an acceleration along a straight line nor a rotational acceleration occur by using Eq. (4.21) in the textbook.
    The approach we follow to solve equilibrium problems for extended rigid objects are similar to the approach we took in Chapters 2 and 3, but an additional plot is required which introduces one more formula in Eq. (4.21).
    In the current case, the entire human body shown in Fig. 4.44 is identified as the system. Since it is an extended body, it is important to know where the center–of–mass of the system lies. In the particular case, the center–of–mass (cm) is shown in Fig. 4.44. Three forces act on the system: the weight (to be drawn at the center–of–mass as discussed in section 4.3), and two normal

24

forces at the two contact points of the system with the environment (at the toes and hands). It is important not to combine these two forces into a single force as they act at different points on the extended system.

Instead of a single free–body–diagram, two plots are required to quantify the problem: the free–body–diagram as before and a *balance of torque plot*. The balance of torque plot is shown in Fig. 4.60. To obtain this plot, first draw a (horizontal) bar representing the object of interest. Such a bar is sufficient since the body is not bend; when a system is not straight, the approach in Example 4.4 or Problem 4.13 must be used.

Next we indicate with a solid dot the point where the axis of rotation lies. Remember that we limit the discussion in this chapter to cases where all forces and (possible) rotations occur in a plane perpendicular to the rotation axis. That plane is the plane of your paper and the axis is represented by a dot as the axis runs into the paper. Confirm for Fig. 4.44 that any possible rotation would occur within the plane of the paper.

We identify the center–of–mass as the axis of rotation. Now we add the forces acting on the body to the sketch. Be careful to not only draw the forces in the right direction as they act, but also to attach them to the bar at the appropriate position. To make sure that you do the latter, always identify the distance from the axis to the point where each force acts on the body. In Fig. 4.60 the length indicators l_1 and l_2 are included for that purpose.

The default choice of coordinate system for a balance of torque plot is based on the axis of rotation as the origin and the direction along the bar as the x–axis. From the free–body–diagram and the balance of torque plot the three formulas in Eq. (4.21) are developed: the first two formulas represent the x– and y–components of Newton's first law and the third formula represents the torque equilibrium condition. In the current case none of the forces has a component acting in the x–direction, thus, the respective formula is omitted. This leaves two formulas for solving the problem:

$$(II) \quad N_1 + N_2 - W = 0$$

$$(III) \quad N_1 l_1 - N_2 l_2 = 0 \tag{5}$$

Note the numbering of the two equations: we consistently label the mechanical equilibrium formula for the x–components of the net force with (I), the formula for the y–components with (II) and the torque equilibrium condition with (III) throughout the solutions in this chapter.

Formula (III) in Eq. (5) does not contain a term with the magnitude of the weight, W. This is due to the

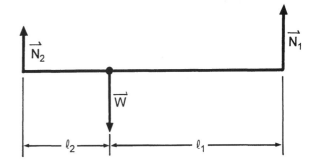

Fig. 4.60: Balance of torque plot for a person doing push–ups.

fact that the weight acts along a line which passes through the axis. Try to pull a door out of its hinges or try to push it into the hinges. No rotation occurs in either case. Since the balance of torque equation contains only possible contributions to a rotational motion of the rigid body, any force acting along a line through the axis does not contribute to the torque equilibrium formula.

The two normal forces acting on the body in Fig. 4.44 are present in the torque equilibrium formula. Based on the torque definition in Eq. (4.20), each of these forces is multiplied with the distance between the axis and the point along the bar at which the force is applied. Note that the angle in Eq. (4.20) is also included, however, we find $\sin \phi = 1$ because both normal forces act perpendicular to the bar.

In the torque equilibrium formula in Eq. (5), one term is positive and one is negative. This is the result of applying the sign–convention of Fig. 4.15: imagine that the force N_1 in Fig. 4.60 succeeds in setting the bar in a rotational motion about the axis. This would be a counter–clockwise rotation; thus, the torque contribution of force N_1 is positive. In turn, if the normal force N_2 were to succeed, the rotation would be clockwise; thus, the torque contribution of force N_2 is negative.

At this point we note another rule of thumb. Because the torque equilibrium equation contains a smaller number of forces (some are excluded as they act towards or away from the axis) it is very often, but not always, the best approach to try to work with the torque equation in a set of equations like Eq. (5) first.

In the current case, Eq. (5) is rather easy to solve for the unknown variables, i.e., the two magnitudes of the normal forces. We do this in the order given in the problem text: the normal force on the arms, N_2, is found first. We rewrite formula (II) in Eq. (5) in the form:

$$N_1 = W - N_2 \tag{6}$$

Then we substitute Eq. (6) into formula (III) of Eq. (5)

to eliminate N_1:

$$(W - N_2) l_1 - N_2 l_2 = 0 \qquad (7)$$

which leads to the magnitude of the normal force at the hands:

$$N_2 = \frac{W l_1}{l_1 + l_2} = \frac{686[N] \; 90[cm]}{90[cm] + 55[cm]}$$

$$\Rightarrow \quad N_2 = 426 \; N \qquad (8)$$

Solution part (b): Substituting the value found in part (a) for N_2 into Eq. (6) yields for the magnitude of the normal force at the feet:

$$N_1 = W - N_2 = 686[N] - 426[N] = 260 \; N \quad (9)$$

Problem 4.3
A person holds the upper arm vertical and the lower arm horizontal with an object of mass M = 6 kg resting on the hand as illustrated in Fig. 4.45. The mass of the lower arm is given as m = 4 kg. We consider four forces acting on the lower arm: (I) the external force $\mathbf{F}_{ext}$, exerted by the bones and ligaments of the upper arm at the elbow (axis), (II) the tension $\mathbf{T}$, exerted by the biceps, (III) the weight $\mathbf{W}_M$ of the object, (IV) the weight $\mathbf{W}_F$ of the lower arm. The points along the lower arm, at which the forces act, are identified in Fig. 4.45: $l_1 = 5$ cm, $l_2 = 15$ cm and $l_3 = 25$ cm.
(a) Calculate the vertical component of the force $\mathbf{F}_{ext}$,
(b) calculate the vertical component of the tension $\mathbf{T}$.

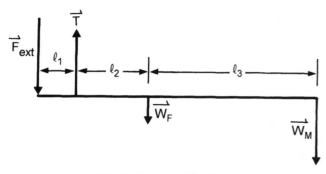

Fig. 4.45 for problem P–4.3.

Solution part (a): For this problem, Fig. 4.45 provides already a balance of torque plot instead of a sketch from

which such a plot would have to be derived. In such a case you want to take extra care to familiarize yourself with the choices made since they may differ from what you might have done yourself. A frequently noted issue of confusion is the fact that the weight of the mass held by the person and not the normal force of the hand acting on the mass is shown at the far right. As discussed in Chapter 2 already, the mechanical equilibrium of an extended object is based on forces which act _on_ the system and is not based on forces which the system exerts on objects in its environment. You may also notice that the free–body–diagram is not shown. It is highly recommended to draw it before proceeding.

Since all the forces in Fig. 4.45 act along a vertical direction which we define as the y–axis, the set of equations corresponding to Eq. (4.21) contains only two formulas, Newton's first law for the y–components of the forces (formula (II)) and the torque equilibrium equation (formula (III)):

$$(II) \quad T - F_{ext} - W_F - W_M = 0$$

$$(III) \quad T l_1 - W_F (l_1 + l_2) - \dots$$

$$\dots - W_M (l_1 + l_2 + l_3) = 0 \qquad (10)$$

In Eq. (10), the axis of rotation is taken at the left end of the bar in Fig. 4.45, at the point where the force $\mathbf{F}_{ext}$ acts on the lower arm. Note that the biceps tendon in a real arm does not act perfectly perpendicular to the lower arm. Thus, assuming that the tension $\mathbf{T}$ is directed in the y–direction is a simplifying assumption. That this assumption is a simplification becomes evident when we later get to examples where some forces do not act perpendicular to the system (bar).

We have two formulas in Eq. (10) and two unknown variables, i.e., the magnitude of the tension and the magnitude of the force $\mathbf{F}_{ext}$. Thus, the set of formulas in Eq. (10) can be solved. We first find the magnitude of the external force. To do this, we rewrite formula (II) in Eq. (10) in the form:

$$T = F_{ext} + W_F + W_M \qquad (11)$$

Next we eliminate the magnitude of the tension, T, from formula (III) in Eq. (10) by inserting Eq. (11):

$$(F_{ext} + W_F + W_M) l_1 - W_F (l_1 + l_2) - \dots$$

$$\dots - W_M (l_1 + l_2 + l_3) = 0 \qquad (12)$$

This allows us to determine the magnitude of $\mathbf{F}_{ext}$:

$$F_{ext} = \frac{l_2}{l_1} W_F + \frac{l_2 + l_3}{l_1} W_M \qquad (13)$$

Next the given numerical values are substituted into Eq. (13):

$$F_{ext} = \frac{15}{5}39.2[N] + \frac{(15+25)}{5}58.8[N] \qquad (14)$$

$$\Rightarrow \quad F_{ext} = 588 \ N$$

The two weights in this equation given in unit [N], were obtained by multiplying each of the two masses in the problem text with the gravitational acceleration constant g.

Solution part (b): The magnitude of $\mathbf{F}_{ext}$ from Eq. (14) is substituted into Eq. (11), yielding for the magnitude of the tension:

$$T = F_{ext} + W_M + W_F = \qquad (15)$$

$$588[N]+39.2[N]+58.8[N] = 686 \ N$$

Problem 4.4

The deltoid muscle holds the arm when it is stretched out horizontally. The major forces acting on the arm in this case are shown in Fig. 4.46. Use m = 8 kg for the mass of the arm, $\alpha = 17^0$ for the angle, $l_1 = 11$ cm for the distance between the shoulder joint and the attachment point of the tendon of the deltoid muscle, and $l_2 = 30$ cm for the distance from the shoulder joint to the center–of–mass of the arm.

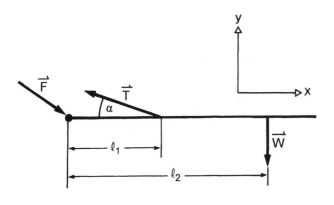

Fig. 4.46 for problem P–4.4.

(a) Calculate the magnitude of the tension **T** in the tendon of the deltoid muscle, and
(b) calculate the magnitude of the external force **F** acting toward the shoulder joint.

Solution part (a): In this problem, we are provided with a balance of torque plot (Fig. 4.46) instead of a more general sketch. In that respect this problem is very similar to the previous problem: you accept this plot but familiarize yourself with it carefully.

What makes this problem different from the previous problem is that some of the forces do not act perpendicularly to the bar (which represents the arm). As a consequence, all three formulas for the mechanical equilibrium of a rigid body in Eq. (4.21) must be written down. For both the free–body–diagram and the shown balance of torque plot we choose the x–axis horizontally towards the right and the y–axis vertically upwards (as indicated in Fig. 4.46). The axis of rotation is identified by the solid dot at the left end of the bar (shoulder joint).

Writing the various terms in Eq. (4.21) is simplified by identifying the x– and y–components of the forces in Fig. 4.46. This is illustrated in Fig. 4.61 for both the force **F** and the tension **T**. Using Figs. 4.46 and 4.61, we write:

$$(I) \quad F_x - T\cos\alpha = 0$$

$$(II) \quad -F_y + T\sin\alpha - W = 0 \qquad (16)$$

$$(III) \quad l_1 T\sin\alpha - l_2 W = 0$$

in which $T_x = -|\mathbf{T}|\cos\alpha$, and $T_y = |\mathbf{T}|\sin\alpha$. Two notes about Eq. (16) are useful:

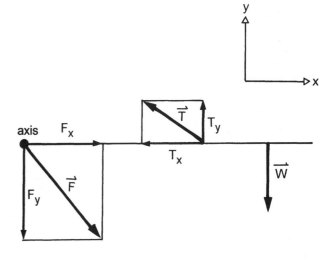

Fig. 4.61: Illustration of the components of the forces which are not directed parallel or perpendicular to the bar in a balance of torque plot.

(I) We have chosen to introduce the x– and y–components for the force **F**. Because part (b) of the problem asks for the magnitude of the external force **F**, we will later have to calculate this magnitude from the two components using the Pythagorean theorem. Alternatively, you can introduce a second angle, e.g. ϕ, between the force **F** and the negative x–axis. It might be useful to try this if you didn't do it in the first place. Note also that the force **F** is not present in formula (III) of Eq. (16) since this force pushes into the axis.

(II) Formula (III) in Eq. (16) shows you how you treat forces in the balance of torque plot which are not perpendicular to the bar. Any such force should be rewritten in component form as done in Fig. 4.61 with one component parallel and one component perpendicular to the bar. The component parallel to the bar does not enter into the torque equilibrium formula since that component is directed either into or away from the axis, i.e., runs in a direction through the axis. Thus, for each non–perpendicular force, only the perpendicular component has to be included in the torque equilibrium formula.

Starting with formula (III) in Eq. (16) is the best approach. In the current case, this allows us to calculate the magnitude of the tension directly as asked for in part (a):

$$T = \frac{l_2\, W}{l_1 \sin\alpha} = \frac{30[cm]\, 78.4[N]}{11[cm]\, \sin 17^0} \qquad (17)$$

$$\Rightarrow \quad T = 731\ N$$

in which we used for the weight W = 8[kg] 9.8[m/s²] = 78.4 N.

Solution part (b): Substituting the result of part (a) into formulas (I) and (II) of Eq. (16), we find the two components of the external force:

$$F_x = T\cos\alpha = 731[N]\cos 17^0$$

$$\Rightarrow \quad F_x = 699\ N \qquad (18)$$

and

$$F_y = T\sin\alpha - W = 731[N]\sin 17^0 - 78.4[N]$$

$$\Rightarrow \quad F_y = 135\ N \qquad (19)$$

leading to the magnitude of the force F:

$$F = \sqrt{699^2 + 135^2}\ [N] = 712\ N \qquad (20)$$

Problem 4.5
An object of mass M = 10 kg is lifted with the aid of a pulley as shown in Fig. 4.47. The upper arm is held vertical and the lower arm has an angle of $\theta = 35^0$ with the horizontal. The label *cm* marks the center–of–mass

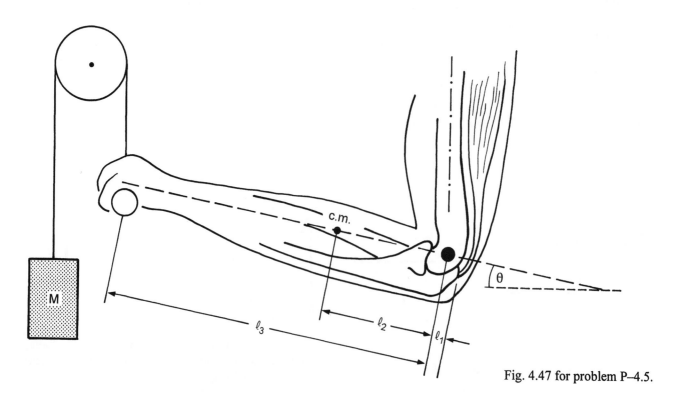

Fig. 4.47 for problem P–4.5.

of the lower arm. Consider the weight of the object M, the weight of the lower arm and hand, the tension due to the triceps muscle and the force due to the humerus. For the lengths we use the following values: $l_1 = 3$ cm, $l_2 = 15$ cm, $l_3 = 40$ cm. The lower arm and the hand have a mass of 2.0 kg.

(a) What is the magnitude of the vertical force exerted on the lower arm by the triceps muscle, and

(b) what is the magnitude of the vertical force exerted on the lower arm by the humerus?

Hint: The triceps muscle pulls vertically upward.

Solution: The sketch in Fig. 4.47 is a combination of a sketch and part of a balance of torque plot. To prevent confusion, it is advisable in such a case to redraw the balance of torque plot separately and make sure that it is complete. It is also advisable not to skip the free–body–diagram. Draw it for the purpose of practice.

The system is the lower arm of the person. The point mass M exerts an upward force on the left end of the lower arm (hand). This force is in magnitude equal to the weight of the object of mass M. We label this force $\mathbf{F_3}$. The lower arm also has a weight $\mathbf{W}$ which acts vertically down at the center–of–mass of the lower arm.

The other forces to be taken into account in this problem are identified in the text, and include the force exerted on the lower arm by the triceps muscle (called $\mathbf{F_1}$) and the force exerted on the lower arm by the humerus through the elbow joint (called $\mathbf{F_2}$). Note that all four forces act vertically, but the lower arm forms an angle of $35°$ with the horizontal.

As noted in the above discussion, the four forces are not perpendicular to the lower arm. This is important to take into account when we draw the balance of torque plot. This plot is shown in Fig. 4.62(b). Note that this time the axis of rotation (the elbow joint) does not lie at the end of the bar since the triceps tendon is attached to the right of the elbow joint. Fig. 4.62 also shows the distances to the axis of the various points at which the forces act on the bar. The standard choice of coordinate system for the balance of torque plot is indicated in Fig. 4.62. For the free–body–diagram in Fig. 4.62(a), a horizontal x– and a vertical y–axis have been chosen. The difference in coordinate systems for both diagrams illustrates that such a choice is acceptable.

Of the three formulas in Eq. (4.21) needed to quantify the mechanical equilibrium of the extended object, the first formula can be omitted because no force components run along the x–axis in Fig. 4.62(a). Thus, we write:

$$(I) \quad F_1 - F_2 + F_3 - W = 0$$

$$(II) \quad l_1 F_1 \cos\theta + l_2 W \cos\theta - ... \qquad \textbf{(21)}$$

$$... - l_3 F_3 \cos\theta = 0$$

Note that the magnitudes $W = mg$ and $F_3 = Mg$ are known. Formula (III) in Eq. (21) is analyzed first to find the magnitude of force $\mathbf{F_1}$:

$$F_1 = \frac{l_3 F_3 - l_2 W}{l_1} = \frac{(l_3 M - l_2 m) g}{l_1} \qquad \textbf{(22)}$$

a)

b)

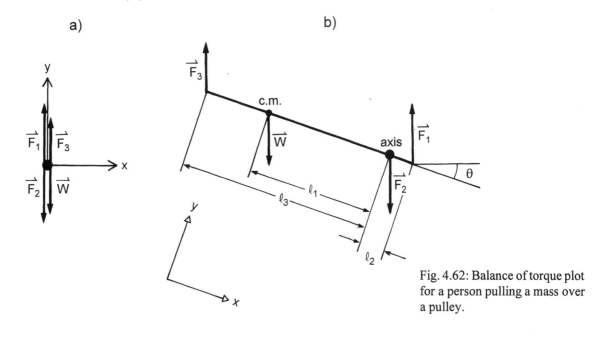

Fig. 4.62: Balance of torque plot for a person pulling a mass over a pulley.

29

Substituting the given numerical values into Eq. (22) yields:

$$F_1 = \frac{\left(0.4[m]10[kg]-0.15[m]2[kg]\right)9.8\left[\dfrac{m}{s^2}\right]}{0.03\;[m]} \quad \textbf{(23)}$$

$$\Rightarrow \quad F_1 = 1209\;N$$

Note that the term $\cos\theta$ did not matter in Eq. (22). This is mathematically due to the fact that we can divide formula (III) in Eq. (21) on both sides by $\cos\theta$. It is important to notice, however, that there is one angle θ for which this mathematical operation is not valid: for $\theta = 90^0$ we find $\cos\theta = 0$ and we cannot divide by zero. However, if $\theta = 90^0$ the whole problem makes no longer sense, and thus, this case can be excluded.

Solution part (b): Substituting the result from part (a) into formula (II) in Eq. (21), we obtain the magnitude of force $\mathbf{F_2}$:

$$F_2 = F_1 + F_3 - W =$$

$$1209[N] + \left(10[kg] - 2[kg]\right)9.8[m/s^2] \quad \textbf{(24)}$$

$$\Rightarrow \quad F_2 = 1287\;N$$

Compare the magnitude of the two forces $\mathbf{F_1}$ and $\mathbf{F_2}$ with the two weights, which are about 20 N for the lower arm and about 100 N for the lifted weight: tremendous forces act on an arm when performing physical tasks, here lifting an object of mass 10 kg.

Problem 4.6
A steel band of a brace exerts an external force of magnitude $F_{ext} = 40$ N on a tooth. The tooth is shown in Fig. 4.48 with point B a distance 1.3 cm above point A, which is the axis of rotation of the tooth. The angle between the tooth and the external force is $\theta = 40^0$. What is the torque on the root of the tooth about point A?

Solution: This is a direct application of the torque definition for an extended body, but contains a geometrical twist. It is simple since there is only one force given, but the angle θ is not the angle we need when analyzing Eq. (4.20) defining the torque.

To use Eq. (4.20), the angle between the exerted force, $\mathbf{F_{ext}}$, and the lever arm vector, given by $\mathbf{AB} = \mathbf{r}$, is needed. This is illustrated in Fig. 4.63, where the angle

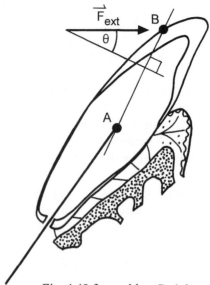

Fig. 4.48 for problem P–4.6.

between both vectors is defined as ϕ. Confirm that the angle θ as shown in Fig. 4.48 and the angle θ as shown in Fig. 4.63 are indeed the same. Remember that vectors can be moved as long as their length and directions are kept the same. In this case, we can move vector $\mathbf{F_{ext}}$ as long as we keep the same angle between $\mathbf{F_{ext}}$ and $\mathbf{AB}$. In particular, we can slide $\mathbf{F_{ext}}$ to the right in Fig. 4.48 so that its tail is at point B. The angles in this problem are related in the following form:

$$\phi = 180^0 - \left(90^0 - \theta\right) = 90^0 + \theta \quad \textbf{(25)}$$

With all necessary parameters defined, we use Eq. (4.20) to calculate the torque:

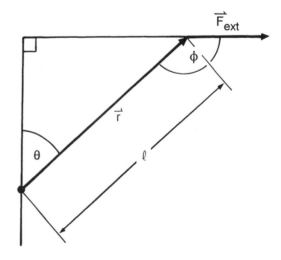

Fig. 4.63: Geometry of the symmetry axis of a tooth and an external force acting on the tooth.

$$\tau = l\,F_{ext}\sin\phi =$$

$$1.3\times10^{-2}[m]\ 40[N]\ \sin130^0 = 0.4\ Nm \qquad \textbf{(26)}$$

Problem 4.7

A person holds an object of mass m = 2 kg on the palm of the hand with the arm stretched as shown in Fig. 4.49. Use the torque equilibrium equation to determine the magnitude of the force **F** which is exerted by the biceps muscle, when a = 30 cm, b = 5 cm and the angle θ = 80⁰. Neglect the weight of the lower arm.

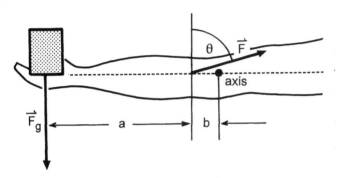

Fig. 4.49 for problem P–4.7.

Solution: Read this problem carefully. Note that we are asked to quantify only one parameter, which is the magnitude of the force **F** (its angle with the arm is defined since a value for the angle θ is given). If there is only one unknown variable, then only one formula is needed. In the current case, the two formulas based on the free–body–diagram are not required. This is indicated in the problem text when it says to use the torque equilibrium equation.

The lower arm is the system. It is an extended body with the rotation axis (elbow joint) at the distance

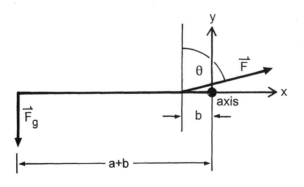

Fig. 4.64: Balance of torque plot for a stretched arm holding a mass.

a + b to the right of the object held in the hand. Two forces act on the lower arm, the force **F** and the weight of the held object, **F**g. The weight of the lower arm itself in neglected.

The balance of torque plot is shown in Fig. 4.64. The standard x– and y–axes for the balance of torque plot are also included in the figure. The rotational equilibrium condition is given in the last formula of Eq. (4.21). It reads for this problem:

$$(III)\quad (a + b)\,F_g - b\,F\cos\theta = 0 \qquad \textbf{(27)}$$

From Eq. (27), the magnitude of the force F is derived:

$$F = \frac{35[cm]\ 2[kg]\ 9.8[m/s^2]}{5[cm]\ \cos80^0} \qquad \textbf{(28)}$$

$$\Rightarrow \quad F = 790\ N$$

Problem 4.8

The quadriceps femoris muscle, shown as (1) in Fig. 4.50(a), is a muscle in the upper leg which serves an analogous purpose to the triceps in the upper arm. Its tendon (2) is attached to the upper end of the tibia (3) as shown in the figure. This muscle exerts the major force of the upper leg on the lower leg when the leg is stretched. Considering also the weight of the lower leg, **W**L, and the weight of the foot, **F**, three forces act on the lower leg as shown in Fig. 4.50(b). Find the magnitude of the tension **T** when the tendon is at an angle of φ = 30⁰ with the tibia using the torque equilibrium. Assume that the lower leg has a mass of 3 kg and the mass of the foot is 1.2 kg. The leg is extended at an angle of θ = 35⁰ with the vertical and the center–of–mass of the lower leg is at its center. The tendon attaches to the lower leg at a point 1/5 of the way down the lower leg.

Solution: As in the previous problem, only one unknown variable is asked for: the magnitude of the force **T**. Thus, a single formula is sufficient to answer the question. The problem directs us to use the torque equilibrium formula.

The lower leg without the foot is the system. The foot is kept separate because it must be treated as an additional mass suspended from the lower leg. If the foot and the lower leg together were considered to form the system, their weights would have to be combined as a single force acting on the center–of–mass of lower leg and foot. Of course, the position at which the weight of the foot acts is important because we are considering torque. All three forces acting on the system are shown

31

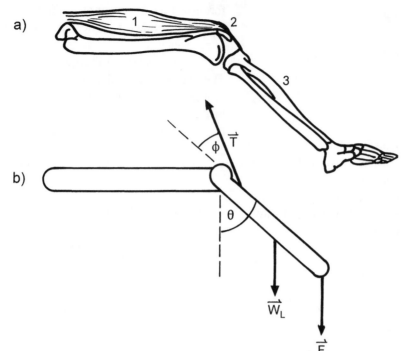

Fig. 4.50 for problem P–4.8.

in Fig. 4.50. These are the weight of the system, the weight of the foot and the tension in the tendon of the large quadriceps muscle.

The balance of torque plot is given in Fig. 4.50(b). Note that we do not need a free–body–diagram to solve this problem since the only formula needed is the one resulting from the balance of torque plot. The torque balance for Fig. 4.50(b) is written in the form:

$$\frac{l}{5}T\sin\phi - \frac{l}{2}W_L\sin\theta - lF\sin\theta = 0 \quad \textbf{(29)}$$

Eq. (29) is solved for T:

$$T = \frac{\left(\dfrac{l}{2}\ 3[kg]\ +\ l\ 1.2[kg]\right)g\ \sin35^0}{\dfrac{l}{5}\ \sin30^0} \quad \textbf{(30)}$$

$$\Rightarrow \quad T = 152\ N$$

Note that we didn't need a value for the length l since l cancels in Eq. (30).

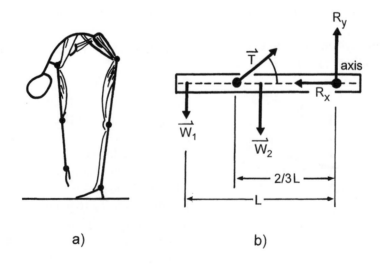

a)   b)

Fig. 4.51 for problem P–4.9.

32

Problem 4.9

A person bends over as shown in Fig. 4.51(a) and lifts an object of mass m = 15 kg while keeping the back parallel with the floor. The muscle that attaches 2/3 of the way up the spine maintains the position of the back. This muscle is called the back muscle or latissimus dorsi muscle. The angle between the spine and the force **T** in this muscle is θ = 11⁰. Use the balance of torque plot in Fig. 4.51(b) and take the mass of the upper body as M = 40 kg.

(a) Find the magnitude of the tension force **T** in the back muscle, and
(b) find the x–component of the compressive force **R** in the spine.

Solution part (a): We choose the spine as our system. All forces to be considered are shown in Fig. 4.51(b). The balance of torque plot is provided in Fig. 4.51(b); draw the free–body–diagram yourself. Using Eq. (4.21), we get for the system in Fig. 4.51:

$$(I) \quad R_x - T\cos\theta = 0$$

$$(II) \quad R_y + T\sin\theta - W_1 - W_2 = 0$$

$$(III) \quad LW_1 - \frac{2L}{3}T\sin\theta + \frac{L}{2}W_2 = 0$$

(31)

in which W_1 = mg and W_2 = Mg. The magnitude of the tension is obtained from formula (III) in Eq. (31):

$$T = \frac{LW_1 + \frac{L}{2}W_2}{\frac{2L}{3}\sin\theta}$$

(32)

Using the given values, we find from Eq. (32):

$$T = \frac{\left(L\, 15[kg] + \frac{L}{2}\, 40[kg]\right)\, 9.8\left[\frac{m}{s^2}\right]}{\frac{2L}{3}\sin 11^0}$$

(33)

$$\Rightarrow \quad T = 2696\ N$$

A value for the length L is not needed since the variable L cancels in Eq. (32).

Solution part (b): The result for T from part (a) is substituted into formula (I) of Eq. (31) to find the component of force **R** lying in the spine, R_x:

$$R_x = T\cos\theta = 2647\ N$$

(34)

Note that formula (II) of Eq. (31) was not needed to solve either part of this problem.

Problem 4.10

A standard man bends the upper body forward, forming a 30⁰ angle with the horizontal, as shown in Fig. 4.52. Considering the mass of the head to be 7 %, the mass of the arms to be 12 % and the mass of the trunk to be 46 % of the body mass, calculate as a multiple of the person's weight

(a) the magnitude of the force **F_M** in the back muscle,
(b) the magnitude of the force **F_B** acting on the fifth lumbar vertebra (at which the axis of rotation lies).

Hint: the figure indicates that the force **F_M** forms a 12⁰ angle with the spinal column.

Solution part (a): The back of the standard man is the system. Using Fig. 4.52, we identify five forces to act on the system, the three weights **W_T**, **W_A** and **W_H**; and the two contact forces **F_M** and **F_B**. From Fig. 4.52, we further conclude that the force **F_M** forms an angle of 18⁰ with the horizontal. The angle of the force **F_B** with the horizontal is not known. No numerical value is given for the length L, but the weight of the person is known because he is a standard man.

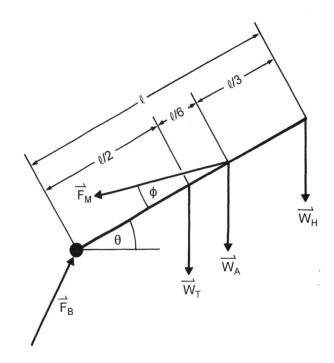

Fig. 4.52 for problem P–4.10.

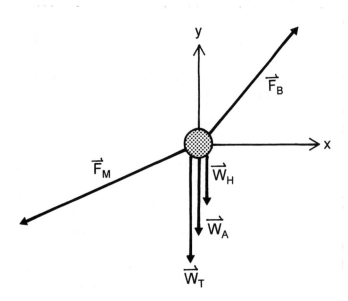

$$\frac{2L}{3} F_M \sin 12^0 = \frac{L}{2} W_T \sin 60^0 + ... \tag{36}$$

$$... + L W_H \sin 60^0 + \frac{2L}{3} W_A \sin 60^0$$

Next, F_M is isolated on the left hand side of Eq. (36):

$$F_M = \frac{3 \sin 60^0}{2 \sin 12^0} \left(\frac{W_T}{2} + W_H + \frac{2 W_A}{3} \right) \tag{37}$$

We use $W_T = 0.46W$, $W_A = 0.12W$ and $W_H = 0.07W$, in which W is the weight of the standard man. This yields:

$$F_M = \frac{3 \sin 60^0}{2 \sin 12^0} 0.38 W = 2.4 W \tag{38}$$

$$\Rightarrow F_M = 1646 N$$

The back muscle must hold two and a half times the weight of the person when bending down!

Solution part (b) : Substituting the result of part (a) in formulas (I) and (II) of Eq. (35) allows us to determine the two components of the force $\mathbf{F_B}$. The x–component reads:

$$F_{B,x} = F_M \cos 18^0 = 2.4 W \cos 18^0 \tag{39}$$

$$\Rightarrow F_{B,x} = 2.3 W$$

and the y–component reads:

$$F_{B,y} = F_M \sin 18^0 + W_H + W_A + W_T \tag{40}$$

$$\Rightarrow F_{B,y} = 1.4 W$$

Using the Pythagorean theorem, Eqs. (39) and (40) yield for the magnitude F_B:

$$F_B = \sqrt{F_{B,x}^2 + F_{B,y}^2} = 2.7 W \tag{41}$$

$$\Rightarrow F_B = 1852 N$$

Fig. 4.65: Free–body–diagram for the back of a person bending down.

The free–body–diagram is shown in Fig. 4.65. We choose the x– and y–axes as shown.

We use the free–body–diagram from Fig. 4.65 and the balance of torque plot from Fig. 4.52 to quantify the problem. Eq. (4.21) is used because the back in the problem is held in rotational equilibrium:

$$(I) \quad F_{B,x} - F_M \cos 18^0 = 0$$

$$(II) \quad F_{B,y} - F_M \sin 18^0 - W_H - W_A - W_T = 0$$

$$(III) \quad -\frac{L}{2} W_T \sin 60^0 - L W_H \sin 60^0 + ... \tag{35}$$

$$... + \frac{2L}{3} \left(- W_A \sin 60^0 + F_M \sin 12^0 \right) = 0$$

Note that formulas (I) and (II) contain two unknown parameters each, formula (I) the magnitude of the force $\mathbf{F_M}$ and the x–component of the force $\mathbf{F_B}$, and formula (II) the magnitude of the force $\mathbf{F_M}$ and the y–component of the force $\mathbf{F_B}$. Formula (III) contains only the magnitude of the force $\mathbf{F_M}$. Thus, the last formula is best suitable to solve for part (a) of the problem.

We rewrite formula (III) of Eq. (35) to isolate the magnitude the magnitude F_M:

Problem 4.11

Fig. 4.53 shows the motion of the thorax during breathing. Air is pulled into the lung and pushed out of the lung by the active change of volume of the lung associated with the change in the volume within the rib cage. Two sets of intercostal muscles allow for the increase and decrease of the volume within the rib cage. These are shown in Fig. 4.54 and include the intercostales interni muscles (connecting points B' and C in the figure) and the intercostales externi muscles (connecting points B and C' in the figure). The ribs are pivoted about the points A and A' which mark the joint with the thoracic vertebra. Determine from Fig. 4.54 which muscle contracts during inhalation (volume increase) and which muscle contracts during exhalation (volume decrease).

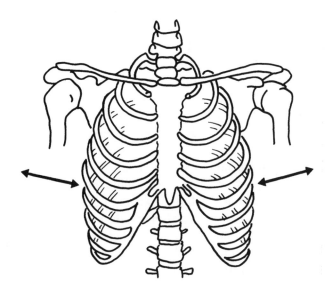

Fig. 4.53 for problem P–4.11.

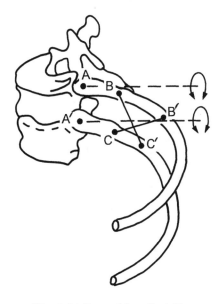

Fig. 4.54 for problem P–4.11.

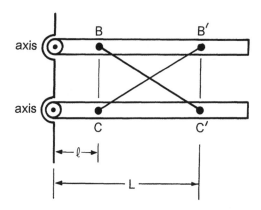

Fig. 4.66: Sketch of the muscle connections of two neighboring ribs.

Solution: Fig. 4.54 contains all the information needed to discuss this problem; however, Fig. 4.66 is a simplified sketch which is better suited to illustrate all the contributions to the motion. In Fig. 4.66, the two points A and A' of Fig. 4.54 are identified as the axes for the rotation of the respective rib bones. The points B and C are a distance l from the axis on either of the ribs and the points B' and C' are a distance L from the axis, with L $\gg$ l. The muscles stretching between the ribs, connect either points B and C' (intercostales externi) or they connect points B' and C (intercostales interni).

We assume first that the intercostales externi contract, i.e., the line connecting points B and C' shortens. This causes a torque on both the upper and the lower rib. On the upper rib the torque is given as $-F_{BC'} l$ (where we assume for simplicity that the trigonometric term containing the angle between the force and the rib, which is of the type $\sin\phi$ as outlined in Eq. (4.20), is included in the magnitude of the force term $F_{BC'}$). This contribution is negative since it would lead to a clockwise rotation of the rib.

For the lower rib, the torque is $+F_{BC'}L$. Thus, the torque on the lower rib is bigger and prevails, moving the lower rib upwards. Since all the ribs are connected in the same form by the intercostales externi, the entire rib cage moves up, which is the rib cage motion associated with inhalation.

The same arguments apply to the intercostales interni, leading to the opposite motion. That motion is typical for the rib cage of an exhaling person.

Problem 4.12

A person is suspended from a high bar as shown on the left side of Fig. 4.55. While at rest, the center–of–mass of the person is directly below the bar. The sketch on the right side in Fig. 4.55 shows the forces acting on the

lower arm of the person. Assume that the forces exerted by the bar on the left hand, $\mathbf{F}_l$, and exerted on the right hand, $\mathbf{F}_r$, are equal in magnitude and directed parallel to each other. Use for the length from the hand to the attachment point of the biceps' tendon $l_1 = 40$ cm and use for the remaining length of the arm to the elbow joint the value $l_2 = 5$ cm. The two angles are $\theta = 10^0$ and $\phi = 20^0$.
(a) Find the x– and y–components of the force $\mathbf{F}_{ext}$ with $\mathbf{F}_{ext}$ the external force exerted by the bar on each of the two hands.
(b) Calculate the magnitude of the tension force $\mathbf{T}$ in the biceps tendon.
(c) $\mathbf{R}$ is the force exerted by the humerus on the lower arm through the elbow. Calculate the magnitude of the force $\mathbf{R}$ and its angle with the lower arm.
Hint: Neglect the weight of the arm and assume that $\mathbf{T}$ and $\mathbf{R}$ are the only forces exerted on the lower arm by the upper arm.

be useful before you get to the last part of a multi–part problem.

Read the solution to this problem carefully as there is a change in what we define as the when proceeding from part (a) to parts (b) and (c). How can you anticipate this? Read part (a) only. This question deals with the entire body. It is the mass of the entire body which hangs on the bar, not only the lower arm. The two forces mentioned in parts (b) and (c), $\mathbf{R}$ and $\mathbf{T}$, are, in turn, only relevant when we focus on physical effects which occur across the interface between the lower arm and the rest of the human body.

In part (a), we are asked to determine the external forces exerted on each hand. The system is the entire human body. Three forces act on the system: the weight and the two contact forces exerted by the bar on each hand. We label these two forces $\mathbf{F}_r$ for the force acting on the right hand and $\mathbf{F}_l$ for the force acting on the left hand. As stated in the problem, we assume that the person holds both lower arms parallel to each other (which leads to the higher score in a competition), and that these two forces are equal in magnitude and direction, i.e., $\mathbf{F}_r = \mathbf{F}_l$. Thus, $\mathbf{F}_{ext} = \mathbf{F}_r = \mathbf{F}_l$ since the external force in Fig. 4.55 is defined as the force exerted on one arm.

We need only a free–body–diagram (and not a balance of torque plot) to determine the external force. This is illustrated with the sketch in Fig. 4.67. For the human body to remain stationary, the center–of–mass of the body must be placed exactly below the bar to avoid a non–zero net torque (this is stated at the beginning of the problem). If the center–of–mass were displaced to either side (front or back with respect to the high bar) a pendulum–type of motion would result similar to that of a child being released on a swing after pulling the child

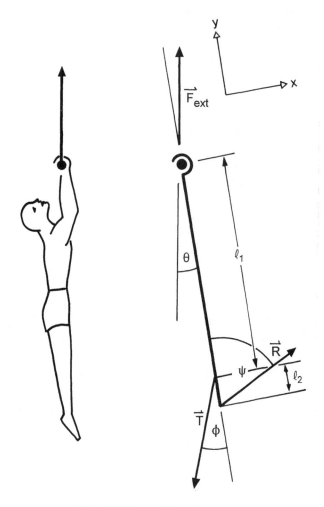

Fig. 4.55 for problem P–4.12.

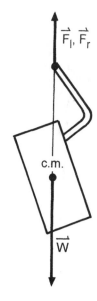

Fig. 4.67: Simplified sketch of a person hanging on a high bar.

Solution part (a): First a bit of common sense. Never work on a problem before you have read it completely. Obviously, a hint given at the end of the problem might

36

backwards. Newton's law in the vertical direction is a simple application of the concepts we introduced in Chapter 2:

$$2 F_{ext} - W = 0$$

$$\Rightarrow \quad F_{ext} = \frac{W}{2} \tag{42}$$

Solutions parts (b) and (c): Now we redefine the system as the lower arm of the person, with the two forces **R** and **T** acting across the interface between the lower arm and the rest of the body. Identified in the problem are three contact forces acting on the lower arm, with their respective directions shown in Fig. 4.55: the tension in the biceps tendon (**T**), the force exerted by the humerus in the upper arm on the lower arm through the elbow joint (**R**) and the external force due to the bar.

Even though the lower arm has a weight, the hint given in the problem text states that we neglect it. This is not done to reduce the mathematical effort, but because the weight is much smaller than the other forces in this problem. How would you make that assumption before calculating the magnitude of these forces? The short answer is: intuition built by experience. After working with problems of this nature for a while you notice that some forces are usually much bigger than others. But even an experienced scientist is expected to validate such assumptions at the end of a calculation. Thus, estimate the magnitude of the weight and compare it with the results we find in this problem.

The free–body–diagram is shown in Fig. 4.68. Note that the coordinate system shown in Fig. 4.55 is used to establish the angles in the free–body–diagram. The balance of torque plot is already given at the right side of Fig. 4.55. The solid dot is the rotation axis (physically representing the high bar) and the thicker solid line represents the lower arm as a bar. The force **R** acts onto the end of the bar (elbow joint) while the tendon (exerting the tension force **T**) is attached a small distance l_2 away from the joint. These two forces form angles ϕ and ψ with the lower arm, where the angle ψ is unknown and the angle ϕ is given. Also given is the angle θ which defines the angle between the vertical and the lower arm.

Using Eq. (4.21), we write the following three formulas for the rotational equilibrium in this problem:

$$(I) \quad F_{ext} \sin\theta + R \sin\psi - T \sin\phi = 0$$

$$(II) \quad F_{ext} \cos\theta + R \cos\psi - T \cos\phi = 0 \tag{43}$$

$$(III) \quad -l_1 T \sin\phi + (l_1 + l_2) R \sin\psi = 0$$

Note that formula (III) in Eq. (43) does not contain a reference to force $\mathbf{F}_{ext}$ since this force acts along a line through the axis. The formula does not contain the x–components of the forces **R** and **T** either for the same reason. To solve Eq. (43) is mathematical slightly more challenging. One reason why Eq. (43) is harder to analyze lies in the fact that it contains three unknown variables, R, T and ψ, and they are present in each of three formulas.

Solution part (b): Between the first and third formula in Eq. (43) we eliminate $R\sin\psi$. For this we first isolate $R\sin\psi$ in formula (I):

$$R\sin\psi = T\sin\phi - F_{ext}\sin\theta \tag{44}$$

Next, we substitute Eq. (44) into formula (III) of Eq. (43):

$$l_1 T\sin\phi = (l_1 + l_2)(T\sin\phi - F_{ext}\sin\theta)$$

$$\Rightarrow \quad T = \frac{(l_1 + l_2) F_{ext}\sin\theta}{l_2 \sin\phi} \tag{45}$$

In Eq. (45), we enter the external force from part (a) and

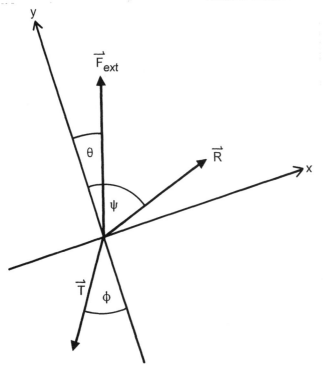

Fig. 4.68: Free–body–diagram for the lower arm of a person hanging on a high bar.

the values given in the problem. This leads to:

$$T = \frac{45[cm]\ \frac{W}{2}\ \sin 10^0}{5[cm]\ \sin 20^0} = 2.28\ W \qquad (46)$$

At this point you see the benefit of calculating the magnitude of various forces as a multiple of the weight $W = mg$ instead of calculating a specific number for a given mass of the person's body. While the force in unit [N] depends on the mass, and thus varies between individuals, the answers in part (a) and (b) are general results.

We found that the force pulling on our hands while hanging on a high bar is equal to half our weight, but that the tension in each of our two biceps tendons is more than twice our weight! Thus, that tendon has to be made of very strong tissue and has to be attached very firmly to the bone and the muscle. Also, the biceps muscle must be strong to exert this force on the bone.

This calculation illustrates what is desirable for an athlete: a small body weight and well trained arm muscles. In turn, a short arm is not an asset since the two lengths l_1 and l_2 are related to each other (scaling).

Solution part (c): To obtain the two remaining unknown variables, R and ψ, we use formulas (II) and (III) in Eq. (43). Substituting the result of part (b) for T, we get:

$$R\cos\psi = T\cos\phi - F_{ext}\cos\theta =$$

$$2.28\ W\cos 20^0 - 0.5\ W\cos 10^0 \qquad (47)$$

$$\Rightarrow \quad R\cos\psi = 1.65\ W$$

and

$$R\sin\psi = \frac{l_1}{l_1 + l_2}\ T\sin\phi =$$

$$\frac{40[cm]}{45[cm]}\ 2.28\ W\ \sin 20^0 \qquad (48)$$

$$\Rightarrow \quad R\sin\psi = 0.69\ W$$

From Eqs. (47) and (48), the magnitude of **R** and the angle ψ follow with standard trigonometric methods:

$$R = \sqrt{R^2\cos^2\psi + R^2\sin^2\psi} =$$
$$\sqrt{(1.65\ W)^2 + (0.69\ W)^2} = 1.79\ W \qquad (49)$$

and

$$\tan\psi = \frac{R\sin\psi}{R\cos\psi} = \frac{0.69\ W}{1.65\ W} \qquad (50)$$

$$\Rightarrow \quad \psi = 22.7^0$$

Again, note that the force **R** is a large force, in each arm almost twice the weight of the person!

Problem 4.13

A disabled arm with the upper arm and elbow in a cast is supported by a sling, which exerts the force **F** on the lower arm. The force **F** is directed perpendicularly to the lower arm upwards, as indicated in Fig. 4.56. The distance between the shoulder joint and the elbow is $l_1 =$

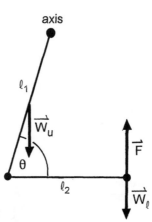

Fig. 4.56 for problem P–4.13.

38

30 cm, the mass of the upper arm (with cast) is 8 kg. For the distance between the elbow and the supported wrist we use $l_2 = 25$ cm, for the mass of the lower arm we use 2 kg. The angle between the lower arm and the upper arm is $\theta = 75^0$. Assuming that the sling supports the lower arm at its center–of–mass, calculate the magnitude of force **F**.

Hint: There are other forces acting on the arm which we assume to act along a line through the shoulder joint. Thus, equating **F** with the weights of the upper and lower arm does not yield the right result. Instead, the problem is solved with the balance of torque equation, into which the unknown forces at the shoulder joint do not enter.

Solution: The axis of rotation is the shoulder joint; some of the forces acting on the arm are exerted below the elbow, i.e., below the point at which the arm is bend. Therefore, this problem is an application of the concepts introduced in section 4.4.2.

The problem text states that the problem has to be approached by using the torque equilibrium equation. Note that we cannot draw a free–body–diagram for this

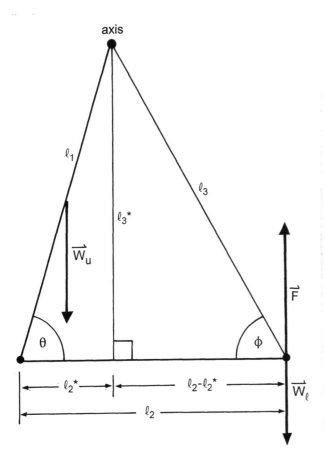

Fig. 4.69: Balance of torque plot for the arm in a sling. This plot defines several additional lengths and angles needed to solve the problem.

problem as not all the forces acting on the arm are identified. Using the concepts discussed in section 4.4.2 we draw a second balance of torque plot which defines several additional distances and angles. This supplementary plot is shown in Fig. 4.69. In addition to the three forces and two lengths shown in Fig. 4.56, the distance l_3 from the axis to the point at which the forces act on the lower arm is included and a new angle ϕ is defined. For the purpose of geometrical construction, the distance $l_3{}^*$ is introduced which is the length of the vector pointing perpendicularly to the lower arm toward the rotation axis.

With these additional variables introduced, formula (III) of Eq. (4.21) is written for the problem:

$$(W_u \cos\theta)\,\frac{l_1}{2} \; + \; (F \cos\phi)\, l_3 \; - \; ...$$

$$... \; - \; (W_l \cos\phi)\, l_3 \; = \; 0 \tag{51}$$

in which $W_u\cos\theta$ is the force component perpendicular to the upper arm, and $F\cos\phi$ and $W_l\cos\phi$ are the force components perpendicular to the line drawn from the axis through the point of attachment of the two forces acting on the lower arm (the length of this line is defined as l_3).

In the form given, Eq. (51) contains not only the magnitude of the force **F** as an unknown variable, but also l_3 and the angle ϕ are not known. Thus, before we can proceed with solving Eq. (51), these two variables must be determined.

l_3 is found with the Pythagorean theorem once the lengths $l_3{}^*$ and $l_2 - l_2{}^*$ are calculated. Trigonometric calculations show:

$$l_3^* \; = \; l_1 \sin\theta \; = \; 30[cm]\sin 75^0 \; = \; 29.0 \; cm$$

$$l_2^* \; = \; l_1 \cos\theta \; = \; 30[cm]\cos 75^0 \; = \; 7.8 \; cm \tag{52}$$

$$\Rightarrow \quad l_2 - l_2^* \; = \; 22.2 \; cm$$

and thus:

$$l_3^2 \; = \; (l_3^*)^2 \; + \; (l_2 - l_2^*)^2 \tag{53}$$

which yields:

$$l_3 \; = \; \sqrt{(29[cm])^2 + (22.2[cm])^2} \; = \; 36.5 \; cm \tag{54}$$

For the angle ϕ, using trigonometry and Fig. 4.69, we get:

$$\tan\phi = \frac{l_3^*}{l_2 - l_2^*} = \frac{29.0 \, [cm]}{22.2 \, [cm]} \tag{55}$$

$$\Rightarrow \quad \phi = 52.6^0$$

In the final step, Eq. (51) is solved for the magnitude of the force **F**:

$$\left(8[kg] \, 9.8 \left[\frac{m}{s^2} \right] \cos 75^0 \right) \frac{0.3[m]}{2} - \ldots$$

$$\ldots - \left(2[kg] \, 9.8 \left[\frac{m}{s^2} \right] \cos 52.6^0 \right) 0.29[m] + \ldots \tag{56}$$

$$\ldots + (F \cos 52.6^0) \, 0.29[m] = 0$$

Eq. (56) yields F = 5.8 N, which means that the sling supports an apparent weight of only 0.6 kg. This small force is intentional as a large force would unnecessarily strain the patient's neck.

CHAPTER V

Bioenergetics: the conservation of energy

Problem 5.1

Fig. 5.25(b) shows in double–logarithmic representation the nerve pulse rate (we use the variable P for the pulse rate) as a function of the speed of an approaching object for a Meissner's corpuscle. Using the power law relation $P = a\,v^b$, determine the constants a and b.

Table 5.8: Data sets from Fig. 5.25 for nerve impulse response of Meissner's corpuscles.

Data set	$\ln(P\ [s^{-1}])$	$\ln(v\ [mm/s])$
#1	0.693	−1.099
#2	2.303	+1.714

Solution: Fig. 5.25(b) is a double–logarithmic plot with logarithmic axes. As outlined in the General Appendix (Chapter 24), you want to supplement both axes with linear axes that show values for lnP and lnv. After generating these additional axes the data analysis proceeds in the same fashion as discussed in the General Appendix: first the power law is rewritten in logarithmic form:

$$P = a\,v^b \quad \Rightarrow \quad lnP = lna + b\,lnv \quad \text{(1)}$$

Eq. (1) is analyzed to obtain the constants a and b.

From Fig. 5.25 we read two data pairs, lnP and lnv. My particular choice is shown in Table 5.8. The two data sets are chosen by reading the speed values at impulse rate values of $P = 2\ s^{-1}$ and $P = 10\ s^{-1}$.

Table 5.8 allows us to write two linear formulas based on Eq. (1):

(I)	$0.693 = b\,(-1.099) + lna$
(II)	$2.303 = b\,(+1.714) + lna$

| (II) − (I) | $1.61 = b\,(1.714 + 1.099)$ |

Solving the last formula for b yields b = 0.57. A value for lna is obtained by substituting the result for b in either of the two formulas (I) or (II), which yields lna = 1.326. This is equivalent to a = 3.8.

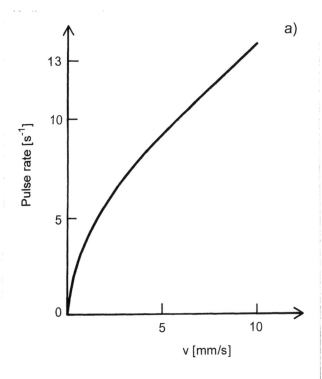

a)

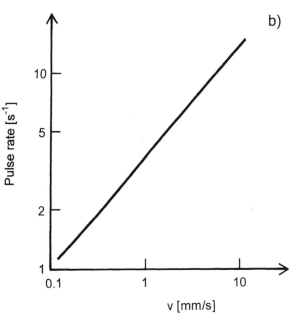

b)

← Fig. 5.25: The impulse rate for a Meissner's corpuscle as a function of the speed of an approaching object. The impulse rate is given in unit [impulses/s] and the speed is given in unit [mm/s].
(a) A linear plot of the data.
(b) A double–logarithmic plot of the same data.

Note that we did not identify a physical concept (or law) which justifies the power law form of Eq. (1), but introduced this relation empirically. This is often done in the sciences and allows you to develop an idea of the physical processes behind the data without having established firm physical laws. There are, of course, several differences between an empirical relation and a physical law. For example, the coefficients a and b have been calculated from experimental data and carry an experimental uncertainty; their true values can only be identified through a physical reasoning for the law relating the impulse rate and the speed of the approaching object. This distinction is important when we ask for the units of the two coefficients. As long as we use an empirical relation, the units of a and b are meaningless and should not be considered further; if we had a proposed physical law, then the units of the coefficients would have to be consistent with the model.

If you check through the large number of laws in the textbook as they are listed for example in the summary sections at the end of each chapter, you will notice that numerical values which are either written as an exponent or as the argument of a function, e.g. x in y^x or $\sin(x)$, never carry a unit. Imagine, as an example, that x has the unit meter [m]. Then $\sin(x)$ would contribute a $\sin[m]$ term to the units of the law. $\sin[m]$ as a unit, however, makes no physical sense.

Problem 5.2
Fig. 5.38 shows the height h [mm] versus mass m [kg]

(solid lines) and the active metabolic rate E [kcal/day] versus height (dashed line) for growing children. Determine the three exponents b in
(a) $h = a_1 m^{b1}$ for m < 25 kg (curve I),
(b) $h = a_2 m^{b2}$ for m > 25 kg (curve II), and
(c) $E = a_3 m^{b3}$ for m < 40 kg (curve III).
The energy conversion is 1 cal = 4.19 J.
For those interested:
(d) Find pictures of children and adults and compare the body proportions to see what causes the differences in the exponents.

Solution part (a): This problem is solved in analogous fashion as problem P–5.1. After supplementing the axes of Fig. 5.38 with linear axes for lnh, lnE and lnm, we proceed as described in the General Appendix.

From Fig. 5.38 we read two data pairs of lnh and lnm from the straight line labelled (I). The data I picked are listed in Table 5.9.

Table 5.9: Data sets from Fig. 5.38 for curve (I).

h [mm]	lnh	m [kg]	lnm
186	5.23	1	0.0
3260	8.09	100	4.605

Using Table 5.9, we write two linear formulas analogous to Eq. (1) in the form lnh = b lnm + lna:

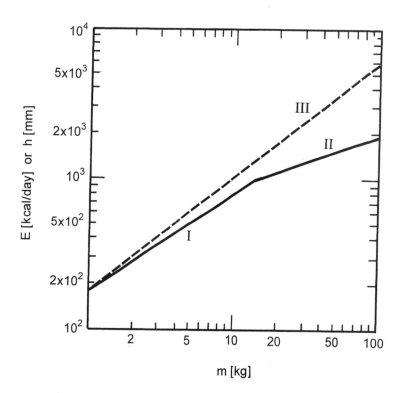

Fig. 5.38 for problem P–5.2.

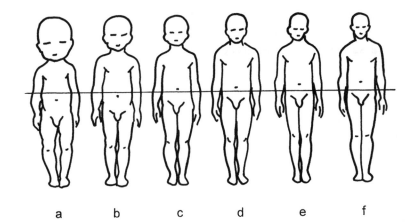

Fig. 5.44: Proportions of human body as function of age. (a) 6 months old fetus, (b) 2 years, (c) 5 years, (d) 13 years, (e) 17 years, (f) adult.

a   b   c   d   e   f

(I)	$5.23 = b\ 0.0 + \ln a$
(II)	$8.09 = b\ 4.605 + \ln a$

(II)–(I)	$2.86 = b\ 4.605$

Thus, $b = 0.62 \approx 2/3$ and $a = 186$.

Solution part (b): Part (b) is done in the same fashion as part (a). From Fig. 5.38 we next read two data pairs of $\ln h$ and $\ln m$ from the straight line labelled (II). My choice is listed in Table 5.10.

Table 5.10: Data sets from Fig. 5.38 for curve (II).

h [mm]	lnh	m [kg]	lnm
419	6.04	1	0.0
1860	7.53	100	4.605

Using Table 5.10 we write two linear formulas:

(I)	$6.04 = b\ 0.0 + \ln a$
(II)	$7.53 = b\ 4.605 + \ln a$

(II)–(I)	$1.49 = b\ 4.605$

Thus, $b = 0.325 \approx 1/3$ and $a = 419$.

Solution part (c): For the linear fit of the dashed line in Fig. 5.38, we read two data pairs of $\ln E$ and $\ln m$ from the curve labelled (III). These data are in Table 5.11.

Table 5.11: Data sets from Fig. 5.38 for curve (III).

E [kcal/day]	lnE	m [kg]	lnm
181	5.20	1	0.0
5540	8.62	100	4.605

Using Table 5.11, we write two linear formulas analogous to Eq. (1) in the form $\ln E = b \ln m + \ln a$:

(I)	$5.20 = b\ 0.0 + \ln a$
(II)	$8.62 = b\ 4.605 + \ln a$

(II)–(I)	$3.42 = b\ 4.605$

Thus, $b = 0.74 \approx 3/4$ and $a = 181$.

Solution part (d): Fig. 5.44 shows the proportions of human bodies as a function of age. Height is clearly not

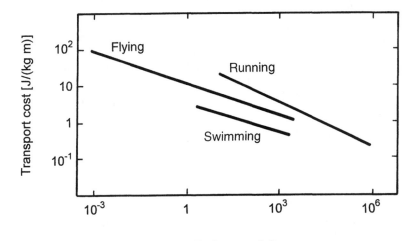

Fig. 5.39 for problem P–5.3.

by itself sufficient to predict the mass of a person as width and depth also contribute to the volume. It is the volume which is ultimately linked to the mass, assuming a constant density of tissue and bone material.

Problem 5.3

In the mid–Cretaceous (110 to 100 million years ago) dinosaurs lived near the poles, e.g. at 80^0N with fossils in North Alaska and the Yukon and at 80^0S with fossils near Melbourne, Australia. The polar regions of the Cretaceous were densely forested with only occasional light freezes in the winter, but non–hibernating ectotherms cannot tolerate prolonged periods without sunlight. Indeed, the most northern fossil find of a large ectotherm is a giant crocodile (phobosuchids) at 55^0N. Fig. 5.39 illustrates the energy consumption in [J/(kg m)] for animals specialized for swimming, flying and running as their normal mode of locomotion. The energy cost for long–distance migration across land is given as:

$$E_{mig} \left[\frac{J}{m} \right] = 14 \left(m \, [kg] \right)^{3/4} \qquad (2)$$

(a) Using Eqs. (2) and (5.2) evaluate the hypothesis that ectothermic southern polar dinosaurs migrated annually between 80^0S and 55^0S latitudes for
(I) Leaellynasaura, which was a 10 kg herbivore,
(II) Dwarf Allosaur, which was a 500 kg carnivore, and
(III) Muttaburrasaurus, which was a 4 tonne herbivore.
(b) Using the energy consumption for running in Fig. 5.39 and Eq. (5.36) for the potential energy, compare the benefits of living in plains versus mountainous terrain for small and large endotherms.

Solution part (a): Eq. (5.2) provides the metabolic rate Mr in [kJ/day] as a function of body mass m in [kg] for ectotherms and endotherms:

$$ectotherm: \ Mr \ [kJ/day] = 20 \left(m \, [kg] \right)^{3/4}$$
$$\qquad (3)$$
$$endotherm: \ Mr \ [kJ/day] = 450 \left(m \, [kg] \right)^{3/4}$$

The problem is solved in the following steps: first, the length of the migration is calculated. Eq. (2) is then used to determine the metabolic requirement for such a migration. Eq. (3) is used to calculate the annual energy production for the same animal. The migration can only occur if its energy requirement is less than the energy production during the same time period.

The distance associated with an annual migration between 80^0S and 55^0S is determined from the radius of the Earth. With $R_{Earth} = 6370$ km, the Earth's

circumference is calculated as $C = 2\pi R_{Earth} \cong 40,000$ km. This circumference corresponds to 360^0; the assumed migration D covered 50^0 (back and forth), which equals:

$$D = 40,000[km] \ \frac{50^0}{360^0} = 5,500 \ km \qquad (4)$$

We multiply this distance with the energy consumption per meter, given in Eq. (2):

$$E_{required} \ [J] = E_{mig} \left[\frac{J}{m} \right] D \ [m]$$
$$\qquad (5)$$
$$\Rightarrow \quad E_{required} \ [J] = \ = 7.7 \times 10^7 \left(m \, [kg] \right)^{3/4}$$

An ectotherm of the same mass m has an annual metabolic rate calculated from Eq. (3):

$$Mr \ [J/yr] = 7.3 \times 10^6 \left(m \, [kg] \right)^{3/4} \qquad (6)$$

From Eqs. (5) and (6) we determine the ratio of energy required to energy available per annum:

$$\frac{E_{required} \ [J]}{Mr \ [J/yr]} = \frac{7.7 \times 10^7 \left(m \, [kg] \right)^{3/4}}{7.3 \times 10^6 \left(m \, [kg] \right)^{3/4}} = 10.5 \quad (7)$$

Note that this result is independent of the mass of the individual species we study. Thus, ectothermic dinosaurs of any size could not have migrated as assumed because the migration would require more than 10 times their annual metabolic rate. Modern predators may use up to 25 % of their metabolic rate walking in search of food.

Solution part (b): Fig. 5.39 and Eq. (2) quantify the energy consumption when running on flat ground. Eq. (2) states that the energy needed per meter travelled is proportional to $m^{3/4}$. In mountainous terrain, a vertical travel component has to be included. The change in potential energy per meter height difference is $\Delta E_{pot}/h \propto mg$, i.e., it is directly proportional to the mass of the animal. Thus, the ratio of energy required for horizontal versus vertical travel for the same animal is:

$$\frac{\Delta E_{horiz} \ [J/m]}{\Delta E_{vert} \ [J/m]} \propto \frac{m^{3/4}}{m} = m^{-1/4} \qquad (8)$$

i.e., lighter animals are favored when a larger component of vertical movement is involved.

Problem 5.4

A gas expands from a volume of 1.0 liter to a volume of 5.0 liters as shown in the pV–diagram of Fig. 5.40. How much work does the gas on the piston?

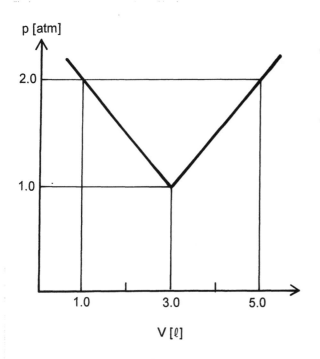

Fig. 5.40 for problem P–5.4.

Solution: The definition of work is based on the area under the curve representing a process in a pV–diagram. If the process occurs at contant pressure, p = const = p_0, the work is calculated from:

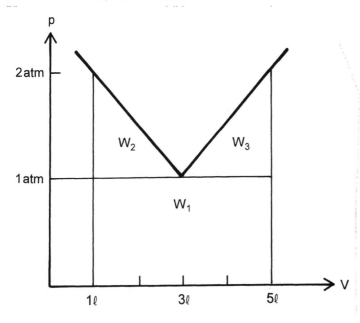

Fig. 5.45: The area under the curve in the pV–diagram of Fig. 5.40 is divided in three parts.

$$W = -p_0 \left(V_{final} - V_{initial} \right) \qquad (9)$$

For any other process, either graphic or numerical methods are needed to obtain the area. Fig. 5.40 represents an intermediate case: the pressure varies along straight line segments. In this case, a geometrical method can be applied to obtain the work.

The area under the curve in Fig. 5.40 is divided into three simple–shaped areas, as shown in Fig. 5.45. We calculate the contribution to the total work of each of these three areas; the total work is then the sum of the three components.

Using geometric features of right triangles and rectangles, we find for the three areas:

$$A_1 = 1[atm] \left(5[l] - 1.0[l] \right) = 4 \; atm \; l$$

$$A_2 = \frac{1}{2} \left(2[atm] - 1[atm] \right) \left(3[l] - 1[l] \right)$$

$$= 1 \; atm \; l \qquad (10)$$

$$A_3 = \frac{1}{2} \left(2[atm] - 1[atm] \right) \left(5[l] - 3[l] \right)$$

$$= 1 \; atm \; l$$

The terms in Eq. (10) were intentionally not labelled W_1, W_2 and W_3 because we did not yet include the sign convention. We determine the sign of the work term only after the geometric analysis is completed which yields the absolute value of the area under the curve. The total work is:

$$W = -\left(A_1 + A_2 + A_3 \right) = -6 \; atm \; l$$
$$\Rightarrow \quad W = -608 \; J \qquad (11)$$

The negative sign in Eq. (11) results from the sign convention: the process in Fig. 5.40 is an expansion for which the work is negative (work done by the gas on the piston).

The unit [atm *l*] in the first formula of Eq. (11) is not a proper energy unit and has been converted with 1 liter = 1×10^{-3} m³ and 1 atm = 1.013×10^5 Pa.

Note that Fig. 5.40 does not represent a typical process. However, it is often possible to approximate the actual curve with a few straight line segments. Thus, the method below is often used to obtain a first approximation of the work in a real system.

45

Problem 5.5

A massless string runs around two massless, frictionless pulleys, as shown in Fig. 5.41. An object with mass m = 15 kg hangs from one pulley. A force **F** is exerted on the free end of the string.

(a) What is the magnitude of the force **F** if the object is lifted at a constant speed?

(b) To lift the object by 2.5 m, how far must the free end of the string be pulled?

(c) During the lift in part (b), what is the work done on the object by the force **F** via the string?

Hint: Use the lower pulley and the attached object as the system.

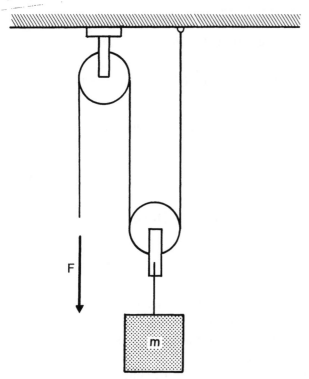

Fig. 5.41 for problem P–5.5.

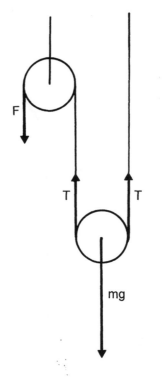

Fig. 5.46: Sketch of the forces acting on the various pulleys in Fig. 5.41.

$$2\,T - mg = 0 \tag{12}$$

We also know that F = T because the string is massless. From Eq. (12), we find the force F in the form:

$$F = T = \frac{1}{2}\,m\,g = \frac{1}{2}\,15[kg]\,9.8\left[\frac{m}{s^2}\right] \tag{13}$$

$$\Rightarrow \quad F = 73.5\ N$$

Solution part (a): The system is the combination of the massless free pulley and the object of mass m. We supplement Fig. 5.41 with a sketch which includes the relevant forces for this problem. Four forces are identified in Fig. 5.46: the weight of the object of mass m, the two tensions in the string extending upwards from the free pulley, and the external force that pulls the string down at the left. Note that the two tensions act on the same body, thus, they are not an action–reaction pair. They are nevertheless equal in magnitude since otherwise a net torque on the free pulley would result, leading to a rotational acceleration of the pulley.

Defining the vertical direction as the y–axis, the mechanical equilibrium in the y–direction is written from Fig. 5.46 using Newton's first law:

Solution part (b) : This part you answer based on your intuition. To lift the free pulley by a given distance d, the upward directed strings on either side of the pulley must each become shorter by that length. Since the string doesn't shrink or stretch, the shortening here must be compensated by the lengthening of the string running down at the left side of the pulley at the ceiling. Thus, the end of that string section has moved a distance d' = 2 d = 2 · 2.5 [m] = 5.0 m.

Solution part (c): This part illustrates that work can be calculated for any force present in a problem. Thus, work is often calculated when only some of the forces are known quantitatively. This is different from the previous chapters where a problem could not be solved unless all forces acting on the system were taken into account.

Note that the force and the displacement d' from part (b) are parallel. Thus, we use Eq. (5.8) to find the work done by the external force **F**:

$$W = (-F)(-d') = \boxed{73.5[N]\ 5.0[m]}$$ (14)

$$\Rightarrow \quad W = +368\ J$$

Since W > 0, this amount of work is invested in the system at the expense of the origin of the external force. In other words, this work is done on the system by the source of the external force.

5.

Problem 5.6
When people run, they dissipate about 0.6 J of mechanical energy per step and per kilogram of body mass. If a certain person of 70 kg body mass dissipates 80 J of energy per second while running, how fast is the person running? Assume that the steps taken are 1.6 m long.

Solution: The best way to proceed with this problem is to focus on the units of the given quantities. We define as N the number of steps taken during the time interval Δt. The work per step and per kilogram of body mass is $W_{step, kg} = 0.6$ J/kg. Note that "step" is not a standard unit, and therefore, is not included in the units of this quantity. The energy dissipation P has the unit [J/s]: P = 80 J/s; this quantity is usually called *power* (therefore, we use the letter P to express this variable). We use the concept power too infrequently in the textbook to justify using the term; therefore, we will continue to refer to it as an energy per time unit.

With the variables defined above we find for the number of steps taken per second:

$$P = \frac{W_{step, kg}\ m\ N}{\Delta t}$$ (15)

$$\Rightarrow \quad \frac{N}{\Delta t} = \frac{P}{m\ W_{step, kg}}$$

substituting in Eq. (15) the values given in the problem text, we obtain:

$$\frac{N}{\Delta t} = \frac{\overset{79}{80\left[\dfrac{J}{s}\right]}}{0.6\left[\dfrac{J}{kg}\right]70\,[kg]} = 1.9\ \frac{steps}{s}$$ (16)

u

The number of steps per second allows us in turn to calculate the speed of the person since we know that each step is 1.6 meters long. Thus:

$$v = \frac{\Delta x}{\Delta t} = \frac{N}{\Delta t}\ l_{step} =$$

$$1.9\left[\frac{steps}{s}\right]1.6\left[\frac{m}{step}\right] = 3.0\ \frac{m}{s}$$ (17)

$$1.22\frac{m}{step} \qquad 2.4\ m/s.$$

Problem 5.7
Two objects are connected by a massless string as shown in Fig. 5.42. The pulley is massless and rotates without friction. The object of smaller mass m = 1.2 kg slides without friction on an inclined plane which makes an angle of $\theta = 35^0$ with the horizontal. The mass of the larger object is M = 2.5 kg and hangs on the string. If the two objects are released from rest with the string taut, what is their total kinetic energy when the object of mass M has fallen 30 cm?

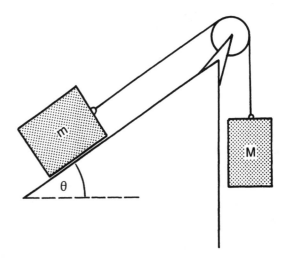

Fig. 5.42 for problem P–5.7.

Solution: This is a problem suitable for the conservation of energy concept. Whenever you use the conservation of energy for a mechanical problem, you start with the following equation:

$$E_{kin,\ init} + E_{pot,\ init} = E_{kin,\ fin} + E_{pot,\ fin}$$ (18)

in which the index "init" stand for *initial* and "fin" is *final*. The left hand side of the equation is the sum of all energies at an initial time instant and the right hand side of the equation is the sum of all energies at a final time

47

instant. Thus, we must first identify these two time instants. Choose them such that the information available at one time instant is a maximum, and the unknown parameter occurs at the other time instant. It doesn't matter, however, on which side the unknown parameter occurs.

In the current problem, we choose as the initial instant the moment of release when both objects are at rest. For the final instant we choose the point in time when the object of mass M has fallen 30 cm since we are asked about the total kinetic energy (unknown variable) at that instant. Now we evaluate each term in Eq. (18).

(I) The initial kinetic energy is zero since both objects start from rest.

(II) The initial potential energy can be chosen arbitrarily since there is no predetermined origin along the vertical axis which defines $y = 0$ in $E_{pot} = mgy$ for either object. For convenience, we choose $y = 0$ at the initial height for each of the two objects, and obtain $E_{pot, init} = 0$ J. We also define the y–axis as directed upwards.

(III) The final kinetic energy of the two objects is sought. We include $E_{kin, final} = \frac{1}{2}(m + M)v^2_{final}$ in Eq. (18).

(IV) The final potential energy has two contributions. The object of mass M is at this time at $y = -0.3$ m, i.e., its contribution to the final potential energy is:

$$E_{pot, final, M} = Mgy =$$

$$2.5[kg] \; 9.8\left[\frac{m}{s^2}\right](-0.3[m]) = -7.35 \; J \tag{19}$$

This value is negative since the object is closer to the Earth, i.e., a state with decreased potential energy.

At the same time, the object of mass m has moved 30 cm up the inclined plane. We know this because the massless string is taut, and therefore, does not change its length during the process. Since the object of

mass m moves along the inclined plane and not vertically up, its position relative to the surface of the Earth has not changed by the length 0.3 m but by a distance of $0.3[m] \sin\theta = 0.3[m] \sin 35°$, i.e., the y–component of the displacement. Remember, the potential energy is a function of the position relative to the surface of the Earth; thus, only the change in the vertical position matters. From this we now calculate the final potential energy of the object of mass m:

$$E_{pot, final, m} = 1.2[kg] \; 9.8\left[\frac{m}{s^2}\right] 0.3[m] \sin 35° \tag{20}$$

$$\Rightarrow \quad E_{pot, final, m} = +2.0 \; J$$

Next we enter all four terms we found into Eq. (18):

$$0[J] + 0[J] = E_{kin, fin} - 7.35[J] + 2.0[J] \tag{21}$$

$$\Rightarrow \quad E_{kin, final} = +5.35 \; J$$

The final kinetic energy is larger than zero since both objects are in motion when the object of mass M passes the 30 cm marker. Eq. (21) yields for the final speed:

$$v_{final} = \sqrt{\frac{2 \, E_{kin}}{m + M}} = 1.7 \; \frac{m}{s} \tag{22}$$

Note that the square–root term contains the sum $m + M$ in the denominator; this is due to the fact that both objects are linked by the string, and therefore, must move with the same speed at every time instant.

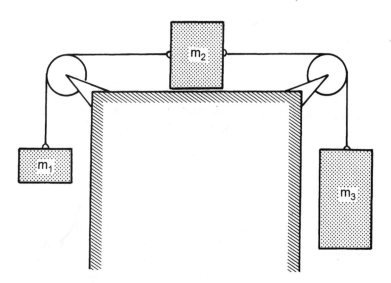

Fig. 5.43 for problem P–5.8.

Problem 5.8

Three objects with masses $m_1 = 5.0$ kg, $m_2 = 10.0$ kg and $m_3 = 15.0$ kg, are attached by massless strings over two frictionless pulleys, as shown in Fig. 5.43. The horizontal surface is frictionless and the system is released from rest. Using energy concepts, find the speed of m_3 after it has moved down 0.4 m.

Solution: We take the same approach as in the previous problem by applying Eq. (18) and choosing the initial instant to be the point of release when the objects are still at rest, and the final instant to be the point at which the object with mass m_3 has moved 0.4 m downwards. For each of the three objects, we identify each of the terms in Eq. (18) separately:

(I) The initial kinetic energy of all three objects is zero since they are connected by taut strings. When one of the objects is at rest, the other two must be at rest, too.

(II) The initial potential energy we choose to be zero by labelling the initial position of each object as the respective origin along the vertical axis.

(III) The final kinetic energy contains the unknown variable. Thus, we leave that term unchanged in Eq. (18) for now.

(IV) The final potential energy has three contributions, one due to each of the three objects. Since the object of mass m_2 moves across a horizontal surface only, its potential energy does not change; the other two objects, however, contribute:

$$m_3 = -m_1 g y_1$$

$$E_{pot,\,total} = m_1\, g\, y_{1,fin} + m_3\, g\, y_{3,fin} \quad {= g y_3}$$

$$g(mg_1)$$

$$\left(5.0[kg]0.4[m] + 15.0[kg](-0.4[m])\right)9.8\left[\frac{m}{s^2}\right] \quad (23)$$

$$\Rightarrow \quad E_{pot,\,total} = -39.2\ J$$

where a downward displacement of $\Delta y_3 = -0.4$ m for the object of mass m_3 means an upward displacement of the object of mass m_1 because the connecting strings are taut: $\Delta y_1 = +0.4$ m.

Next we enter all energy contributions at the initial and final states of the system into Eq. (18):

$$0 = -39.2\ [J] + \frac{1}{2}\left(m_1 + m_2 + m_3\right)v_{final}^2 \quad (24)$$

There is only one speed, v_{final}, associated with the total final kinetic energy because all three objects move at the same speed at all times due to the fixed distance resulting from taut connecting strings. Eq. (24) yields for the final speed:

$$v_{final} = \sqrt{\frac{2 \cdot 39.2[J]}{(5+10+15)[kg]}} = 1.62\ \frac{m}{s} \quad (25)$$

Problem 5.9

A pendulum consists of an object of mass $m = 1.5$ kg swinging on a massless string of length $l = 3.0$ m. The object has a speed of 2.0 m/s when it passes through its lowest point.

(a) If the gravitational potential energy is taken to be zero at the lowest point of the trajectory of the object, what is the total mechanical energy of the system?

(b) What is the speed of the object when the string is at 75^0 below the horizontal?

(c) What is the greatest angle with the vertical that the string reaches during the motion of the object?

Solution part (a): The total mechanical energy is conserved. Thus, we can choose any time instant to evaluate it. The best choice is the lowest point of the path of the object, since the potential energy at that point is zero and we know the speed of the object at that point. We find:

$$E_{total} = E_{kin,\,initial} = \frac{1}{2}\,m\,v_0^2 = 3.0\ J \quad (26)$$

Solution part (b): We start again with Eq. (18). The initial time instant is chosen when the object passes through the lowest point (since we know a lot about that instant) and the final time instant is chosen when the string is at 75^0 (because we are asked about the system at that time).

(I) The initial potential energy we choose to be zero by defining the origin of the vertical axis at the lowest point of the trajectory of the object.

(II) The initial kinetic energy is calculated from the given initial speed:

$$E_{kin,\,init} = \frac{1}{2}mv_0^2 = \frac{1.5[kg]}{2}\left(2.0\left[\frac{m}{s}\right]\right)^2 \quad (27)$$

$$\Rightarrow \quad E_{kin,\,init} = 3.0\ J$$

(III) To determine the final potential energy, we draw Fig. 5.47. The figure shows the position of the object when the string forms an angle of 75^0 with the horizontal, i.e., when the string is at an angle of 15^0 with the vertical. At that instant, the object is raised to the height

49

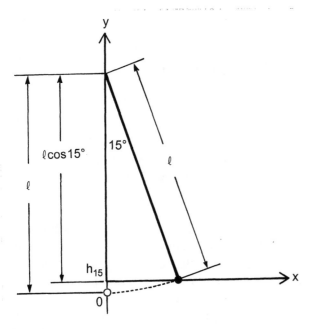

Fig. 5.47: Sketch illustrating the potential energy of the point mass in the pendulum.

$y = h_{15}$ above the lowest position at $y = 0$, and its potential energy is:

$$E_{pot, \, final} = mgh_{15} = mg \left(l - l\cos 15^0 \right)$$

$$\Rightarrow \quad E_{pot, \, final} = mgl \left(1 - \cos 15^0 \right) \qquad (28)$$

(IV) The formula for the final kinetic energy contains the final speed, and therefore contains the unknown variable.

Substituting these results into Eq. (18) leads to:

$$\frac{1}{2}mv_0^2 = \frac{1}{2}mv_{15}^2 + mgl \left(1 - \cos 15^0 \right) \qquad (29)$$

In this formula, we isolate the final kinetic energy term on the left side of the equation and then multiply by 2/m. This yields:

$$v_{15} = \sqrt{v_0^2 - 2gl \left(1 - \cos 15^0 \right)} \qquad (30)$$

With the given data we find:

$$v_{15} = \sqrt{\left(2 \left[\frac{m}{s} \right] \right)^2 - 2 \cdot 9.8 \left[\frac{m}{s^2} \right] 3 [m] 0.034} \qquad (31)$$

Thus, the final speed is $v_{15} = 1.41$ m/s.

Solution part (c) : We continue to use the same initial time instant (when the point mass is at its lowest point) but change the final time instant to the time instant when the object reaches its highest point. This leads to two new terms for the right hand side of Eq. (18):

(III) The final kinetic energy is zero at the highest point where the object comes momentarily to rest while reversing its direction of motion.

(IV) The final potential energy contains the final height above the lowest point as the unknown variable. Because we are asked for the angle of the string with the vertical at that instant, we are using Eq. (28) but exchange the 15^0 angle with the unknown angle θ_{max}. Substituting all terms in Eq. (18) leads this time to:

$$\frac{1}{2}mv_0^2 = mgl \left(1 - \cos\theta_{max} \right)$$

$$\qquad (32)$$

$$\Rightarrow \quad \cos\theta_{max} = 1 - \frac{v_0^2}{2gl} = 0.932$$

Thus, the maximum angle is $\theta_{max} = 21.3^0$.

Problem 5.10
Table 5.6 shows the metabolic rate for given activities of the adult human body and Table 5.7 gives the energy content of the three most important components of food. Answer the following two questions using the two tables:

Table 5.6 for problem P–5.10

Activity	Metabolic rate [cal/s kg]
Sleeping	0.263
Sitting	0.358
Standing	0.621
Walking	1.0
Biking	1.81
Swimming	2.63
Running	4.3

Table 5.7 for problem P–5.10

Food	Energy content [cal/g]
Carbohydrate	4100
Protein	4200
Fat	9300

(a) how much energy is expended by a person of mass of 75 kg who walks for one hour every morning?

(b) If the body of the person consumes body fat reserves to produce this energy, how much mass will be lost per day? Use 1 cal = 4.19 J.

Solution part (a): From Table 5.6, we find the metabolic rate for walking as Mr = 1.0 cal/(s kg). Note that the non–standard unit [cal] is still often used in the context of energy content in food or other organic compounds. You also find the unit [Cal] (with a capital letter C) which converts as 1 [Cal] = 1 [kcal] = 1×10^3 [cal]. As discussed before, it is advisable to convert such non–standard units as early as possible. In the current case, the result is Mr = 1.0 cal/(s kg) = 4.19 J/(s kg), using the conversion factor given in the problem text.

From this value of the metabolic rate Mr we determine the total energy when a person of 75 kg body weight walks for 1 h = 3600 s. Note that the non–standard unit [h] for *hours* is used. The energy consumption ΔE_{walk} is given as:

$$\Delta E_{walk} = 4.19 \left[\frac{J}{s \ kg} \right] 75[kg] \ 3600 \left[\frac{s}{h} \right] \qquad (33)$$

$$\Rightarrow \quad \Delta E_{walk} = 1130 \ kJ$$

Solution part (b): Using the result in Eq. (33) and Table 5.7, the fat consumption during the walking exercise is calculated. The table shows that 1 g = 0.001 kg fat provides 9300 cal ≈ 39 kJ, when converted into energy. Thus, the total fat consumption of the person, represented by the variable Fc, is:

$$Fc = \frac{1130 \ [kJ]}{39 \ [kJ/g]} \ 1 \times 10^{-3} \left[\frac{kg}{g} \right] \qquad (34)$$

$$\Rightarrow \quad Fc = 0.029 \ kg$$

i.e., only 29 g of fat are consumed ("lost").

Problem 5.11

A person of body mass 50 kg climbs 10 m up a vertical rope. How much energy in calories is dissipated as heat in a single climb if 20 % of the total energy required is used to do the work?

Solution: When a person climbs up a rope, the (gravitational) potential energy of the person changes. To increase the potential energy of the body, work must be done on the body. The amount of work or change in potential energy when climbing up a rope of length *l* is given by:

$$\Delta E_{pot} = m \ g \ l = 50[kg] \ 9.8 \left[\frac{m}{s^2} \right] 10[m] \qquad (35)$$

$$\Rightarrow \quad \Delta E_{pot} = + 4900 \ J$$

The text states that this is only 20 % of the total energy required. Thus, the total energy required for the rope climbing is 24.5 kJ.

Where does this energy come from? Remember, the first law of thermodynamics states that energy cannot be created, it can only be converted from one form into another. The energy in this case is the energy stored in the muscles of the person. This also explains why the question is asked the way it is stated. The term "dissipating" implies that chemical energy is converted into mechanical energy.

It is not unusual, albeit not particularly up to date, to request that the result is stated in a non–standard unit (here [cal]). Using the conversion factor from the General Appendix (Chapter 24), we find for the change in potential energy ΔE_{pot} = 1.17 kcal and for the total energy required 5.85 kcal.

Problem 5.12

Assume that Joule's brewery horses did each 750 J of work per second (this corresponds roughly to the definition of horse power). If he had 4 horses moving in a circle for one hour to operate a stirrer in a well isolated container filled with 1 m³ water at initial temperature of 25^0C, to what final value did the water temperature rise? Use Fig. 5.33 for the specific heat of water at 25^0C.

Solution: Four brewery horses perform work at a rate of W/t = 4 · 750 J/s = 3000 J/s. Thus, the total work, which is the energy transferred to the water per hour (= 3600 s) is given by the value of W = W/t · 1 h = 10,800 kJ. If the work is stored in the water in the form of heat as assumed in the text, then we apply the definition of the heat in the form:

$$Q = c \cdot m \cdot \Delta T \qquad (36)$$

in which c is the specific heat capacity of water, m is its mass and ΔT is the temperature change. We obtain the heat capacity of H_2O at 25^0C from Fig. 5.33 with a value of c_{H2O} = 4185 J/(^{0}C kg), which, after unit conversion, is equal to c_{H2O} = 4185 J/(K kg) since a one degree change

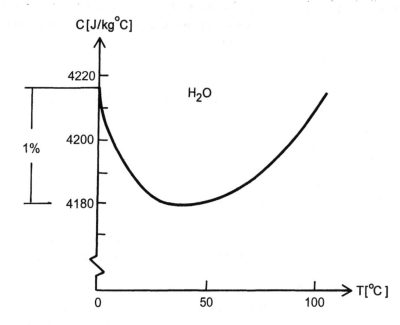

Fig. 5.33: Heat capacity for water between 0^0C and 100^0C.

in temperature is the same change for the Celsius and the Kelvin scales. Substituting the given values in Eq. (36) yields:

$$10800 \ kJ = m_{H_2O} \ c_{H_2O} \ \Delta T \qquad (37)$$

which yields for the temperature difference:

$$\Delta T = \frac{10800 \ [kJ]}{\rho_{H_2O} \ V_{H_2O} \ c_{H_2O}} =$$

$$\frac{10800 \ [kJ]}{1 \times 10^3 \left[\dfrac{kg}{m^3}\right] 1.0[m^3] \ 4.185 \left[\dfrac{kJ}{K \ kg}\right]} \qquad (38)$$

in which ρ_{H2O} is the water density, $\rho_{H2O} = 1.0$ g/cm³. This yields the result:

$$\Delta T = 2.58 \ K \qquad (39)$$

The temperature change in Eq. (39) is measurable but small, increasing from 25^0C to 27.6^0C.

CHAPTER VI

Respiration: the properties of gases

Problem 6.1

(a) Draw a graph for the volume of 1.0 mol of an ideal gas as a function of temperature in the range from 0 K to 400 K at constant gas pressures of, first, 0.2 atm and, secondly, 5 atm.

(b) Draw a graph for the pressure of 1.0 mol of an ideal gas as a function of volume between 0 liter and 20 liter at constant temperatures of 150 K and 300 K.

Use: 1 atm = 1.01×10^5 Pa.

Solution part (a): We use the ideal gas law in the form

$$p V = n R T \qquad (1)$$

For the first plot, we need the volume to be the independent variable and the temperature to be the dependent variable, i.e.,

$$V = \frac{n R}{p} T \qquad (2)$$

In this equation, we substitute the values of R from the table of constants in the General Appendix, n = 1.0 mol,

and either p = 0.2 atm = 20,260 Pa, or p = 5.0 atm = 506,500 Pa for the pressure. Then we plot two curves:

$$(I) \quad V\,[m^3] = 4.1 \times 10^{-4}\; T[K]$$
$$(II) \quad V\,[m^3] = 1.6 \times 10^{-5}\; T[K] \qquad (3)$$

These two curves are shown in Fig. 6.34.

Solution part (b): This time the ideal gas equation is rewritten such that the pressure is the independent variable and the volume is the dependent variable:

$$p = nRT\, \frac{1}{V} \qquad (4)$$

Using again n = 1, we find for the two temperatures given in the problem text:

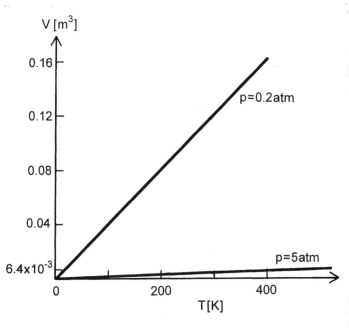

Fig. 6.34: V–T diagram for an ideal gas at two different pressure values.

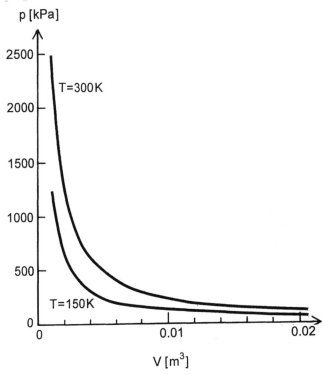

Fig. 6.35: p–V diagram for an ideal gas at two different temperatures.

53

(I) $T = 300K \Rightarrow p[kPa] = \dfrac{2.494}{V[m^3]}$

$$\tag{5}$$

(II) $T = 150K \Rightarrow p[kPa] = \dfrac{1.247}{V[m^3]}$

These two curves are shown in Fig. 6.35.

Problem 6.2

A container of volume 1 mm³ is initially filled with air. The container is then evacuated at 25°C to a pressure of 1.0×10^{-6} torr. How many molecules are in the container after evacuation if we assume that air is an ideal gas?

Solution: In the first step we determine the n [mol] from the ideal gas law n = pV/RT. We convert the values given in the problem to standard units: for the pressure $p = 1.0 \times 10^{-6}$ torr $= 1.33 \times 10^{-4}$ Pa, for the volume $V = 1.0 \times 10^{-9}$ m³ and for the temperature T = 298 K. Thus:

$$n = \frac{1.33 \times 10^{-4}[Pa]\ 1.0 \times 10^{-9}[m^3]}{8.314[J/(K\,mol)]\ 298[K]} \tag{6}$$

$$\Rightarrow \quad n = 5.4 \times 10^{-17}\ mol$$

In the next step, we multiply n with Avogadro's number, N_A, to obtain the number of molecules in the container N:

$$N = n\,N_A = 5.4 \times 10^{-17}[mol]\ 6 \times 10^{23}\left[\frac{1}{mol}\right] \tag{7}$$

$$\Rightarrow \quad N = 3.2 \times 10^7\ molecules$$

Problem 6.3

A container of volume V = 500 cm³ has a mass of 38.7340 g when evacuated. When the container is filled with air of pressure p = 1 atm at temperature T = 24°C, the mass of the system increases to 39.3135 g. Assuming that air behaves like an ideal gas, calculate from these data the average molar mass of air.

Solution: This problem is an application of the ideal gas law. Since the mass of the gas is given and the molar mass is sought, we rewrite the ideal gas law in the form:

$$pV = nRT = \frac{m}{M}\,RT \quad \Rightarrow \quad M = \frac{mRT}{pV} \tag{8}$$

In Eq. (8), m is the mass of air which is obtained from the given data by calculating:

$$m = m_{full} - m_{evac} = 0.5795 \times 10^{-3}\ kg \tag{9}$$

By substituting the remaining data given in the problem, including a temperature of 24°C = 297 K, and the air pressure in the container of 1.0 atm = 1.013×10^5 Pa, we find:

$$M = \frac{0.5795 \times 10^{-3}[kg]\,8.314\left[\dfrac{J}{K\,mol}\right]297[K]}{1.013 \times 10^5[Pa]\ 500 \times 10^{-6}[m^3]} \tag{10}$$

$$\Rightarrow \quad M = 0.02825\ \frac{kg}{mol} = 28.25\ \frac{g}{mol}$$

We usually use a value of 29 g/mol for the molar mass of air.

Problem 6.4

A container of volume 10.0 dm³ contains 1.03×10^{23} hydrogen gas molecules (H_2). If the pressure of the gas is 30.0 torr, what is
(a) the temperature, and
(b) the root–mean–square speed of the molecules?
Hint: Treat hydrogen as an ideal gas and use the conversion 1 torr = 133.32 Pa. The molecular mass of hydrogen is $M(H_2) = 2.0$ g/mol.

Solution part (a): As stated in the problem text, we treat hydrogen as an ideal gas. Note that this assumption is not valid in all cases, as discussed in the textbook; however, we cannot solve any gas problems at this point without this assumption since we haven't introduced any equation other than the ideal gas law for describing a gas.

We use the ideal gas law in the form T = pV/nR to determine the temperature. The given pressure value converts to p = 30 torr = 4000 Pa, the volume converts to V = 10 dm³ = 1.0×10^{-2} m³ and the molar mass equals $M(H_2) = 2.0$ g/mol = 0.002 kg/mol. The number of moles of hydrogen gas, n, is determined from the given number of gas molecules, $N = 1.03 \times 10^{23}$, and the Avogadro number, N_A, using the formula $n = N/N_A = 0.17$ mol.

Thus:

$$T = \frac{pV}{nR} = \frac{4000[Pa]\ 1.0\times 10^{-2}[m^3]}{0.17[mol]\ 8.314[J/(K\,mol)]} \quad \textbf{(11)}$$

$$\Rightarrow \quad T = 28.3\ K$$

Solution part (b): We determine the root–mean–square speed of the hydrogen molecules by substituting the results from part (a) into Eq. (6.70):

$$\sqrt{<v^2>} = \sqrt{\frac{3RT}{M}} = \quad \textbf{(12)}$$

$$\sqrt{\frac{3 \cdot 8.314[J/(K\,mol)]\ 28.3[K]}{0.002[kg/mol]}}$$

which yields:

$$\sqrt{<v^2>} = 594\ \frac{m}{s} \quad \textbf{(13)}$$

Thus, the speed of hydrogen molecules at this low temperature is still faster than the speed of nitrogen molecules at room temperature, as calculated in Eq. (6.71). This is one of the reasons why hydrogen is still a gas when cooled to 30 K.

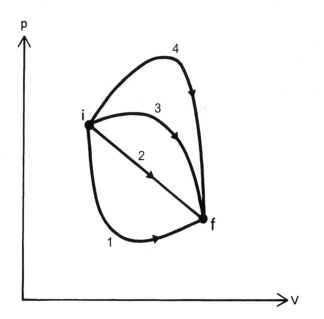

p

4

i

3

2

1

f

V

Fig. 5.19: Four possible paths for a process operating between an initial state (i) and a final state (f) of a system shown in a pressure versus volume diagram.

Problem 6.5

Fig. 5.19 shows a p–V diagram with four paths that a gas can take from an initial state i to a final state f. Rank the paths in decreasing order according to (a) the change of internal energy ΔU, and (b) the amount of heat transfer Q between the system and the environment.

Solution part (a): Note that we used the same figure in Example 5.5 to determine the ranking of the work done in each process from highest to lowest. All four paths lead to the same change of the internal energy of the system because:

$$\Delta U = U_f - U_i \quad \textbf{(14)}$$

and the initial and final states are the same in all cases.

Solution part (b): The first law of thermodynamics for a closed system states that the change in the internal energy is $\Delta U = Q + W$. From this follows that $Q = \Delta U - W$. Using the result for the order of the four work terms from Example 5.5, i.e., the result reported in Eq. (5.20), we find for the order of the heat terms:

$$Q_4 > Q_3 > Q_2 > Q_1 \quad \textbf{(15)}$$

Problem 6.6

1.0 mol of an ideal gas is expanded from an initial pressure of 10 atm to a final pressure of 0.4 atm in the same fashion as discussed in section 6.6. Calculate separately for two constant temperatures, 0^0C and 25^0C,
(a) the work done by the gas,
(b) the change of internal energy of the gas, and
(c) the amount of heat taken from the environment.

Solution part (a): This problem requires that the same type of calculation is done twice, once for an isothermal expansion at $T_1 = 0^0$C = 273.15 K and once for an isothermal expansion at $T_2 = 25^0$C = 298.15 K.

For the work of an isothermal expansion, we use the formulas developed in Eqs. (6.80) and (6.81) with the pressure as independent variable instead of the volume. At the first temperature, we find:

$$W = -nRT \ln\left(\frac{p_i}{p_f}\right) = \quad \textbf{(16)}$$

$$-1[mol]8.314\left[\frac{J}{K\,mol}\right]273.1[K]\ln\left(\frac{10}{0.4}\right)$$

which yields for the work:

$$W_1 = -7.31 \ kJ \qquad (17)$$

At the second temperature we obtain:

$$W = -nRT \ \ln\left(\frac{p_i}{p_f}\right) = \qquad (18)$$

$$-1[mol]8.314\left[\frac{J}{K\ mol}\right]298.1[K]\ \ln\left(\frac{10}{0.4}\right)$$

which yields:

$$W_2 = -7.98 \ kJ \qquad (19)$$

The second result can also be obtained relative to the first result by calculating:

$$W_2 = W_1 \ \frac{T_2}{T_1} \qquad (20)$$

Solution part (b): The change of the internal energy of an ideal gas during an isothermal process is zero, i.e., $\Delta U = 0$ since $\Delta T = 0$. This applies at any temperature.

Solution part (c): Using the first law of thermodynamics for closed systems, we obtain:

$$Q = \Delta U - W = -W \quad \Rightarrow$$

$$Q_1 = +7.31 \ kJ \ \ ; \ \ Q_2 = +7.98 \ kJ \qquad (21)$$

Problem 6.7
Fig. 6.32 shows the p–V relationship in the left ventricle of the human heart. The curve is traversed counter-clockwise with increasing time. The stroke volume is 100 ml − 35 ml = 65 ml. The systolic pressure is 118 torr (which is equal to 15.7 kPa) and the diastolic pressure is 70 torr (which is equal to 9.3 kPa). The ventricular pressure drops below the diastolic pressure while the pressure in the arteries remains about 70 torr because the aortic valve has closed and prevents back flow. Determine graphically the amount of work done in a single cycle.
Hint: Simplify the calculation by using the dashed straight lines in the p–V diagram instead of curved segments.

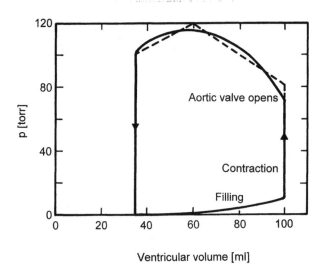

Fig. 6.32 for problem P–6.7.

Solution: Work is defined as the area under the curve in a p–V diagram, as discussed in the context of Figs. 5.17 and 5.18. To conveniently analyze the area under the curve in Fig. 6.32 (using the dashed lines instead of the curved upper line), the area is subdivided into six sections, as shown in Fig. 6.36. Note that sections 1 to 5 contribute to the area under the curve which is traversed from larger toward smaller volume, and thus, leads to positive work contributions, analogous to the discussion of Example 5.5 (see in particular Fig. 5.18). Area 6 represents an area which must be subtracted from the combined areas 1 through 5 to properly describe the enclosed

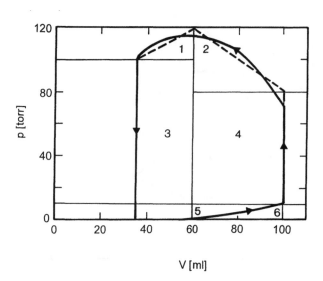

Fig. 6.36: p–V relation for the left ventricle of the heart. The area under the curve is determined from 6 rectangular or triangular segments.

area.

Note that all six areas are either rectangular or triangular with a 90° angle. The area of these two shapes are one or one–half times the width times the height, respectively. Thus, we find (all values given in units [torr *ml*]):

area 1 = ½ (25 · 20) = 250,
area 2 = ½ (40 · 40) = 800,
area 3 = (100 · 25) = 2500,
area 4 = (70 · 40) = 2800,
area 5 = (10 · 40) = 400, and
area 6 = ½ (10 · 40) = 200.

We obtain for the work from these data: W = 6750 – 200 = 6550 [torr *ml*]. This is converted to standard unit with 1 *ml* = 1 × 10⁻⁶ m³ and 1 torr = 133.32 Pa, yielding a work of W = + 0.87 J.

The work is positive, i.e., work is done on the fluid in the heart (here not an ideal gas but the liquid blood).

Problem 6.8

(a) How much heat is needed to increase the temperature of 3.45 g neon gas (Ne) in a 10 liter container from 0°C to 100°C? Treat Ne as an ideal gas and use M(Ne) = 20.18 g/mol.
(b) By how many percent does $<v^2>$ of the neon atoms in the gas increase in this process?
Hint: part (b) does not ask for v_{rms}.

Solution part (a): The argument for the amount of heat is based on the first law of thermodynamics for a closed system. We know that W = 0 J since the volume in this problem remains constant (no provision is given to allow for an increase or decrease of the container size). Therefore, $\Delta U = Q$. Finding the increase in the internal energy allows us to determine the amount of heat required.

For an ideal gas, we use Eq. (6.63) for ΔU with n = (3.45[g]) / (20.18[g/mol]) = 0.17 mol. Thus:

$$\Delta U = \frac{3}{2} nR\Delta T =$$

$$\frac{3}{2} \ 0.17[mol] \ 8.314\left[\frac{J}{K \, mol}\right] 100[K] \quad \textbf{(22)}$$

$$\Rightarrow \quad \Delta U = 212 \ J$$

Solution part (b): Note that the question is not for the root–mean–square speed but for $<v^2>$. The relative increase of this quantity is defined as:

$$\frac{\Delta <v^2>}{<v^2>_{initial}} = \frac{<v^2>_{final} - <v^2>_{initial}}{<v^2>_{initial}} \quad \textbf{(23)}$$

i.e., the relative increase is a fraction of the initial value. The result is multiplied by 100 to express it as a percentage value. Using Eq. (6.70) we rewrite Eq. (23):

$$\frac{\Delta <v^2>}{<v^2>_i} = \frac{\frac{3R}{M}T_{final} - \frac{3R}{M}T_{initial}}{\frac{3R}{M}T_{initial}} =$$

$$= \frac{T_{final} - T_{initial}}{T_{initial}} = \frac{100[K]}{273[K]} = 0.37 \quad \textbf{(24)}$$

This is a 37 % increase relative to the initial value.

3 3 7 6 0 6

3 6 8 5 0 6.

Problem 6.9

Show that Eq. (6.94) leads to Eq. (6.96) when using the operations specified in the text.

Solution: We start with Eq. (6.94) in the form given in the second formula. In this formula we replace T by the term pV/nR (ideal gas law):

$$VT^{C_V/R} = V\left(\frac{pV}{nR}\right)^{C_V/R} = const \quad \textbf{(25)}$$

$$p^{\frac{C_V}{R}} V^{\frac{C_V}{R}+1} = const \ (nR)^{C_V/R} = const^*$$

in which const* is indeed a constant since both n and R in the middle term of the second formula in Eq. (25) do not vary. Now we rewrite the exponent of the volume:

$$p^{\frac{C_V}{R}} V^{\frac{C_V}{R}+1} = p^{\frac{C_V}{R}} V^{\frac{C_V+R}{R}} = const^* \quad \textbf{(26)}$$

In the last step, we raise both sides of the formula to the (R/C_V)–th power:

$$p \ V^{\frac{C_V+R}{C_V}} = \left(const^*\right)^{\frac{R}{C_V}} = const^I \quad \textbf{(27)}$$

in which const' is also constant since the middle term in Eq. (27) does not contain any variables. Eq. (27) is

57

easily transformed into Eq. (6.96) when using the relation between C_V and C_p, as given in section 6.6.3. This converts the exponent of the volume term to $\kappa = C_p/C_V$.

Problem 6.10
One mol of an ideal gas which starts at 1.0 atm and 25^{0}C does 1.0 kJ of work during an adiabatic expansion.
(a) What is the final temperature of the gas?
(b) What is the final volume of the gas?

Solution part (a): The term adiabatic process implies that no heat exchange occurs between the system and the environment. From the first law of thermodynamics, we therefore conclude for an adiabatic process $\Delta U = W$, as stated in section 6.6.4.

Since the system in this problem is an ideal gas, we use Eq. (6.93) for the change of the internal energy during the process. With the values given in the problem, we determine the change in temperature:

$$\Delta T = \frac{2\ \Delta U}{3\ n\ R} = \frac{2\ (-1.0 \times 10^3 [J])}{3 \cdot 1[mol] 8.314 \left[\dfrac{J}{K\ mol}\right]} \quad (28)$$

$$\Rightarrow \quad \Delta T = -\ 80.2\ K$$

With an initial temperature of 25^{0}C = 298.15 K, we get for the final temperature:

$$T_{fin} = T_{init} + \Delta T = 298.15[K] - 80.2[K]$$

$$\tag{29}$$

$$\Rightarrow \quad T_{final} = 218\ K = -55^0 C$$

Solution part (b): The final volume is found it two steps: first we use the ideal gas law to determine the initial volume and then we use the relation of adiabatic states.

The given data in the problem allow us to calculate the initial volume:

$$V_{init} = \frac{nRT}{p} =$$

$$\frac{1[mol]\ 8.314 \left[\dfrac{J}{K\ mol}\right]\ 298.1[K]}{1.013 \times 10^5 [Pa]} \quad (30)$$

$$\Rightarrow \quad V_{initial} = 0.0245\ m^3 = 24.5\ litre$$

With this, we find the final volume from Eq. (6.94):

$$V_{final} = V_{initial} \left(\frac{T_{initial}}{T_{final}} \right)^{C_V/R}$$

$$\tag{31}$$

$$V_{final} = 24.5[l] \left(\frac{298.1[K]}{218[K]} \right)^{\frac{3}{2}} = 39.1\ l$$

Problem 6.11
Compare the efficiency coefficient for a Carnot machine operating between a low temperature heat reservoir at room temperature (25^{0}C) and a high temperature heat reservoir at the boiling point of water at two different pressures:
(a) 5 atm with $T_{boil} = 152^0$C, and
(b) 100 atm with $T_{boil} = 312^0$C.

Solution part (a): This is a straight–forward substitution problem for Eq. (6.115); at a pressure of 5 atm we find:

$$\eta = \frac{T_b - T_a}{T_b} = \frac{425[K] - 298[K]}{425[K]}$$

$$\tag{32}$$

$$\Rightarrow \quad \eta = 30\ \%$$

Solution part (b): at a pressure of 100 atm we find

$$\eta = \frac{T_b - T_a}{T_b} = \frac{585[K] - 298[K]}{585[K]}$$

$$\tag{33}$$

$$\Rightarrow \quad \eta = 49\ \%$$

It is important to notice, however, that the higher efficiency coefficient in part (b) is not a direct result of the changed pressure, but follows only indirectly from the pressure change as a boiling point change is involved.

Problem 6.12
A Carnot process is operated with 1.0 mol of an ideal gas of heat capacity $C_V = 3R/2$. The pressure of the gas is 10.0 atm and the temperature is 600 K in the most compressed state. From there, an isothermal expansion leads to a pressure 1.0 atm. The lower process temperature is 300 K.
(a) Calculate for each step of this Carnot process the

work and heat exchange with the environment.
(b) What is the efficiency coefficient of this machine?
(c) Draw this Carnot process as a p–V diagram, then sketch it as a p–T diagram, a V–T diagram, and a U–T diagram.

Solution part (a) : Fig. 6.37 shows the Carnot process with the two processing temperatures of 600 K and of 300 K. The data given in the problem text for the four corner states of the Carnot process are supplemented with the initial volume in Table 6.3. The volume values are calculated using the ideal gas law.

With these preliminary steps we can now answer the various parts of the problem. For the work, heat and energy terms, we evaluate the terms in Table 6.2 for the Carnot process, leading to Table 6.4.

Solution part (b): The efficiency is determined from Eq. (6.115):

$$\eta = \frac{T_b - T_a}{T_b} = \frac{600[K] - 300[K]}{600[K]} \tag{34}$$

$$\Rightarrow \quad \eta = 50\%$$

This result can be found also by using Eq. (6.114) in the form:

$$\eta = \frac{|W_I + W_{III}|}{Q_I} = \frac{|-11.5[kJ] + 5.7[kJ]|}{+11.5[kJ]} \tag{35}$$

$$\Rightarrow \quad \eta = 0.5$$

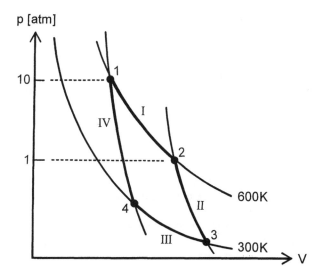

Fig. 6.37: Sketch of the specific Carnot process discussed in problem P–5.11.

Table 6.3: p, V, and T data relevant to the Carnot process in Fig. 6.37.

State	p	V	T
1	10 atm	4.94 l	600 K
2	1 atm	49.4 l	600 K
3			300 K
4			300 K

Table 6.4: Work and heat values for the Carnot process in Fig. 6.37.

Process	work W	heat Q
I	− 11.5 kJ	+ 11.5 kJ
II	− 3.7 kJ	0
III	+ 5.7 kJ	− 5.7 kJ
IV	+ 3.7 kJ	0

Note: $V_2/V_1 = V_3/V_4$ due to Eq. (6.109).

in which the work and heat terms are taken from Table 6.4.

Solution part (c): The various plots are shown in Fig. 6.38. Note that all five plots illustrate the same cyclic process!

In the U–T diagram, all processes are represented by straight line segments because the change of the internal energy and the temperature change are related in a linear fashion, $\Delta U \propto \Delta T$. To determine the curvature of the adiabatic steps in the p–T diagram, we rewrite the equation for the adiabatic process in Eq. (6.94), with p and T as the variables by using the ideal gas law in the form V = nRT/p:

$$p^{-1}T^{C_V/R + 1} = p^{-1}T^{C_p/R} = const^* \tag{36}$$

$$\Rightarrow \quad p \propto T^{5/2}$$

For the adiabatic steps in the V–T diagram, we rewrite Eq. (6.94) in the form $V \propto T^{2/3}$.

Problem 6.13
The cyclic process in Fig. 6.33 consists of (I) an isothermal expansion, (II) an isochoric cooling and (III) an adiabatic compression. If the process is done with n = 2.5 mol of an ideal gas, what are
(a) the total work done by the gas,
(b) the heat exchanged with the environment, and
(c) the change of the internal energy for one cycle.

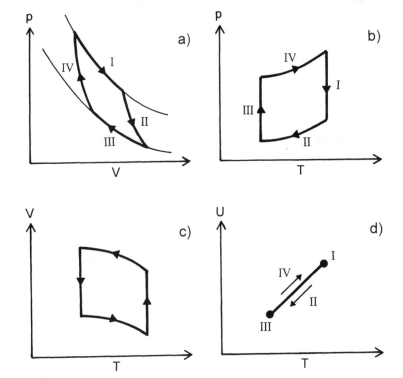

Fig. 6.38: Carnot process of Fig. 6.37, redrawn in various plots: (a) p – V diagram, (b) p – T diagram, (c) V – T diagram, and (d) U – T diagram.

(d) Sketch the cyclic process of Fig. 6.33 as p–T, V–T and U–T diagrams.

Solution part (a): Any cyclic process of this type is treated the same way that we dealt with the Carnot process in the previous problem. In the first step we summarize the work, heat and internal energy contributions due to the single steps involved in the cyclic process, in analogy to Table 6.2. For this, we need not to calculate any of the

contributions since each individual step is already covered in sections 6.6.1 to 6.6.4. The contributions are summarized in Table 6.5.

To quantify the terms in Table 6.5, the temperatures of the two isothermal curves in Fig. 6.33 must be calculated. The temperature T_1 is obtained from the ideal gas law applied to the first state of the system:

$$T_1 = \frac{p_1 V_1}{n R} = \frac{1.013 \times 10^5 [Pa] 0.01 [m^3]}{8.314 \left[\frac{J}{K\, mol}\right] 2.5 [mol]} \quad (37)$$

$$\Rightarrow \quad T_1 = 48.7 \ K$$

The second temperature is obtained from the adiabatic step (step III) in Fig. 6.33, using Eq. (6.94) with $C_V/R = 3/2$ for an ideal gas:

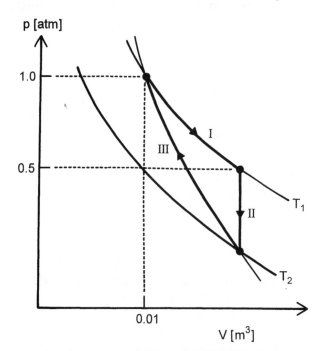

Fig. 6.33 for problem P–6.13.

Table 6.5: Heat and work contributions to the cyclic process shown in Fig. 6.33.

Process step	work W	heat Q
I	$-nRT_1 \ln(p_i/p_f)$	$-W_I$
II	0	$-(3/2)nR(T_1-T_2)$
III	$+(3/2)nR(T_1-T_2)$	0

$$T_2 = \left(\frac{V_1}{V_2}\right)^{2/3} T_1 = 0.5^{2/3} \; 48.7[K] \qquad \textbf{(38)}$$

$$\Rightarrow \quad T_2 = 30.7 \; K$$

in which the ratio of the two volumes is 0.5 because of Boyle's law applied to step (I) in Fig. 6.33 $p_2/p_1 = V_1/V_2$. The total work is the sum of the three work terms in Table 6.5, with:

$$W_I = -2.5[mol]8.314\left[\frac{J}{Kmol}\right]48.7[K]\ln\frac{1.0}{0.5}$$

$$\Rightarrow \quad W_I = -700 \; J \qquad \textbf{(39)}$$

$$W_{III} = +\frac{3}{2}\;2.5[mol]8.314\left[\frac{J}{K\,mol}\right]18[K]$$

$$\Rightarrow \quad W_{III} = +560 \; J$$

in which $T_1 - T_2 = 48.7 \, K - 30.7 \, K = 18.0 \, K$ is the temperature difference in the third work term. Thus, the work per cycle is $W_{cycle} = W_I + W_{III} = -140$ J. Because this is a negative value, the work is done by the gas.

Solution part (b): Studying Table 6.5, we note that $Q_{II} = -W_{III}$ and that $Q_I = -W_I$. Thus, $Q_{cycle} = -W_{cycle} = +140$ J. Since the value is positive, we conclude that the system receives this amount of energy as heat per cycle.

Solution part (c): For any cyclic process the change per cycle in the internal energy must be zero because the internal energy is a variable of state of the system. This is confirmed by adding Q_{cycle} and W_{cycle}, as calculated.

Solution part (d): The three graphs are shown in Fig. 6.39. They are derived in the following fashion:
The p–T plot: The first step is an isothermal expansion or isothermal decompression. Since temperature is constant for isothermal processes, the initial and final state must lie on a common, vertical line. The second step is an isochoric cooling, i.e., both, temperature and pressure decrease while the volume stays constant. The third step must bring the system back to the initial state.
The V–T plot: The first step is an isothermal expansion, i.e., the volume increases and the temperature remains the same (vertical line). The second step is an isochoric cooling, i.e., the temperature is reduced while the volume is constant (horizontal line). The last step must connect back to the initial state. Both curves for the last step are bent because the adiabatic process is not a linear relation between either pressure and temperature or volume and temperature.
The U–T plot: Since the first step is isothermal, both the temperature and the internal energy of the ideal gas do not change. Thus, during the first step the system does not change its position in this type of plot. The second step is an isothermal cooling, i.e., the temperature decreases, and with it the internal energy. This relationship is linear due to $\Delta U \propto \Delta T$. The third step must bring the system back to the initial state.

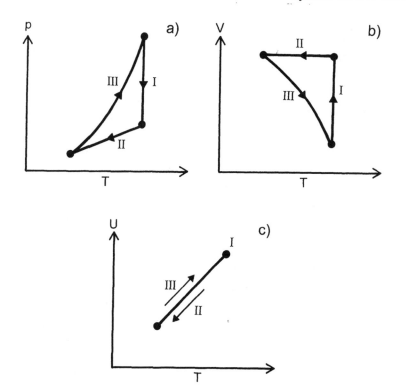

Fig. 6.39: Cyclic process of Fig. 6.33, redrawn in various plots: (a) p–T diagram, (b) V–T diagram, and (c) U–T diagram.

Problem 6.14

In section 6.6.3 it is stated that $C_p = C_v + R$ holds for an ideal gas. Derive this result for an isobaric expansion of 1.0 mol of ideal gas without using the enthalpy concept. For this, start with the work in Eq. (6.82) and the change of internal energy in Eq. (6.63) for the expansion in Fig. 6.23. Then use the first law of thermodynamics and the definition

$$Q = n C_p \Delta T \qquad (40)$$

which applies for an isobaric process.

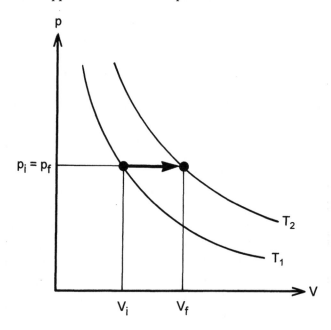

Fig. 6.23: The bold arrow indicates an isobaric expansion from an initial volume V_i to a final volume V_f. Note that the temperature increases during the process from T_1 to T_2.

Solution: We rewrite the first law of thermodynamics, $\Delta U = W + Q$, using Eq. (6.82) in the form $W = -np\Delta V$ and Eq. (6.63) in the form $\Delta U = nC_v\Delta T$. We further use Eq. (40) as given in the problem text:

$$\Delta U = nC_v\Delta T = -np\Delta V + nC_p\Delta T \qquad (41)$$

which leads to:

$$C_p - C_v = \frac{np\Delta V}{n\Delta T} = \frac{p\Delta V}{\Delta T} = R \qquad (42)$$

Problem 6.15

A boy wants to pretend that he has a fever. He notices that air he breathes onto his arm feels warmer than the arm itself. Reasoning that breathing on a thermometer should effectively drive up the mercury column, will he succeed to deceive his parents?

Solution: This problem is based on what we have already discussed with regard to the temperature of the human body. The issue also reaches along the lines of our everyday intuition forward into Chapter 7: the human body is losing continuously heat to the environment when it is immersed in an environment of less than 37^0C. As Fig. 7.5 in the next chapter will illustrate, this leads to a surface temperature of our body which may be as much as 9 degree Celsius below the core temperature. When the healthy boy breathes at his skin, the air from his lungs (which is at 37^0C) is blown at a cooler surface. The boy perceives the breath as warmer than the air in the room and he judges it, correctly, to be warmer than the skin of his arm. Similarly, a mercury (fever) thermometer, which shows room temperature before being used, responds to the breathed air with an increased temperature reading, but it cannot exceed 37^0C as nothing in this case is warmer than that temperature. For the thermometer to show a temperature higher than 37^0C, it has to be brought into thermal contact (and thermal equilibrium) with a medium which has that higher temperature.

Problem 6.16

We study a tidal volume (0.5 liter) of dry air at two frequently used reference states. With index 1 we refer to the gas at STPD conditions, (which are: $p_1 = 101.3$ kPa, $T_1 = 0^0$C, $V_1 = 0.5$ liters); with index 2 we refer to the gas at BTPS conditions, but excluding the water vapor component added during inhalation, i.e., $p_2 = 95.0$ kPa, $T_2 = 37^0$C, $V_2 = 0.605$ liters.
(a) Why is V_2 not also given as 0.5 liters?
(b) We transfer the gas from state 1 to state 2. Assuming that we adjust the pressure first in an isothermal step and then the temperature in an isobaric step, what fraction of the total volume change occurs in the isothermal step?
(c) Assuming that we invert the order of the two steps in part (b), i.e., we start with an isobaric step followed by an isothermal step, is the fraction of the total volume change after the first step the same as in part (b)?
(d) Can the process from STPD to BTPS conditions also be achieved with an initial isochoric step followed by an isobaric step?

Solution part (a): Because we want to consider the same amount of gas, which is n = 0.022 mol.

Solution part (b): 31.4 % to an intermediate volume of V = 0.533 liter.

Solution part (c): No. The step is this time 64.8 % to an intermediate volume of 0.568 liter.

Solution part (d): yes.

CHAPTER VII

Membranes: transport of energy and matter

Problem 7.1

We quantify Fourier's experiment, shown in Fig. 7.4, for a cylindrical copper rod of a length of 1.2 m and a cross–sectional area 4.8 cm². The rod is insulated to prevent heat loss through its surface. A temperature difference of 100 K is maintained between the ends. Find the rate at which heat is conducted through the rod.

Solution: Fourier's law is used with the thermal conductivity for copper taken from Table 7.1:

$$\frac{Q}{t} = \lambda_{Cu} A \frac{\Delta T}{l} = \tag{1}$$

$$\frac{390[J/(m\,s\,K)]\ 4.8{\times}10^{-4}[m^2]\ 100[K]}{1.2\ [m]}$$

which yields:

$$\frac{Q}{t} = 15.6\ \frac{J}{s} \tag{2}$$

Note that this is less than a tenth of the amount of heat that your body loses in the winter with dry clothing (see Example 7.1). Why would we compare these results? The answer is that we build an intuition for such numbers, as the loss of heat in winter is a process to which we can relate while the heat flowing in a metal rod eludes our daily experience.

Problem 7.2

We confirm the concept of the geothermal effect in an alternative fashion to the discussion in the text (Example 7.3). We know that the average rate at which heat is conducted through the surface of the ground in North America is 54.0 mJ/(s m²). Assuming a surface temperature of 10^0C, what is the temperature at a depth of 35 km (near the base of the Earth's crust)?

Hint: Ignore the heat generated by the presence of radioactive elements and use 2.5 J/(m s K) for the average thermal conductivity of the near–surface rocks. Start with Fourier's law.

Solution: In this application of Fourier's law, Eq. (7.1), is first rewritten to isolate the unknown temperature which is the independent variable:

$$T_{high} = \frac{\left(\dfrac{Q}{t}\right) l}{\lambda\ A} + T_{low} \tag{3}$$

then we substitute the given values, including $(Q/t)/A = 54.0\ [mJ/(s{\cdot}m^2)]$, as given in the problem text:

$$T_{high} = \frac{5.4{\times}10^{-2}\left[\dfrac{J}{m^2 s}\right]3.5{\times}10^4[m]}{2.5\left[\dfrac{J}{m\,s\,K}\right]} + 283[K] \tag{4}$$

$$\Rightarrow\quad T_{high} = 1039\ K = 766^0C$$

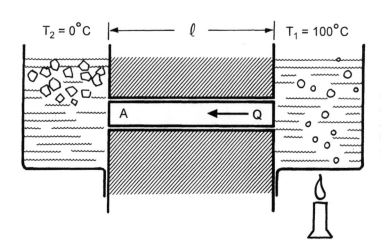

Fig. 7.4: Fourier's experiment of heat conduction. A steady–state heat flow across a rod of length l is achieved by providing for a thermal contact to heat reservoirs at 0 ^{0}C and 100^{0}C, respectively, at the two ends of the rod.

64

Therefore, the temperature at the base of Earth's crust is about 750⁰C. This clearly precludes science fiction ideas like those in "Voyage au centre de la terre" by Jules Verne, published in 1864. Indeed, we couldn't even travel 0.5 % of the distance to the center of the Earth and expect to live to tell about it!

Problem 7.3

For poor heat conductors a thermal resistance R has been introduced. The thermal resistance of a piece of material of thermal conductivity λ and thickness l is defined as:

$$R = \frac{l}{\lambda} \qquad (5)$$

(a) Show that Eq. (5) allows us to rewrite Fourier's law in the form:

$$\frac{Q}{t} = A \frac{T_{high} - T_{low}}{R} \qquad (6)$$

in which A is the cross–sectional area of the piece of material.
(b) What is the SI unit of the thermal resistance R?

Solution part (a): Eq. (6) is obtained by substituting Eq. (5) in the form $\lambda/l = 1/R$ into Fourier's law in Eq. (7.1).

Solution part (b): We determine the unit of R from Eq. (5):

$$unit\ (R)\ =\ unit\left(\frac{l}{\lambda}\right)\ =\ \frac{[m]}{\left[\dfrac{J}{m\,s\,K}\right]} \qquad (7)$$

$$\Rightarrow\quad unit\ (R)\ =\ \left[\frac{s\,K\,m^2}{J}\right]$$

Problem 7.4

In a table you find $\lambda = 2.9 \times 10^{-3}$ cal/(cm s K) for the thermal conductivity of Pyrex glass at 0⁰C.
(a) Express this value in standard units.
(b) What is the thermal resistance of a Pyrex glass sheet of thickness 0.635 cm (or ¼ inch)?

Solution part (a): A first, useful step in any problem is to convert the energy unit "cal" into standard unit "J". Conversion factors for non–standard units are given in the General Appendix (Chapter 24). Also, the length unit is converted into meters:

$$2.9 \times 10^{-3}\left[\frac{cal}{cm\,s\,K}\right] \frac{4.184\left[\dfrac{J}{cal}\right]}{0.01\left[\dfrac{m}{cm}\right]} = 1.2\left[\frac{J}{m\,s\,K}\right] (8)$$

Solution part (b): Using Eq. (5), which was discussed in problem 7.3, we find:

$$R = \frac{l}{\lambda} = \frac{0.635 \times 10^{-2}[m]}{1.2[J/(m\,s\,K)]}$$
$$\qquad (9)$$
$$\Rightarrow\quad R = 5.2 \times 10^{-3}\left[\frac{m^2\,s\,K}{J}\right]$$

Problem 7.5

If it takes two days to defrost a frozen 5 kg turkey, estimate how long it would take to defrost a 2 tonnes Siberian Mammoth from the same initial temperature.
Hint: treat both animals as spherically shaped and use the same approach we applied in Example 7.3.

Solution: We isolate the time in Eq. (7.1):

$$t = \frac{Q}{\lambda\,A\,\dfrac{\Delta T}{l}} \qquad (10)$$

i.e., the time for the process is proportional to the amount of heat required and inversely proportional to the temperature gradient in the meat. The required heat is rewritten with Joule's definition Q = c m ΔT:

$$t = \frac{c\,m\,\Delta T}{\lambda\,A\,\dfrac{\Delta T}{l}} \qquad (11)$$

The specific heat capacity and the thermal conductivity of turkey and mammoth are assumed to be the same. Thus we rewrite Eq. (11) as a ratio:

$$\frac{t_{mammoth}}{t_{turkey}} = \frac{\left(\dfrac{A}{l}\right)_{mammoth}}{\dfrac{m_{turkey}}{\left(\dfrac{A}{l}\right)_{turkey}}} \quad \text{(12)}$$

The mass scales with L³ where L is the size (typical length) for an object of uniform density. This leads to $A/l \propto L \propto m^{1/3}$. Thus, we rewrite Eq. (12) in terms of the respective body masses:

$$\frac{t_{mammoth}}{t_{turkey}} = \frac{m_{mammoth}^{2/3}}{m_{turkey}^{2/3}} = \left(\frac{2,000\ [kg]}{5\ [kg]}\right)^{2/3} \quad \text{(13)}$$

$$\Rightarrow \quad \frac{t_{mammoth}}{t_{turkey}} = 55$$

Defrosting the mammoth takes 110 days.

Problem 7.6
We want to measure the thermal conductivity of an unknown insulator material. For this we use the following set–up: A 3 mm thick plate of the unknown material is placed between two iron plates of thickness 2 cm each. All three plates are 20 cm by 20 cm in size. The upper iron plate is heated to 80 °C and the lower iron plate is kept at 20°C. Once a stationary temperature profile has developed across the insulator, the heater is removed from the upper iron plate. We observe that the temperature of the upper iron plate drops by 2.7 K after 1 min. Neglecting any loss of heat to the environment, what is the thermal conductivity coefficient λ for the unknown insulator material?
Hint: approach this problem in the same fashion as we solved Example 7.3. The density of iron is $\rho = 7.9$ g/cm³, the specific heat capacity of iron is c = 450 J/(kg K).

Solution: We use Fourier's law with the unknown thermal conductivity isolated in the form:

$$\lambda = \frac{\dfrac{Q}{t}}{A\ \dfrac{\Delta T}{d_2}} \quad \text{(14)}$$

in which we wrote $d_2 = 0.003$ m for the thickness of the unknown material. During the $\Delta t = 1$ minute time interval in which the upper plate temperature drops 2.7 K, the amount of heat released by the upper plate is calculated with Joule's definition, taken for the interval Δt:

$$\frac{\Delta Q}{\Delta t} = c_{plate}\ m_{plate}\ \frac{\Delta T}{\Delta t} \quad \text{(15)}$$

The mass of the upper plate needed in Eq. (15) follows from the given data, $d_1 = 0.02$ m for the iron plate thickness and A = 0.2[m] · 0.2[m] = 0.04 m²:

$$m_{plate} = \rho_{Fe}\ d_1\ A =$$

$$7.9\times10^3 \left[\frac{kg}{m^3}\right] 0.02[m]\ 0.04[m^2] \quad \text{(16)}$$

$$\Rightarrow \quad m_{platte} = 6.32\ kg$$

Substituting this value in Eq. (15), we find for the heat loss in Δt:

$$\frac{\Delta Q}{\Delta t} = 0.45\times10^3\left[\frac{J}{kg\ K}\right]6.32[kg]\frac{2.7[K]}{60[s]} \quad \text{(17)}$$

$$\Rightarrow \quad \frac{\Delta Q}{\Delta t} = 128.0\ \frac{J}{s}$$

This value is now substituted into Eq. (14) for Q/t:

$$\lambda = \frac{128.0\left[\dfrac{J}{s}\right]}{0.04[m^2]\ \dfrac{60[K]}{0.003[m]}} \quad \text{(18)}$$

$$\Rightarrow \quad \lambda = 0.16\ \frac{J}{m\ s\ K}$$

Note that we neglected the temperature change across the unknown material in this last formula. A more appropriate value to use would be $\Delta T = 58.65$ K, which is the average between the initial and final temperature differences.

Problem 7.7
Fig. 7.21 shows a block which consists of two materials with different thicknesses l_1 and l_2 and different thermal

conductivities, λ_1 and λ_2. The temperatures of the outer surfaces of the block are T_{high} and T_{low}, as shown in the figure. Each face of the block has a cross–sectional area A.

(a) Show that the formula

$$\frac{Q}{t} = \frac{A\,(T_{high} - T_{low})}{(l_1/\lambda_1) + (l_2/\lambda_2)} \tag{19}$$

correctly expresses the steady state rate of heat transfer. Hint: in the steady state the heat transfer through any part of the block must be equal to the heat transfer through the other part of the block. Introduce a temperature T_x at the interface of the two parts as shown in Fig. 7.21, and in the first step express the rate of heat transfer for each part of the block separately.

(b) Rewrite Eq. (19) using Eq. (5), which introduces R_1 and R_2 as the thermal resistances for the two parts of the block. By comparing the result with Eq. (6), determine how thermal resistances are combined for materials in sequence.

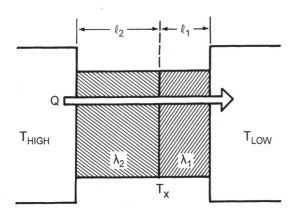

Fig. 7.21 for problems P–7.7 and P–7.8

Solution part (a): In this problem, the underlying assumption is that the heat transfer is a steady process, i.e., that (i) the temperature profile across the block and (ii) the rate of heat transfer do not change with time. Later in the textbook, we will define this as a distinguished state of the system called the "steady state". In the steady state, the heat transferred through the two blocks per time unit must be the same. Otherwise, we would either have a depletion of heat at the interface between both blocks and the interface zone would have to cool down or we would have an accumulation of heat at the interface and that zone would become hotter and hotter.

As a consequence, we can use Fourier's law twice, once for each block. The implication of the steady state requires $(Q/t)_1 = (Q/t)_2 = Q/t$, in which the indices

1 and 2 represent each of the blocks. Labelling the temperature at the interface T_x we obtain:

$$\frac{Q}{t} = \frac{\lambda_2 A (T_{high} - T_x)}{l_2} = \frac{\lambda_1 A (T_x - T_{low})}{l_1} \tag{20}$$

Note that Eq. (20) contains three formulas, as the first and second or first and third or second and third terms are equal.

First, we use the equality of the second and third terms in Eq. (20) to derive a formula for the temperature at the interface, T_x. We multiply both sides of the equation with $l_1 l_2$ and divide both sides by the area A:

$$\lambda_2 l_1 T_{high} - \lambda_2 l_1 T_x = \lambda_1 l_2 T_x - \lambda_1 l_2 T_{low} \tag{21}$$

In the next step we group together the terms containing T_x:

$$T_x(\lambda_1 l_2 + \lambda_2 l_1) = \lambda_2 l_1 T_{high} + \lambda_1 l_2 T_{low} \tag{22}$$

In the last step we isolate T_x:

$$T_x = \frac{\lambda_2 l_1 T_{high} + \lambda_1 l_2 T_{low}}{\lambda_1 l_2 + \lambda_2 l_1} \tag{23}$$

Now this result is substituted into either one of the other two formulas in Eq. (20). Choosing the equality between the first and the second term, the following calculation follows. For convenience, we do not substitute Eq. (23) into that equation right away since the formula would become very long and cumbersome. Instead, we initially substitute Eq. (23) only into the term $(T_{high} - T_x)$, which is part of the second term in Eq. (20). Once this bracket has been simplified, we return to the full formula in Eq. (20) and determine the flow rate of heat, i.e., Q/t. Starting, as said, with the bracket $(T_{high} - T_x)$ we find:

$$
\begin{aligned}
T_{high} - T_x &= T_{high} - \frac{\lambda_2 l_1 T_{high} + \lambda_1 l_2 T_{low}}{\lambda_1 l_2 + \lambda_2 l_1} \\[2mm]
&= \frac{\lambda_1 l_2 T_{high} + \lambda_2 l_1 T_{high} - \lambda_2 l_1 T_{high} - \lambda_1 l_2 T_{low}}{\lambda_1 l_2 + \lambda_2 l_1} \\[2mm]
&= \frac{\lambda_1 l_2 (T_{high} - T_{low})}{\lambda_1 l_2 + \lambda_2 l_1}
\end{aligned}
\tag{24}
$$

67

The result in Eq. (24) is now substituted for the term $(T_{high} - T_x)$ in the first equality of Eq. (20):

$$\frac{Q}{t} = \frac{\lambda_2 A}{l_2} \frac{\lambda_1 l_2 (T_{high} - T_{low})}{\lambda_1 l_2 + \lambda_2 l_1}$$

$$= A \frac{\lambda_1 \lambda_2}{\lambda_1 l_2 + \lambda_2 l_1} (T_{high} - T_{low}) \qquad (25)$$

Lastly, we divide both the numerator and the denominator of the right hand side of Eq. (25) by $\lambda_1 \lambda_2$, leading to:

$$\frac{Q}{t} = A \frac{(T_{high} - T_{low})}{\dfrac{l_2}{\lambda_2} + \dfrac{l_1}{\lambda_1}} \qquad (26)$$

which is the result we sought.

Solution part (b): Eq. (26) is now rewritten by applying Eq. (5) to each of the two blocks where we use $R_1 = l_1/\lambda_1$ and $R_2 = l_2/\lambda_2$:

$$\frac{Q}{t} = A \frac{(T_{high} - T_{low})}{R_1 + R_2} \qquad (27)$$

Thus, the R values, which are the thermal resistances, are simply added for blocks through which heat is passing in sequence. When we study fluid flow through tubes placed in sequence (Chapter 11), we will find that fluid flow resistances are also added; in Chapter 13 we will find the same to apply to electric resistances, which are added when electric charges flow through sequential re-sistors. This illustrates that our finding is broadly applicable: resistances have to be added if the flow is through several components in sequence. We will also find that flow resistances have to be added inversely when the components are placed in parallel, i.e., such that the flow is divided and passes through all components simultaneously.

Problem 7.8

Show that the temperature T_x at the interface of the block in Fig. 7.21 is given by:

$$T_x = \frac{R_1 T_{high} + R_2 T_{low}}{R_1 + R_2} \qquad (28)$$

Solution: We quantified the interfacial temperature T_x in Eq. (23). We divide both numerator and denominator of Eq. (23) by $\lambda_1 \lambda_2$ and obtain:

$$T_x = \frac{\dfrac{l_1}{\lambda_1} T_{high} + \dfrac{l_2}{\lambda_2} T_{low}}{\dfrac{l_1}{\lambda_1} + \dfrac{l_2}{\lambda_2}} \qquad (29)$$

Using Eq. (5) for both blocks in the form $R_1 = l_1/\lambda_1$ and $R_2 = l_2/\lambda_2$, we rewrite Eq. (29):

$$T_x = \frac{R_1 T_{high} + R_2 T_{low}}{R_1 + R_2} \qquad (30)$$

This equation is the result we sought.

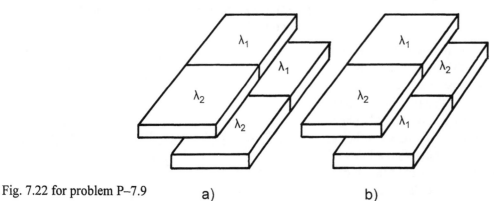

Fig. 7.22 for problem P–7.9   a)   b)

Problem 7.9

Four square pieces of insulation of two different materials, all with the same thickness and cross–sectional area A, are used to cover an opening of total area 2A. This can be done in either of the two ways shown in Fig. 7.22. Which arrangement, (a) or (b), gives the lower heat flow if $\lambda_1 \neq \lambda_2$?

Solution: We start with arrangement (a). After combining the two blocks we obtain an insulation layer of area 2A with 50 % of this area covered with material 1 of (combined) thickness 2 l where l is the thickness of a single piece of insulator. For this arrangement Fourier's law reads:

$$\frac{Q}{t}\bigg|_{(a)} = \left(\frac{Q}{t}\right)_1 + \left(\frac{Q}{t}\right)_2 =$$

$$\frac{A\lambda_1}{2l}\left(T_{high} - T_{low}\right) + \frac{A\lambda_2}{2l}\left(T_{high} - T_{low}\right) \quad (31)$$

We rewrite Eq. (31) for later comparison in the form:

$$\frac{Q}{t}\bigg|_{(a)} \equiv \frac{A}{2l}\,\lambda_{comb}^{(a)}\left(T_{high} - T_{low}\right)$$

$$with: \quad \lambda_{comb}^{(a)} = \lambda_1 + \lambda_2 \quad (32)$$

Now we consider arrangement (b). Both half–sides of the combined insulator consist of two layers with a 1–2 sequence of the two materials. To describe such an arrangement, we derived Eq. (19) in problem P–7.7. Using this formula for a total area of 2A in the current problem, we write:

$$\frac{Q}{t}\bigg|_{(b)} = \frac{2A\left(T_{high} - T_{low}\right)}{(l/\lambda_1) + (l/\lambda_2)} \quad (33)$$

which we rewrite in analogy to Eq. (32) above:

$$\frac{Q}{t}\bigg|_{(b)} \equiv \frac{A}{2l}\,\lambda_{comb}^{(b)}\left(T_{high} - T_{low}\right)$$

$$with: \quad \lambda_{comb}^{(b)} = \frac{4\lambda_1\lambda_2}{\lambda_1 + \lambda_2} \quad (34)$$

in which the factor 4 in the last formula is due to the prefactor 2 moving from the numerator to the denominator between Eqs. (33) and (34). The remaining factors in the

formula for $\lambda_{comb}^{(b)}$ are due to the following mathematical step:

$$\frac{1}{\dfrac{1}{\lambda_1} + \dfrac{1}{\lambda_2}} = \frac{1}{\dfrac{\lambda_1 + \lambda_2}{\lambda_1\lambda_2}} = \frac{\lambda_1\lambda_2}{\lambda_1 + \lambda_2} \quad (35)$$

In order to compare Eqs. (32) and (34), we divide Eq. (32) by Eq. (34). Since all other terms in both equations are equal, this corresponds to a division of the two combined λ factors:

$$\frac{\lambda_{comb}^{(a)}}{\lambda_{comb}^{(b)}} = \frac{\left(\lambda_1 + \lambda_2\right)^2}{4\lambda_1\lambda_2} \quad (36)$$

We use a mathematical trick to determine whether the ratio in Eq. (36) is larger or smaller than 1: since we know that the square of any number is positive the following holds:

$$\left(\lambda_1 - \lambda_2\right)^2 = \lambda_1^2 - 2\lambda_1\lambda_2 + \lambda_2^2 =$$

$$\lambda_1^2 + 2\lambda_1\lambda_2 + \lambda_2^2 - 4\lambda_1\lambda_2 = \quad (37)$$

$$\left(\lambda_1 + \lambda_2\right)^2 - 4\lambda_1\lambda_2 > 0$$

which is true for any pair of values λ_1 and λ_2 if the condition $\lambda_1 \neq \lambda_2$ is fulfilled. Thus, we find the inequality $(\lambda_1 + \lambda_2)^2 > 4\lambda_1\lambda_2$ and from this we get:

$$\frac{\lambda_{comb}^{(a)}}{\lambda_{comb}^{(b)}} > 1 \quad \Rightarrow \quad \lambda_{comb}^{(a)} > \lambda_{comb}^{(b)} \quad (38)$$

The smaller combined thermal conductivity for arrangement (b) leads to a smaller amount of heat transported per time unit.

Problem 7.10

Two identical rectangular rods of metal are welded end to end, as shown in Fig. 7.23(a), and 1 J of heat is conducted in a steady state process through the combined rod in 2.0 minutes. How long would it take for 1 J to be conducted through the rods if they were welded together as shown in Fig. 7.23(b)?

Solution: We start with Fourier's law, which is applied

69

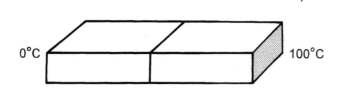

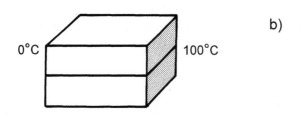

a)

0°C   100°C

b)

0°C   100°C

Fig. 7.23 for problem P–7.10

to cases (a) and (b) in Fig. 7.23:

$$(I) \quad \left.\frac{Q}{t}\right|_{(a)} = \lambda A_a \frac{\Delta T}{l_a}$$

$$(II) \quad \left.\frac{Q}{t}\right|_{(b)} = \lambda A_b \frac{\Delta T}{l_b}$$

(39)

Dividing the two formulas in Eq. (39) leads to the ratio of the two heat flow rates:

$$\frac{(Q/t)_a}{(Q/t)_b} = \frac{A_a/l_a}{A_b/l_b}$$

(40)

To find the values to substitute into Eq. (40) we study the geometric properties of the arrangements in Fig. 7.23. We find:

$$l_b = \frac{l_a}{2} \quad and \quad A_b = 2\,A_a$$

(41)

Substituting Eq. (41) in Eq. (40) gives:

$$\frac{(Q/t)_a}{(Q/t)_b} = \frac{A_a(l_a/2)}{2\,A_a l_a} = \frac{1}{4}$$

(42)

With $Q = 1.0$ J and $t_a = 2.0$ min., we find from Eq. (42) that $t_b/t_a = 0.25$, and therefore, $t_b = 0.5$ min.

Problem 7.11
Heat loss via convection occurs only when heat is carried by a moving fluid. For example, when heating water in a beaker from below, the increase of the water temperature at the bottom leads to a decrease of the water density and causes the warmer water to rise due to buoyancy. The rising water carries excess heat to the surface. (a) Compare bare skin to skin covered with clothes. Why is the heat loss of the body significantly reduced when wearing clothes?
(b) At temperate lakes and ponds it is often observed that algae bloom for a short period during spring and autumn. Consider Fig. 7.24 which shows the stratification during summer (top) as well as the seasonal turnover in spring and autumn (bottom), how can the convection driven turnover cause algal blooms?

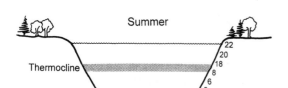

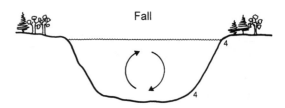

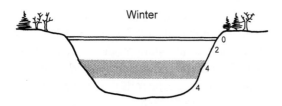

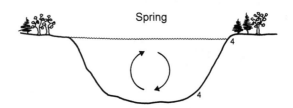

Fig. 7.24 for problem P–7.11

Solution part (a): A major heat loss mechanism at moderate environmental temperatures is convection, as listed in Table 7.2. Convection requires that an air flow pass across the skin to carry the heat away. Clothes have air–filled pores of variable size in which the air cannot move. Thus, heat that would otherwise be lost from the bare skin by convection, must be conducted by the air in the pores of the clothes. Heat conduction (Fourier's law) is a much less effective mechanism than convection, particularly since the thermal conductivity coefficient λ of air is very small.

$$D = \frac{5.7 \times 10^{-15} \left[\frac{kg}{s} \right]}{2 \times 10^{-4} [m^2] \; 3 \times 10^{-2} \left[\frac{kg}{m^4} \right]} \quad \textbf{(44)}$$

$$\Rightarrow \quad D = 9.5 \times 10^{-10} \; \frac{m^2}{s}$$

Solution part (b): The algal blooms that one can observe in temperate lakes during the transitional seasons (autumn and spring) are caused by convective currents in the water of the lake. As illustrated in Fig. 7.24, the temperature profile of the lake during summer is layered with (i) a warm zone near the surface (since this zone is heated by the warm air and the sun's radiation), (ii) an intermediate layer called *thermocline*, and (iii) a cold layer near the bottom of the lake. During the transitional seasons the temperature change in the upper layer causes the thermocline layer to break down, which in turn causes convection to mix the water. The water currents associated with convection transport nutrients from the bottom of the lake to the surface. The nutrient–rich water brought that way to the surface can cause a rapid increase in the algae population as algae also need sun light to grow.

Problem 7.12
Determine the diffusion coefficient for glycerine in H_2O using the following observations: glycerine diffuses along a horizontal, water–filled column that has a cross–sectional area of 2.0 cm². The density step from one end to the other is $\Delta\rho/l = 3.0 \times 10^{-2}$ kg/m⁴ and the steady state diffusion rate is 5.7×10^{-15} kg/s.

Solution: We use Fick's law in the form given in Eq. (7.19) and rewrite it so that the diffusion coefficient is the independent variable:

$$D = \frac{1}{A} \left(\frac{m}{t} \right) \frac{1}{\Delta\rho/l} \quad \textbf{(43)}$$

in which $\Delta\rho/l$ is the change of the density per unit length and is called a *density gradient*. We now substitute the data given in the problem into Eq. (43):

Problem 7.13
We want to test a statement we will make in Chapter 12: carbon–dioxide diffuses easier than oxygen across the membrane between the lung's alveoli and the blood capillaries. To show this, calculate the ratio of the diffusion coefficient of CO_2 and the diffusion coefficient of O_2 in tissue at 37⁰C.
Hint: Start with Eq. (7.21). Rewrite the concentration difference as a pressure difference using the ideal gas law. Applying this equation for both gases separately, determine the ratio of the diffusion coefficients. For the pressure differences across the membranes in the lungs use the values $\Delta p(CO_2) = 0.8$ kPa and $\Delta p(O_2) = 8.0$ kPa. The number of moles of both gases diffusing across the interface alveoli/capillaries can be determined from the data given in Example 6.3.

Solution: We use Fick's law in the form given in Eq. (7.21). The concentration difference on the right hand side is rewritten as a pressure difference using the ideal gas law:

$$pV = nRT \quad \Rightarrow \quad p = \frac{n}{V}RT = cRT \quad \textbf{(45)}$$

which yields:

$$\frac{n_i}{t} = DA \frac{\Delta c_i}{l} = DA \frac{\Delta p_i}{RTl} \quad \textbf{(46)}$$

In this equation, we allow the index i to refer first to the oxygen component in air and blood and secondly to the carbon–dioxide component in air and blood. Applying the equation to these two cases generates two equations. Note that the pressure difference in Eq. (46) applies specifically to a certain component i in the gas mixture (or to a gas component dissolved in blood). In Chapter 12 we introduce for this concept the term *partial pres-*

sure; for the current problem it is sufficient to follow the hint provided with the problem text. In particular, we use for Δp_i the two pressure differences given in the problem text, i.e., $\Delta p(CO_2) = 0.8$ kPa and $\Delta p(O_2) = 8.0$ kPa, which allows us to apply Eq. (46) to these two gases as:

$$(I) \quad \frac{n_{O_2}}{t} = D_{O_2} A \frac{\Delta p_{O_2}}{RTl}$$

$$(II) \quad \frac{n_{CO_2}}{t} = D_{CO_2} A \frac{\Delta p_{CO_2}}{RTl} \quad \textbf{(47)}$$

Now we calculate the ratio of the two formulas in Eq. (47) because we are primarily interested in a relative statement about the two diffusion coefficients:

$$\frac{n_{O_2}/t}{n_{CO_2}/t} = \frac{D_{O_2}}{D_{CO_2}} \frac{\Delta p_{O_2}}{\Delta p_{CO_2}} \quad \textbf{(48)}$$

The left hand side of Eq. (48) is quantified using a rate of 0.3 *l*/min exchange of oxygen and 0.25 *l*/min of carbon–dioxide, as introduced in Example 6.3. We can use these data because we assume that both gases are ideal and the ideal gas law yields a direct proportionality between the mole number n and the volume V, $n \propto V$, when p and T are kept constant. Thus:

$$\frac{n_{O_2}/t}{n_{CO_2}/t} = \frac{0.3 \ [l/min]}{0.25 \ [l/min]} = 1.2 \quad \textbf{(49)}$$

With this result, we determine the ratio of the two diffusion coefficients:

$$\frac{D_{O_2}}{D_{CO_2}} = 1.2 \frac{\Delta p_{CO_2}}{\Delta p_{O_2}} = 1.2 \frac{0.8[kPa]}{8.0[kPa]}$$

$$\Rightarrow \quad \frac{D_{O_2}}{D_{CO_2}} = 0.12 \quad \textbf{(50)}$$

Thus, we have found that in tissue:

$$D_{CO_2} \cong 8.3 \ D_{O_2} \quad \textbf{(51)}$$

Problem 7.14

Why can bacteria rely on passive diffusion for their oxygen supply but not human beings?

Hint: Calculate from Eq. (7.30):

(a) the time it takes for oxygen to diffuse from the interface with the environment to the center of a bacterium of radius r = 1.0 μm, and

(b) the time it takes for oxygen to diffuse from the external air to an organ 10 cm below human skin.

Note: for an upper limit use the diffusion coefficient of oxygen in water and for a lower limit use the diffusion coefficient of oxygen in tissue from Table 7.4. These two values give you a good approximation since humans consist roughly of 10 liters [*l*] of extracellular fluid and 30 *l* of cells.

(c) *If you are interested*: why can many relatively large invertebrates such as hydras survive without a cardio-vascular system?

Solution part (a): Aerobic bacteria need to have oxygen present throughout their body in order for their metabolisms to function. Let us assume a spherical bacterium of average size, e.g. with a radius of 1 μm (although they are often not spherical, as their name implies). For this bacterium we calculate the time that it takes for oxygen to diffuse from the outer surface to the center, using Einstein's equation in Eq. (7.30). The diffusion length is $\Lambda = 1.0 \times 10^{-6}$ m. We obtain a lower limit for the diffusion time by using the diffusion coefficient for oxygen in water at room temperature from Table 7.4:

$$t = \frac{\Lambda^2}{2D} = \frac{(1.0 \times 10^{-6}[m])^2}{2 \cdot 1.0 \times 10^{-9}[m^2/s]} \quad \textbf{(52)}$$

$$\Rightarrow \quad t = 5 \times 10^{-4} \ s$$

which is just half a millisecond.

In the same way, we use the diffusion coefficient of oxygen in tissue at room temperature from Table 7.4 to obtain an upper limit:

$$t = \frac{\Lambda^2}{2D} = \frac{(1.0 \times 10^{-6}[m])^2}{2 \cdot 1.0 \times 10^{-11}[m^2/s]} \quad \textbf{(53)}$$

$$\Rightarrow \quad t = 5 \times 10^{-2} \ s$$

which is still less than a tenth of a second. Thus, an average sized bacterium at room temperature has no problem assimilating the oxygen it needs for its metabolism through passive diffusion.

72

Solution part (b): Now we focus on a human body with an oxygen consuming organ, such as the heart, at an assumed depth of 10 cm below the surface of the outer skin. This leads to a required diffusion length $\Lambda = 0.1$ m for the human organ to be supplied with oxygen. We calculate the same two limiting cases as for the bacterium, assuming that oxygen is brought to the organ by passive diffusion. Note that a body temperature of endotherms of 37^0C instead of 20^0C improves the following result only insignificantly. For diffusion in water we find:

$$t = \frac{\Lambda^2}{2D} = \frac{(0.1 \, [m])^2}{2 \cdot 1.0 \times 10^{-9} \, [m^2/s]} \qquad (54)$$

$$\Rightarrow \quad t = 5 \times 10^6 \, s \simeq 58 \, days$$

and for diffusion in tissue we obtain:

$$t = \frac{\Lambda^2}{2D} = \frac{(0.1 \, [m])^2}{2 \cdot 1.0 \times 10^{-11} \, [m^2/s]} \qquad (55)$$

$$\Rightarrow \quad t = 5 \times 10^8 \, s \simeq 15.9 \, years$$

This result shows clearly that a larger organism cannot rely on passive diffusion to provide the oxygen required for its metabolism.

It is interesting to correlate this result with Table 7.3, which provides a brief history of life on Earth. When you read that table carefully, you notice that it took just over 500 million years for life to actually emerge after conditions that permit life to exist developed. It took five times this time, a staggering 2.5 billion years, to have the first single–celled bacteria develop into a larger, multicelled organisms. Once this had been achieved, a rapid diversification of life took place about 670 million years ago, called the Cambrian Explosion. Thus, Eq. (7.30) can be considered to represent the single biggest hurdle in the development of life, not the

occurrence (creation) of life itself. It is noteworthy that material transport within cells remains diffusion–limited, and thus, even the largest mammalian cells have diameters of no more than 20 μm.

Solution part (c): Hydras possess a central gastrovascular cavity that is lined by a layer of two cells thick to allow diffusive material exchange.

Problem 7.15

We want to determine the relation between the diffusion coefficient and the molecular mass of macromolecules. Using a double–logarithmic plot of the data listed in Table 7.7, determine the coefficients a and b in

$$D = a \cdot M^b \qquad (56)$$

Solution: Since you are producing the double logarithmic plot yourself, it is easier to rewrite Table 7.7 for lnD and lnM data than to use double–logarithmic paper. These calculated data are given in Table 7.8.

The data from Table 7.8 are plotted in Fig. 7.26. Note that the data points do not line up perfectly (which experimental data never do due to measurement uncertainties). The straight line is a best fit to the data.

From the straight line fit we pick two data pairs to use in Eq. (56), which we rewrite as:

$$lnD = lna + b \, lnM \qquad (57)$$

The two data pairs (lnD, lnM) I picked are $(-14.0, 10.64)$ and $(-16.5, 16.8)$, thus:

$$(I) \quad -14.0 = lna + b \, 10.64$$
$$(II) \quad -16.5 = lna + b \, 16.80 \qquad (58)$$

In the same fashion as done in the General Appendix, we find $b = -0.4$ and $a = 5.8 \times 10^{-5}$. Note that the numerical

Table 7.7: Diffusion coefficients in solution at 20^0C.

Protein	D [cm²/s]	M [g/mol]
Insulin	8.2×10^{-7}	41 000
Haemoglobin	6.3×10^{-7}	67 000
Catalase	4.1×10^{-7}	250 000
Urease	3.5×10^{-7}	470 000
Tobacco mosaic virus	5.3×10^{-8}	31 000 000

Table 7.8: lnD vs. lnM using data of Table 7.7.

Protein	ln(D [cm²/s])	ln(M [g/mol])
Insulin	-14.01	10.62
Haemoglobin	-14.28	11.11
Catalase	-14.71	12.43
Urease	-14.87	13.06
T. M. virus	-16.75	17.25

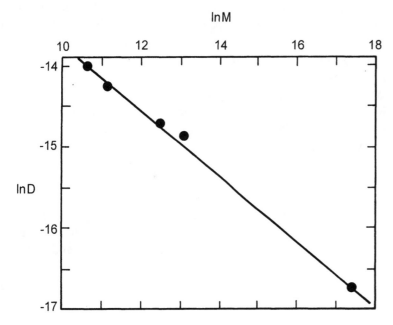

InM

Fig. 7.26: Double–logarithmic plot of diffusion coefficients versus molecular mass for various biochemical compounds.

value of the constant a depends on the units in which D and M are recorded; in the present case these are [cm²/s] for D and [g/mol] for M. The fact that the data obey the power law of Eq. (56) indicates that the diffusion coefficient is indeed linked to the molar mass of the moving species, but not inversely because $b \neq -1$.

Problem 7.16

(a) How far does a Tobacco mosaic virus move in water at 20^0C in 1 hour?

(b) Using the ratio of the diffusion coefficients for oxygen and carbon–dioxide in tissue from problem P–7.13, what is the ratio of diffusion lengths for these molecules in tissue at 20^0C?

Solution part (a): We use Einstein's equation Eq. (7.30). The diffusion coefficient of the tobacco mosaic virus in water is taken from Tables 7.4 or 7.7:

$$\Lambda = \sqrt{2 \cdot 5\times10^{-12}[m^2/s] \ 3600[s]}$$

$$\Rightarrow \quad \Lambda = 1.9 \times 10^{-4} \ m = 0.19 \ mm$$

(59)

This performance of the tobacco mosaic virus isn't impressive. It takes 1 hour to travel about 0.2 mm, 4 days to travel about 2 mm and more than 13 months to travel a distance of 2 cm. Clearly, viruses choose other modes of transportation, such as drag effects in air or water, which allow them to spread more quickly.

Solution part (b): The two formulas for the diffusion lengths read:

$$\Lambda_{O_2} = \sqrt{2 \ D_{O_2} \ t}$$

$$\Lambda_{CO_2} = \sqrt{2 \ D_{CO_2} \ t}$$

(60)

and their ratio is given by:

$$\frac{\Lambda_{CO_2}}{\Lambda_{O_2}} = \sqrt{\frac{D_{CO_2}}{D_{O_2}}} = \sqrt{8.3} = 2.9$$

(61)

in which we have used the result of Eq. (51) in P–7.13. This means that carbon–dioxide diffuses in tissue roughly three times further than oxygen under the same conditions.

Problem 7.17

Determining the pre-exponential factor D_0 in the manner shown in Example 7.6 leads to a large uncertainty of the value. To illustrate this, we focus on the diffusion of carbon (C) in silicon. Fig. 7.25 shows the Arrhenius plot of the available data (note that silicon melts at about 1400^0C). Use the solid line and the dashed line to determine

(a) the variation of the activation energy ΔE, and

(b) the variation of the pre–exponential factor D_0.

Solution parts (a) and (b): We compare the solid and the dashed line in Fig. 7.25. Since the logarithmic plot in the figure yields straight lines in both cases, just two data point pairs are needed for the dashed and the solid line to obtain the pre–exponential factor and the activation

74

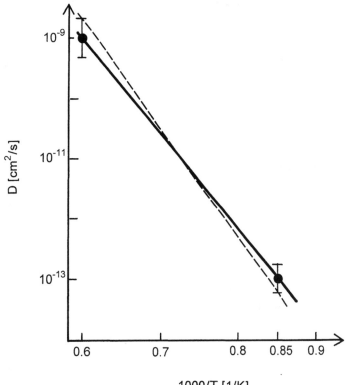

Fig. 7.25 for problem P–7.17

energy in each case, as defined in Eq. (7.26). We analyse both lines at the same temperature points for convenience, and obtain the data listed in Table 7.9.

Table 7.9.

1/T [1/K]	ln(D [cm²/s]) (solid line)	ln(D [cm²/s]) (dashed line)
6.0×10^{-4}	-20.72	-20.02
8.5×10^{-4}	-29.93	-30.54

Substituting the data from Table 7.9 for the solid line into Eq. (7.26) yields $\Delta E/k = 36840$ K, which corresponds to (a) $\Delta E = 5.1 \times 10^{-19}$ J $= 3.2$ eV, and to (b) $\ln D_0 = 1.38$, which gives $D_0 = 4$ cm²/s.

Substituting in Eq. (7.26) the data from Table 7.9 for the dashed line yields $\Delta E/k = 42080$ K, which corresponds to $\Delta E = 5.8 \times 10^{-19}$ J $= 3.6$ eV; and $\ln D_0 = 5.23$, which provides to a prefactor of $D_0 = 190$ cm²/s.

Note the significant difference between the two prefactors D_0 for the solid line and the dashed line. This large variability limits the usefulness of D_0 in fundamental, atomic level mechanism studies.

CHAPTER VIII

Order and evolution: the dynamics of processes

Problem 8.1

We revisit the Carnot process discussed in P–6.12. This process is operated with 1.0 mol of an ideal gas of heat capacity $C_V = 3R/2$. The pressure of the gas is 10.0 atm and the temperature is 600 K in the most compressed state. From there, an isothermal expansion leads to a pressure of 1.0 atm. The lower process temperature is 300 K. Draw this Carnot process in an S–T diagram.

Solution: Fig. 8.23 shows the plot for this cyclic process. Adiabatic means also *isentropic* (no entropy change).

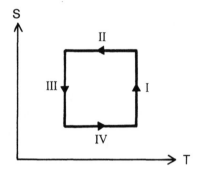

Fig. 8.23: S–T diagram for a Carnot process.

Problem 8.2

(a) Calculate the entropy change of 5 mol of an ideal gas which is isothermally and reversibly expanded from a pressure of 2 atm to 1 atm at 25^0C.
(b) How large is the entropy change in the environment within the isolated superstructure?
(c) How large is the entropy change if the expansion is done adiabatically instead?

Solution part (a): For a reversible, isothermal expansion of an ideal gas we know that $Q = -W$ since $\Delta U = 0$. We obtain the heat exchange from Eqs. (6.79) and (6.80):

$$Q = +nRT \ln\left(\frac{V_{final}}{V_{initial}}\right) =$$

$$= +nRT \ln\left(\frac{p_{initial}}{p_{final}}\right) \qquad (1)$$

We substitute the given values into Eq. (1), using the definition of the entropy change from Eq. (8.6):

$$\Delta S = \frac{Q}{T} = nR \ln\left(\frac{p_i}{p_f}\right) =$$

$$5[mol] \; 8.314\left[\frac{J}{K\,mol}\right] \ln\left(\frac{2[atm]}{1[atm]}\right) \qquad (2)$$

which yields:

$$\Delta S = +28.8 \; \frac{J}{K} \qquad (3)$$

Solution part (b): No processes occur in the current problem except for the isothermal expansion. The isothermal expansion is reversible. Therefore, we know that $\Delta S = 0$ for the isolated superstructure, yielding:

$$\Delta S_{environ.} = -\Delta S_{system} = -28.8 \; \frac{J}{K} \qquad (4)$$

This value is negative because the environment loses heat to the system during the process.

Solution part (c): An adiabatic process is characterized by $Q = 0$, i.e., no heat exchange occurs between the system and the environment. Therefore, $\Delta S = 0$ for this process.

Problem 8.3

Calculate the entropy change during melting of 1.0 mol benzene. The melting point of benzene at 1 atm pressure is $T_m = 5.4^0$C and the latent heat of melting is 126 kJ/kg.

Solution: We use the definition of the entropy change for the process, $\Delta S = Q/T$. To express the entropy in unit [J/(K mol)], we need to convert the latent heat to a molar value. The molar mass of benzene is:

$$M_{C_6H_6} = 6\left(M_C + M_H\right) =$$

$$6\left(12.01\left[\frac{g}{mol}\right] + 1.01\left[\frac{g}{mol}\right]\right) = 78.1 \frac{g}{mol} \quad (5)$$

With this mass, we convert the latent heat of melting:

$$\Delta H_{melt} = 126\left[\frac{kJ}{kg}\right] 78.1\left[\frac{g}{mol}\right]$$

$$\Rightarrow \quad \Delta H_{melt} = 9840 \frac{J}{mol} \quad (6)$$

Note that the latent heat of melting is written as an enthalpy because the process is done at constant pressure, not at constant volume. With the melting temperature $T_{melt} = 5.4^0C = 278.55$ K, we find:

$$\Delta S_{melt} = \frac{\Delta H_{melt}}{T_{melt}} = \frac{9840\left[\frac{J}{mol}\right]}{278.55\,[K]} \quad (7)$$

$$\Rightarrow \quad \Delta S_{melt} = 35.3 \frac{J}{K\,mol}$$

Problem 8.4
Calculate the entropy of evaporation for 1 mol of the materials listed in Table 8.8.

Solution: In each case, the process entropy is calculated from its definition as $\Delta S = \Delta H/T_b$, where the boiling temperature is given in [K]. This yields the results in Table 8.10.

Table 8.8: Boiling point T_b and latent heat of evaporation for various materials.

Material	$T_b[^0C]$	ΔH [kJ/mol]
Argon (Ar)	− 185.7	7.86
Mercury (Hg)	356.6	64.85
CCl$_4$	76.7	30.0
C$_6$H$_6$ (benzene)	80.1	30.75

Table 8.10: Boiling point T_b in [K] and entropy of evaporation for the materials of Table 8.8.

Material	T_b[K]	ΔS [J/(K mol)]
Argon (Ar)	87.45	89.9
Mercury (Hg)	629.8	103.0
CCl$_4$	349.9	85.7
C$_6$H$_6$ (benzene)	353.3	87.0

Problem 8.5
10 g ice at 0^0C are placed in a calorimeter with 20 g water at 90^0C. The latent heat of melting is 5980 J/mol for ice. For the molar heat capacity of liquid water we use 75.3 J/(K mol) and assume that this value is temperature independent.
(a) What is the final temperature of the water?
(b) If the process is done reversibly, what is the entropy change of the combined system ice/water?
(c) What is the entropy change in the environment for the reversible process.
(d) What is the entropy change if the process is done irreversibly in an isolated beaker?
Hint: Use Eq. (8.27) for the temperature dependence of the entropy.

Solution part (a): We first calculate the amount of energy needed to melt 10 g of ice. This energy is extracted from the water at 90^0C. In the last step, we mix the 10 g now liquid at 0^0C with the 20 g of warmer water.

The energy needed to melt 10 g of water is obtained from the given latent heat of melting and the molar mass of water, M = 18 g/mol:

$$E_{melt} = \frac{5890\left[\frac{J}{mol}\right]}{18\left[\frac{g}{mol}\right]} 10[g] \quad (8)$$

$$\Rightarrow \quad E_{melt} = 3322\ J$$

This energy is obtained from cooling water from $T_{init} = 90^0$C = 363 K to T_{final}. We use C_p because the process is done at constant pressure:

$$\Delta H = n\ C_p\ \Delta T =$$

$$\frac{20\,[g]}{18\left[\frac{g}{mol}\right]} 75.3\left[\frac{J}{k\,mol}\right]\left(363[K] - T_{final}\right) \quad (9)$$

We use $\Delta H = 3322$ J in Eq. (9) to find $T_{final} = 323.4$ K = 50.3^0C. Mixing 10 g water at 0^0C and 20 g of water at 50.3^0C leads to 30 g of water at 33.5^0C.

Solution part (b): The entropy change is determined in two parts: the contribution of the phase change of the ice and the contribution due to the temperature changes in the liquid water. For the latter, we use from the text Eq. (8.27):

$$\Delta S = n \; C_p \; \ln\left(\frac{T_f}{T_i}\right) \qquad (10)$$

The first contribution to the entropy change is the melting of 10 g ice. We saw that the energy needed for that process is $E = 3322$ J. The associated entropy value is $\Delta S = + 12.16$ J/K since the melting happens at 273.1 K.

Eq. (10) is now applied for each of the two amounts of water in the system, for 10 g to heat from the freezing point to 33.5^0C, and for 20 g of water to cool from 90^0C to 33.5^0C. Note that the heating leads to a positive entropy change and the cooling to a negative change:

$$\Delta S = \frac{10[g]}{18\left[\frac{g}{mol}\right]} \; 75.3\left[\frac{J}{K \; mol}\right] \cdot \; ...$$

$$... \cdot \left\{\ln\left(\frac{306.6}{273.1}\right) + 2 \; \ln\left(\frac{306.6}{363.1}\right)\right\} \qquad (11)$$

The factor two in the last bracket of Eq. (11) recognizes that 20 g water are cooled, not just 10 g. Eq. (11) yields $\Delta S = - 9.3$ J/K.

We combine both contributions to the entropy change of the system:

$$\Delta S_{system} = 12.16\left[\frac{J}{K}\right] - 9.3\left[\frac{J}{K}\right]$$

$$\Rightarrow \quad \Delta S_{system} = + 2.9 \; \frac{J}{K} \qquad (12)$$

Solution part (c) : For the process to be reversible, the change in the environment must be equal but opposite to the change in the system. Thus, $\Delta S_{env} = - 2.9$ J/K.

Solution part (d): In this case we get $\Delta S_{system} = + 2.9$ J/K and $\Delta S_{env} = 0$ J/K; i.e., the total entropy change is an increase of 2.9 J/K. This is a thermodynamically possible process.

Problem 8.6

Calculate the entropy of 1 mol nitrogen gas (N_2) at p = 1 atm and T = 150^0C. Use for the molar heat capacity of nitrogen $C_p = 28.8$ J/(K mol).

Solution: In the text, Table 8.4 provides the value of the standard entropy at $25°$C and 1 atm for various materials. For nitrogen (N_2), the table states $S^0 = 191.2$ J K^{-1} mol^{-1}. This is not the answer, however, as we are asked to provide the entropy at another temperature. We use Eq. (10) to calculate the temperature related change:

$$\Delta S = 28.8\left[\frac{J}{K}\right] \; \ln\left(\frac{423.1[K]}{298.1[K]}\right)$$

$$\Rightarrow \quad \Delta S = + 10.1 \; \frac{J}{K} \qquad (13)$$

Thus,

$$S_{150\,K} = S^0 + \Delta S = 191.2\left[\frac{J}{K}\right] + 10.1\left[\frac{J}{K}\right]$$

$$\Rightarrow \quad S_{150\,K} = + 201.3 \; \frac{J}{K} \qquad (14)$$

Problem 8.7

Determine graphically the standard entropy of silver from the data given in Table 8.9.

Table 8.9: Molar heat capacity C_p for silver (Ag) at various temperatures.

T[K]	C_p [J/(K mol)]	T[K]	C_p [J/(K mol)]
15	0.67	170	23.61
30	4.77	190	24.09
50	11.65	210	24.42
70	16.33	230	24.73
90	19.13	250	25.02
110	20.96	270	25.31
130	22.13	290	25.44
150	22.97		

Solution: The standard entropy for 1 mol is determined from the definition:

$$\Delta S = S_{final} - S_{initial} = \sum_i \frac{Q_i}{T_i} \qquad (15)$$

in which we choose the initial state at temperature 0 K, at which S = 0 J/K and the final state as the standard state at temperature 298 K. To obtain a value at constant pressure, the heat term in Eq. (15) is replaced by the term Q = C_p ΔT:

$$S^0 = \sum_{T = 0\,K}^{298\,K} \frac{C_p}{T} \Delta T \qquad (16)$$

We obtain the standard entropy from the data in Table 8.9 by plotting C_p/T versus the temperature. This plot is shown in Fig. 8.24.

Problem 8.8
The standard entropy of diamond is S^0 = 2.5 J/(K mol) and the standard entropy of graphite is S^0 = 5.7 J/(K mol). Both are phases of elementary solid carbon. Which of the two phases is more stable if we establish a thermal equilibrium between the two phases in an isolated system?

Solution: Diamond and graphite are two different solid state phases of carbon. For the argument below we consider the following phase transition:

$$C_{diamond} \rightarrow C_{graphite} \qquad (17)$$

The entropy change for one mol of carbon to undergo this reaction is calculated from the given values:

$$\Delta S = S^0_{graphite} - S^0_{diamond} =$$
$$= 5.71 \left[\frac{J}{K\,mol}\right] - 2.45 \left[\frac{J}{K\,mol}\right] > 0 \qquad (18)$$

The transition from diamond to graphite is a spontaneous process because the result in Eq. (18) is positive. Thus, diamond is the more stable solid state of carbon.

Problem 8.9
For a certain chemical reaction we find ΔH = – 94.5 kJ and ΔS = – 189.1 J/K. Neglect the temperature dependence of these two values. What is the Gibbs free energy for the reaction at
(a) 300 K, and
(b) 1000 K?

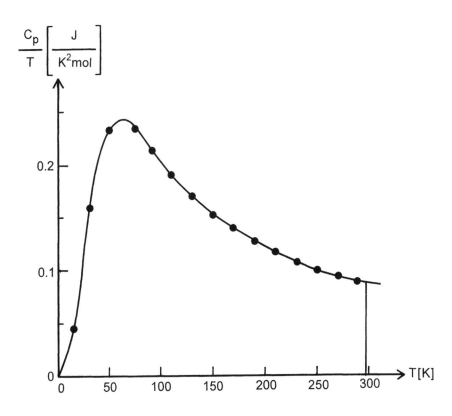

Fig. 8.24: C_p/T plot versus temperature for the data of Table 8.9.

Solution part (a): The Gibbs free energy change of a chemical reaction, ΔG, is defined as:

$$\Delta G = \Delta H - T \Delta S \qquad (19)$$

in which the given data are substituted:

$$\Delta G = -94.5 \, [kJ] - 300[K]\left(-189.1\left[\frac{J}{K}\right]\right) \qquad (20)$$

$$\Rightarrow \quad \Delta G_{300\,K} = -37.8 \; kJ$$

Because ΔG is negative, the reaction occurs spontaneous as written.

Solution part (b): The change in temperature has a profound effect on this reaction; at 1000 K it is no longer a spontaneous process:

$$\Delta G = -94.5[kJ] - 1000[K]\left(-189.1\left[\frac{J}{K}\right]\right) \qquad (21)$$

$$\Rightarrow \quad \Delta G_{1000\,K} = +94.5 \; kJ$$

Problem 8.10

Calculate ΔS and ΔG for the evaporation of 1 mol of water at $T = 100^0C$ and $p = 1$ atm. The latent heat of evaporation of water is 9.7 kcal/mol.

Solution: We start with the entropy change. We use n = 1 mol, T = 373 K, and convert the latent heat to standard unit:

$$\Delta H_{evap} = 9.7 \, \frac{kcal}{mol} = 40.6 \, \frac{kJ}{mol} \qquad (22)$$

with these values, we find:

$$\Delta S_{evap} = \frac{\Delta H_{evap}}{T} = \frac{40.6\left[\frac{kJ}{mol}\right]}{373 \, [K]} \qquad (23)$$

$$\Rightarrow \quad \Delta S_{evap} = 108.8 \, \frac{J}{K\,mol}$$

Before combining the results in Eqs. (22) and (23) to obtain the Gibbs free energy, we notice that water evaporation at 100^0C (at 1 atm) is a process between two

states of the water system which are in thermal equilibrium at that temperature. Therefore, we expect at $T = T_{evap}$ that $\Delta G = 0$:

$$\Delta G_{evap} = \Delta H_{evap} - T \Delta S_{evap}$$

$$= \Delta H_{evap} - T \frac{\Delta H_{evap}}{T_{evap}} = 0 \qquad (24)$$

Problem 8.11

Derive Eq. (8.4) from Eq. (8.3).

Solution: We want to show how we get from the formula for the efficiency coefficient of the Carnot process:

$$\eta = \frac{|W|}{Q_b} = \frac{Q_a + Q_b}{Q_b} = \frac{T_b - T_a}{T_b} \qquad (25)$$

to the formula which motivates the introduction of the entropy concept:

$$\frac{Q_a}{T_a} + \frac{Q_b}{T_b} = 0 \qquad (26)$$

We start with the last two terms in Eq. (25). Eliminating the denominators through multiplication yields:

$$Q_a T_b + Q_b T_b = Q_b T_b - Q_b T_a$$

$$\Rightarrow \quad Q_a T_b = - Q_b T_a \qquad (27)$$

Eq. (27) is divided on both sides by $T_a T_b$:

$$\frac{Q_a}{T_a} = - \frac{Q_b}{T_b} \qquad (28)$$

This is equivalent to Eq. (26).

CHAPTER IX

Water and aqueous solutions: static electricity

Problem 9.1

We study 3 point charges at the corners of a triangle, as shown in Fig. 9.31. The charges are $q_1 = 5.0 \times 10^{-9}$ Cb, $q_2 = -4.0 \times 10^{-9}$ Cb, and $q_3 = 2.5 \times 10^{-9}$ Cb. Two distances of separation are also given, $l_{12} = 4$ m and $l_{13} = 6$ m. Find the net electric force on q_3.

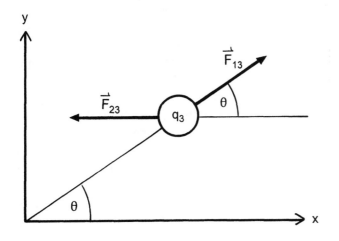

Fig. 9.31 for problem P–9.1.

Fig. 9.38: Two forces acting on a charged particle.

Solution: The force on the charge q_3 is the superposition of the forces due to charges q_1 and q_2, i.e., $\mathbf{F}_{13}$ and $\mathbf{F}_{23}$. We calculate each of these two force vectors separately using Coulomb's law. Then we add them to obtain the resulting force.

Starting with the magnitude of the force exerted by q_1 on q_3, $|\mathbf{F}_{13}|$ we find:

$$|\mathbf{F}_{13}| = k \frac{|q_1|\,|q_3|}{r_{13}^2} = \tag{1}$$

$$9\times10^9\left[\frac{Nm^2}{Cb^2}\right]\frac{5\times10^{-9}[Cb]\,2.5\times10^{-9}[Cb]}{(6.0[m])^2}$$

which yields:

$$|\mathbf{F}_{13}| = 3.1 \times 10^{-9}\ N \tag{2}$$

The direction of this force is along the line connecting the charges q_1 and q_3 and is directed away from charge q_1 since the two charges repel each other. This leads to a vector which forms an angle θ with the positive x–axis, as illustrated in Fig. 9.38. The angle θ is obtained from geometric analysis of Fig. 9.38. We find, sin θ = 4.0m/6.0m = 0.667 which corresponds to θ = 41.8°. This allows us to express the x– and y–components of the force in the form:

$$F_{13,\,x} = |\mathbf{F}_{13}|\cos\theta = 2.31 \times 10^{-9}\ N$$
$$F_{13,\,y} = |\mathbf{F}_{13}|\sin\theta = 2.07 \times 10^{-9}\ N \tag{3}$$

We apply again Coulomb's law to obtain the magnitude of the second force, $\mathbf{F}_{23}$. Fig. 9.38 is used for the required distance between the two charges q_2 and q_3. Applying standard trigonometry we find:

$$l_{23}^2 + l_{12}^2 = l_{13}^2 \tag{4}$$

which leads to:

$$l_{23} = \sqrt{l_{13}^2 - l_{12}^2} = \sqrt{(6[m])^2 - (4[m])^2} \quad (5)$$

This yields:

$$l_{23} = 4.47 \ m \quad (6)$$

Now the given data and the value from Eq. (6) are substituted into Coulomb's law:

$$|F_{23}| = k \frac{|q_2| \ |q_3|}{r_{23}^2} =$$

$$9 \times 10^9 \left[\frac{Nm^2}{Cb^2} \right] \frac{4 \times 10^{-9}[Cb] \ 2.5 \times 10^{-9}[Cb]}{(4.47[m])^2} \quad (7)$$

which yields:

$$|F_{23}| = 4.50 \times 10^{-9} \ N \quad (8)$$

The direction of this force is along the connecting line between the charges q_2 and q_3 and is pointed toward q_2 since the two charges attract each other. This is illustrated in Fig. 9.38.

With the two individual forces acting on charge q_3 identified, we now calculate the total force acting on that charge. For the x–component we find:

$$F_{total, \ x} = F_{13, \ x} - |F_{23}| =$$

$$2.31 \times 10^{-9} \ [N] - 4.50 \times 10^{-9} \ [N] \quad (9)$$

$$\Rightarrow \quad F_{total, \ x} = -2.19 \times 10^{-9} \ N$$

for the y–component we get:

$$F_{total, \ y} = F_{13, \ y} = + 2.07 \times 10^{-9} \ N \quad (10)$$

Providing the Cartesian components of a vector is one way to express it. Alternatively, you can calculate the magnitude of the vector, $| \mathbf{F}_{total}|$, and its angle with the positive x–axis, ϕ (which is the polar coordinate representation). For the vector with its components given in Eqs. (9) and (10), this yields:

$$|F_{total}| = \sqrt{F_{total, \ x}^2 + F_{total, \ y}^2} \quad (11)$$

$$\Rightarrow \quad |F_{total}| = 3.01 \times 10^{-9} \ N$$

and

$$\tan\phi = \frac{F_{total, \ y}}{F_{total, \ x}} = \frac{+ 2.07 \times 10^{-9} \ [N]}{- 2.19 \times 10^{-9} \ [N]} \quad (12)$$

$$\Rightarrow \quad \phi = 136.6^0$$

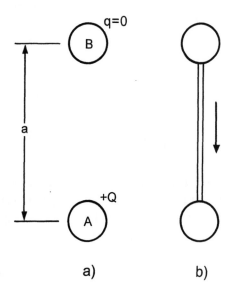

Fig. 9.32 for problem P–9.2.

Problem 9.2
In Fig. 9.32(a) we study two identical, electrically isolated spheres A and B. The surface of each sphere is conducting which allows for a uniform charge distribution. The spheres are separated by a distance a that is large compared to the diameter of each of the two spheres. Sphere A has initially a positive charge of +Q and sphere B is electrically neutral (q = 0). Thus, there is no electrostatic force acting between the spheres.

Suppose the spheres are now connected with a conducting wire as shown in Fig. 9.32(b). We assume that the wire is thin enough so that any net charge on it can be neglected. However, the repulsive force between the charges on sphere A leads to an equal distribution of charges between the two spheres, i.e., all the charges move to a maximum mutual distance. What is the electrostatic force between the spheres after the wire is removed?

Solution: Initially, there is no electrostatic force since sphere B doesn't carry any charge. After connecting both spheres, the mutual repulsion of the mobile positive charges from sphere A leads to a maximum charge separation, given when $q_A = Q/2$ and $q_B = Q/2$.

At this point we make a less obvious assumption. We assume that the uniformity of the charge distribution on either sphere is not disturbed by the other sphere. This assumption is reasonably justified as long as the sizes of the two spheres are small in comparison to their distance. When this assumption is valid, the entire charge on either sphere behaves as if it were a point charge at the center of the sphere. Note that we would have to consider all the individual charges on each sphere separately without this assumption.

Using Coulomb's law we find for the magnitude of the force between the two spheres:

$$|F| = \frac{1}{4\pi\epsilon_0} \frac{\frac{Q}{2}\frac{Q}{2}}{a^2} = \frac{1}{16\pi\epsilon_0}\left(\frac{Q}{a}\right)^2 \quad (13)$$

The two spheres repel each other with this force as they are both charged positively.

Problem 9.3
The radius of atomic nuclei follows closely the formula

$$r\ [m] = 1.2 \times 10^{-15}\ A^{1/3} \quad (14)$$

in which A is the atomic mass in unit [g/mol].
(a) Confirm that the density of the material in the nuclei is independent of the type of atom studied. This density is 2×10^{17} kg/m³!
(b) Using Eq. (9.75) and A(Bi) = 209.0 g/mol, find the magnitude of the repulsive electrostatic force between two of the protons in a bismuth nucleus when they are separated by the diameter of the nucleus.

Solution part (a): The density is defined by $\rho = m/V$. For the material in the nucleus, the mass is the atomic mass, A. The volume of the nucleus is proportional to the cube

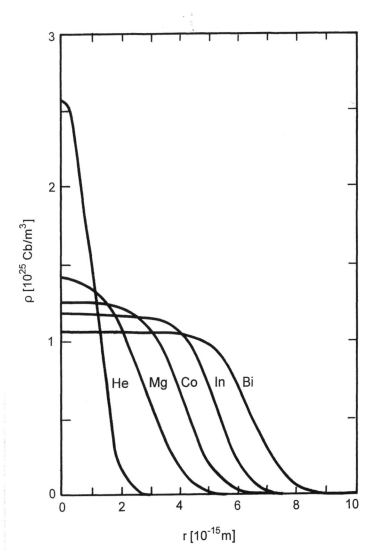

Fig. 9.39: The charge density of nuclear matter in an atomic nucleus as a function of distance from the nucleus' center. The same uniformity is also observed for the nuclear potential energy across the nucleus.

of the radius of the nucleus, $V \propto r^3$. Substituting Eq. (14) into this relation, we find for the volume $V \propto (A^{1/3})^3 = A$. Thus, the density is independent of the atomic mass because $\rho = m/V \propto A/A$.

Note that we made an implicit assumption when using the density, $\rho = m/V$: this formula is only useful if the density is constant across the entire volume. Is this assumption justified for a nucleus? Surprisingly, the assumption of a constant density is a very good one for the nuclei of heavier atoms. This is illustrated in Fig. 9.39 showing the charge density in the nucleus. Only close to the edge does the nuclear density tail off.

Solution part (b): Substituting the given atomic mass of bismuth in Eq. (14), we find for the radius of Bi nuclei:

$$r = 1.2 \times 10^{-15}\ 209^{1/3} = 7.1 \times 10^{-15}\ m \quad (15)$$

The diameter of the nucleus is twice its radius. The charge of a proton is equal in magnitude to the elementary charge e, with $e = 1.6 \times 10^{-19}$ Cb. Therefore, the Coulomb force between two protons equals:

$$|F| = k\ \frac{e^2}{(2r)^2} =$$

$$9 \times 10^9 \left[\frac{Nm^2}{Cb^2}\right] \frac{(1.6 \times 10^{-19}\ [Cb])^2}{(14.2 \times 10^{-15}\ [m])^2} \quad (16)$$

$$\Rightarrow \quad |F| = 1.1\ N$$

This is a small force when acting on a macroscopic object, but it is a tremendous force when acting at an atomic length scale. It should lead to the explosion of this and any other nucleus, except for the hydrogen nucleus with only one proton. Luckily there is an even stronger attractive force acting between the protons and neutrons in a nucleus, which is the nuclear force.

However, the nuclear force falls off much more steeply than the Coulomb force and the latter starts to dominate at about the distance used in this problem. Therefore, there are no stable nuclei larger than bismuth's nucleus, with two heavier elements only coming close: the thorium isotope Th–232 with a half–life of 14 billion years and the uranium isotope U–238 with a half–life of 4.5 billion years.

Problem 9.4
How much negative charge is in 1.0 mol of neutral helium gas? Each He atom has two electrons in its atomic shell.

Solution: Helium has two electrons in its atomic shell, electrically balancing the two protons in its nucleus. Thus, the total amount of negative charge is:

$$Q = (2e) \cdot N_A =$$

$$3.2 \times 10^{-19} \left[\frac{Cb}{atom}\right] 6 \times 10^{23} \left[\frac{atoms}{mol}\right] \quad (17)$$

which yields:

$$Q = 1.9 \times 10^5\ \frac{Cb}{mol} = 0.19\ \frac{MCb}{mol} \quad (18)$$

Note that there are also two neutrons in each helium nucleus. Free neutrons are not stable but decay into an electron and a proton with a half–life of 14 minutes. In above calculation we neglected these additional electrons because neutrons in a nucleus are stable.

Problem 9.5
A CsCl (cesium chloride) salt crystal is built from unit cells, as shown in Fig. 9.33. Cl^- ions form the corners of a cube and a Cs^+ ion is at the center of the cube. The edge length of the cube, which is called the lattice constant, is 0.4 nm.
(a) What is the magnitude of the net electrostatic force exerted on the cesium ion by its eight shown Cl^- neighbors?
(b) If the Cl^- in the lower left corner is removed, what is the magnitude of the net electrostatic force exerted on the cesium ion at the center by the seven remaining chlorine ions? In what direction does this force act on the cesium ion?

Solution part (a): Each of the eight Cl^- ions at the corners of the unit cell of the CsCl crystal exerts the same magnitude of electrostatic force on the Cs^+ ion at the center of the unit cell. All of these pair–wise forces are attractive since they act between a positive Cs ion and a negative Cl ion. Since, therefore, there are four pairs of equal but opposite forces, the net force on the central Cs ion is zero. Note: the same is true for the chlorine ions as well because each Cl^- ion lies in the same fashion at the center of eight Cs^+ ions. This becomes evident when you keep in mind that the unit cell of the CsCl crystal is (infinitely often) repeated in all three Cartesian directions.

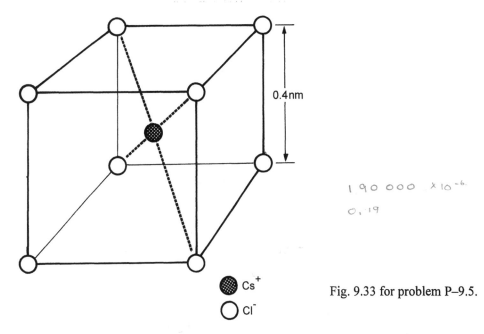

0.4nm

$190\ 000 \times 10^{-6}$
0.19

Cs⁺ (filled circle)
Cl⁻ (open circle)

Fig. 9.33 for problem P–9.5.

Solution part (b): From an electric point of view it is the same to remove a Cl⁻ ion from one of the corners of the unit cell shown in Fig. 9.33 or to add a positive elementary charge to that same chlorine ion. Thus, the change from the answer in part (a) to part (b) is one additional pair–wise force between that additional positive charge and the central charge of the Cs⁺ ion.

We determine first the distance between the added charge and the center of the unit cell. The distance is half of the length of a line drawn through the cube of side length a. From trigonometry we know that the diagonal line in such a cube has the length $(\sqrt{3})\,a$. Thus, the additional force is:

$$|\mathbf{F}| = \frac{1}{4\pi\epsilon_0}\frac{e^2}{\left(\dfrac{\sqrt{3}a}{2}\right)^2} =$$

$$9\times 10^9\left[\frac{Nm^2}{Cb^2}\right]\frac{(1.6\times 10^{-19}\ [Cb])^2}{\dfrac{3}{4}\left(0.4\times 10^{-9}\ [m]\right)^2}$$

(19)

which yields:

$$|\mathbf{F}| = 1.9\times 10^{-9}\ N \qquad \textbf{(20)}$$

This is a repulsive force, i.e., it acts on the central ion in the direction pointing away from the missing ion at the corner of the unit cell. It is interesting to compare this force with the force we calculated in problem P – 9.3,

showing the significant difference between electrostatic forces at the length scale of a nucleus and at atomic length scales.

Problem 9.6

Fig. 9.34 shows three positive charges, two charges of magnitude q at a distance a along the x– and the y–axis, and one charge of magnitude 2q at the origin. Calculate the electric field at point P for q = 1.0 nCb and the distance a = 1.0 m.

Solution: The electric field is closely related to the electric force and as such a vector. Thus, for a two–dimensional problem as illustrated in Fig. 9.34, we need to find two electric field components. Fig. 9.34 already identifies the two Cartesian coordinates, the x–direction horizontally toward the right and the y–direction vertically up. With respect of this coordinate system, we are asked to find E_x and E_y.

Usually, a calculation like this, in the current case for three point charges, can become extensive. It is, therefore, highly recommended to search for symmetries in the problem. You will notice for the current problem how this may greatly reduce the effort.

We notice that the two charges with value +q, at positions (0, a) and (a, 0), are located at the same distance from point P at opposite sides, i.e., along the dashed line. Thus, the field contributions of these two charges cancel each other. As a result, we need only to determine the field contribution of the charge with value +2q to answer the problem.

Since this charge is a point charge, we apply Eq.

85

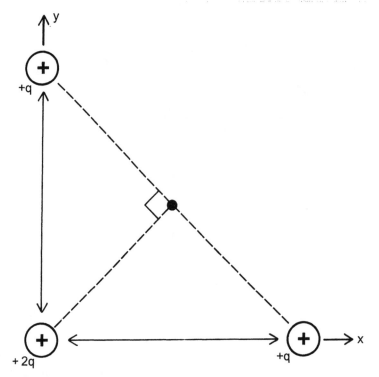

+q

+2q

+q

x

Fig. 9.34 for problem P–9.6.

(9.20) (and not Eq. (9.21), which we would have to choose if more than one point charge would contribute to the net electric field). In Eq. (9.20), the distance of point P and the point charge is required. This distance is determined from Fig. 9.34: point P lies in the center of a square of side length a. The length of a diagonal line through a square is $a\sqrt{2}$. Thus, the distance between the point charge and the point P is ½ $a\sqrt{2} = a/\sqrt{2}$. This allows us to express the electric field at point P:

$$|E(P)| = \frac{1}{4\pi\epsilon_0} \frac{2q}{\left(\frac{a}{\sqrt{2}}\right)^2} = \frac{q}{\pi\epsilon_0 a^2} \qquad (21)$$

The direction of the electric field is illustrated in Fig. 9.40: the electric field is directed away from the positive charge at the origin (compare Fig. 9.12).

Fig. 9.40 defines an angle θ between the direction of the electric field and the positive x–axis. Thus, with the magnitude in Eq. (21) and the angle θ the task of this problem is complete. In particular, the two components of the electric field can then be expressed as:

$$E_x = \frac{q}{\pi\epsilon_0 a^2} \cos\theta$$

$$\qquad (22)$$

$$E_y = \frac{q}{\pi\epsilon_0 a^2} \sin\theta$$

The angle θ is easiest determined from Figs. 9.34 and 9.40. The angle θ is equal to the angle the line from the origin to point P forms with the x–axis, i.e., $\theta = 45^0$.

Substituting the values given in the problem into Eq. (22) yields for the x–component:

$$E_x = \frac{1\times10^{-9}[Cb] \cos 45^0}{\pi\ 8.85\times10^{-12}\left[\dfrac{Cb}{Vm}\right](1.0[m])^2} \qquad (23)$$

$$\Rightarrow \quad E_x = 25.4\ \frac{V}{m}$$

and for the y–component:

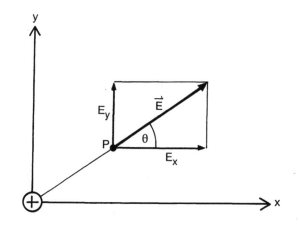

Fig. 9.40: The electric field components at point P due to a charge at the origin.

86

$$E_y = \frac{1\times10^{-9}[Cb]\;\sin 45^0}{\pi\;8.85\times10^{-12}\left[\dfrac{Cb}{Vm}\right](1.0[m])^2} \tag{24}$$

$$\Rightarrow \quad E_y = 25.4\;\frac{V}{m}$$

Problem 9.7
Calculate the electric field half way between two charges, where one charge is $+10.0 \times 10^{-9}$ Cb and the second charge is
(a) $+ 5.0 \times 10^{-9}$ Cb at a distance of 20 cm;
(b) $- 5.0 \times 10^{-9}$ Cb at a distance of 20 cm.

Solution part (a): The electric field for an arrangement of two charges is the sum of the two electric fields for each charge separately. The two electric field vectors at the point half way between the two charges are sketched in Fig. 9.41. Note that $l_1 = l_2 = r$. The respective directions of the two vectors are determined from the convention introduced in Fig. 9.12.

The first charge we consider has the value of $+10.0 \times 10^{-9}$ Cb and is shown at left in Fig. 9.41. The distance to the half way point is r = 0.1 m, and thus, the field contribution at that point is:

$$|E_1| = \frac{k\;q_1}{r^2} = 9\times10^9\left[\frac{Nm^2}{Cb^2}\right]\frac{1\times10^{-8}[Cb]}{(0.1[m])^2} \tag{25}$$

$$\Rightarrow \quad |E_1| = 9\times10^3\;\frac{N}{Cb}$$

The field of the second charge at the same point is:

$$|E_2| = \frac{k\;q_2}{r^2} = 9\times10^9\left[\frac{Nm^2}{Cb^2}\right]\frac{5\times10^{-9}[Cb]}{(0.1[m])^2} \tag{26}$$

$$\Rightarrow \quad |E_2| = 4.5\times10^3\;\frac{N}{Cb}$$

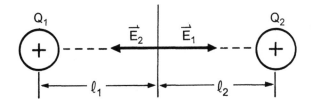

Fig. 9.41: Electric field components of charged particles.

Both fields, given as a magnitude in Eqs. (25) and (26), have only x–components, as shown in Fig. 9.41. The resulting field has, therefore, also only an x–component which is given by:

$$E_{total,\,x} = E_{1,\,x} + E_{2,\,x} = |E_1| - |E_2|$$

$$\Rightarrow \quad E_{total,\,x} = +\,4.5\times10^3\;\frac{N}{Cb} \tag{27}$$

with the y–component of the resulting field zero.

Solution part (b): The only change in comparison to part (a) is the sign of the second charge, which causes a 180^0 change in the direction of field vector $\mathbf{E}_2$ in Fig. 9.41. This changes the corresponding sign in Eq. (27), leading to:

$$E_{total,\,x} = E_{1,\,x} + E_{2,\,x} = |E_1| + |E_2|$$

$$\Rightarrow \quad E_{total,\,x} = +\,1.35\times10^4\;\frac{N}{Cb} \tag{28}$$

The y–component of the resulting field vanishes again.

Problem 9.8
In the Millikan oil–drop apparatus of Fig. 9.2 a drop of radius r = 1.9 μm has an excess charge of two electrons. What are the magnitude and direction of the electric field that is required to balance the drop so it remains stationary in the apparatus? Use for the density of oil the value ρ = 0.925 g/cm³.

Solution: To establish a mechanical equilibrium for the drop, i.e., to maintain a zero–acceleration in the vertical y–direction, an upward acting electrostatic force must compensate the downwards directed weight:

$$\sum_i F_{i,\,y} = 0 = q|E| - mg = q|E| - \rho Vg$$

$$\Rightarrow \quad ne|E| = \rho\left(\frac{4}{3}\pi r^3\right)g \tag{29}$$

in which the charge on the oil drop is expressed as q = ne, with n an integer number and e the magnitude of the elementary charge. The mass of the spherical drop has been rewritten as the product of the density and the volume of a sphere of radius r. With n = 2 given in the problem text we find for the magnitude of the required electric field:

$$|E| = \frac{4\pi r^3 \rho g}{3ne} =$$

$$\frac{4\pi \left(1.9\times10^{-6}[m]\right)^3 \ 925\left[\frac{kg}{m^3}\right] 9.8\left[\frac{m}{s^2}\right]}{6 \cdot 1.6\times10^{-19}[Cb]} \quad \text{(30)}$$

which yields:

$$|E| = 8.14 \times 10^5 \ \frac{N}{Cb} \quad \text{(31)}$$

While the electrostatic force is directed upwards, the electric field is pointing downwards with the magnitude calculated in Eq. (31). This direction of the electric field is due to the negative charge carried by the drop. To design such a field, a parallel plate capacitor is used with the positively charged plate above the region in which the oil drop is levitating and the negatively charged plate is below this area.

Problem 9.9
An electron is released into a uniform electric field of magnitude 1.5×10^3 N/Cb. Calculate the acceleration of the electron, neglecting gravitation.

Solution: The magnitude of the force acting on the electron is given by $F = e|E|$ in which e is the elementary charge, carried by an electron. $|E|$ is the magnitude of the electric field at the actual location of the electron. Thus, the present problem would be mathematically challenging for any other arrangement of fixed charges than a parallel plate capacitor since the electric field is only in that device the same at every point. The acceleration of the electron in the electric field is determined with above force from Newton's second law:

$$\sum_i F_i = q|E| = ma \quad \text{(32)}$$

which yields:

Table 9.1: Elementary particles in the atom

Particle	Mass [kg]	Charge [Cb]
Electron	9.11×10^{-31}	-1.6×10^{-19}
Proton	1.673×10^{-27}	$+1.6 \times 10^{-19}$
Neutron	1.675×10^{-27}	0

$$a = \frac{e|E|}{m} = \frac{1.6\times10^{-19}[Cb] \ 1.5\times10^3\left[\frac{N}{Cb}\right]}{9.11\times10^{-31}[kg]} \quad \text{(33)}$$

$$\Rightarrow \quad a = 2.6 \times 10^{14} \ \frac{m}{s^2}$$

in which the mass of the electron was taken from Table 9.1. The tremendous acceleration found in Eq. (33) reflects both the very small mass of the electron and the strength of the electric force.

Problem 9.10
Determine the magnitude of the force between an electric dipole with a dipole moment of 3×10^{-29} Cb m and an electron. The electron is positioned 20 nm from the center of the dipole, along the dipole axis.
Hint: assume that the given distance is large relative to the charge separation of the dipole.

Solution: We use Eq. (9.29), which gives us the electric field far from a dipole in the axial direction. For the force between the charge and the dipole we find:

$$F = q_{electron} \ |E| = \frac{e \ qd}{2\pi\epsilon_0 \ x^3} = 2k \ \frac{e \ qd}{x^3} \quad \text{(34)}$$

in which e is the elementary charge. qd in Eq. (34) is the dipole moment with qd $= 3 \times 10^{-29}$ Cb m. Thus:

$$F = 2 \cdot 9\times10^9\left[\frac{Nm^2}{Cb^2}\right] \cdot \ ...$$

$$... \ \frac{1.6\times10^{-19}[Cb] \ 3.0\times10^{-29}[Cb \ m]}{(20\times10^{-9}[m])^3} \quad \text{(35)}$$

$$\Rightarrow \quad F = 1.1 \times 10^{-14} \ N$$

Problem 9.11
Humid air breaks electrically down when its molecules become ionized. This happens in an electric field $|E| = 3.0 \times 10^6$ N/Cb. In that field, calculate the magnitude of the electrostatic force on
(a) an electron, and
(b) an ion with a single positive charge.

Solution part (a): This is a straight forward substitution problem using Eq. (9.19):

$$F = e|\boldsymbol{E}| = 1.6 \times 10^{-19}[Cb] \; 3 \times 10^6 \left[\frac{N}{Cb}\right] \quad \textbf{(36)}$$

$$\Rightarrow \quad F = 4.8 \times 10^{-13} \; N$$

Solution part (b): The second part of the question does not require a calculation. Eq. (36) still applies since the magnitude of charge of a single positive charge is equal the magnitude of the charge of an electron, i.e., the elementary charge e. The only difference is that the force on the ion acts in the opposite direction of the force acting on the electron.

Problem 9.12

A constant electric field is experimentally obtained with the set–up shown in Fig. 9.35: a 12 V battery is connected to two parallel metal plates separated by a distance of $d = 0.25$ cm. Calculate the magnitude of the electric field between the plates.

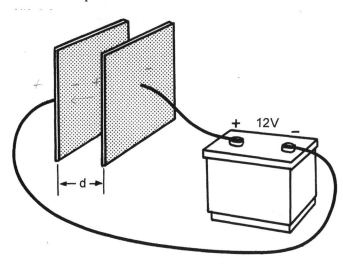

Fig. 9.35 for problem P–9.12.

Solution: The electric field in this set–up is uniform (except near the edges of the metal plates where fringe effects have to be included). Thus, Eq. (9.58) provides the appropriate relation between the potential difference and the magnitude of the electric field:

$$V_B - V_A = + |\boldsymbol{E}|d \quad \textbf{(37)}$$

Substituting the given values in this equation we obtain:

$$|\boldsymbol{E}| = \frac{\Delta V}{d} = \frac{12[V]}{0.25 \times 10^{-2}[m]} \quad \textbf{(38)}$$

$$\Rightarrow \quad |\boldsymbol{E}| = 4.8 \times 10^3 \; \frac{V}{m}$$

The direction of this electric field is toward the negatively charged plate due to the convention we introduced in Fig. 9.12.

Problem 9.13

A large number of energetic cosmic–ray particles (more on these in Chapter 20) reach the Earth's atmosphere continuously and knock electrons out of the molecules in the air. Once an electron is released, it responds to an electrostatic force which is due to an electric field **E** that is produced in the atmosphere by other charged particles. Near the surface of the Earth this electric field has a magnitude of E = 150 N/Cb and is directed downwards, as shown in Fig. 9.36. Calculate the change in electric potential energy of a released electron when it moves vertically upward through a distance d = 650 m.

Solution: The electric energy of a test charge between two uniformly charged parallel plates is given in Eq. (9.48). But can we apply this formula to the charge distribution causing the processes shown in Fig. 9.36? The answer is yes in an approximated fashion: Eq. (9.48) holds if we identify the origin of the motion of charges

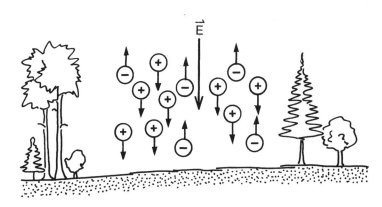

Fig. 9.36 for problem P–9.13.

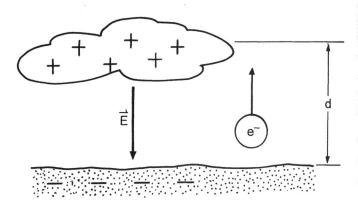

Fig. 9.42: Electric field between a cloud and the ground. An electron accelerates towards the cloud due to this electric field.

in Fig. 9.36 in the form done in Fig. 9.42. In this figure, we treat the cloud cover as one and the Earth's surface as the other of two conducting plates of a parallel plate capacitor. The surface of the Earth is charged negative and the cloud is charged positive since the electric field is pointing downwards (see the convention in Fig. 9.12). As shown in Fig. 9.42, a free electron accelerates toward the cloud since negative charges free to move accelerate always toward a region of positive charges.

The motion of the electron is accompanied by a reduction in its electric potential energy, as discussed in Eq. (9.48). The change in the electric potential energy is given by:

$$\Delta E_{el} = -e\,|E|\,\Delta y =$$

$$-1.6 \times 10^{-19} [Cb] \ 150 \left[\frac{N}{Cb}\right] \ 650[m] \qquad \textbf{(39)}$$

in which the negative sign on the right hand side of the first formula is the result of a decreasing potential energy in the direction of an increasing height y. This yields:

$$\Delta E_{el} = -1.56 \times 10^{-14} \ J \qquad \textbf{(40)}$$

Problem 9.14
(a) What is the electric potential V at a distance of r = 2.1×10^{-8} cm from a proton?
(b) What is the electric potential energy in units [J] and [eV] of an electron at the given distance from the proton?
(c) Why is this value close to the potential energy of an hydrogen atom?

(d) If the electron moves closer to the proton, does the electric potential energy increase or decrease?

Solution part (a): For a point charge, Eq. (9.59) gives us the potential:

$$V = \frac{1}{4\pi\epsilon_0}\frac{e}{r} = 9 \times 10^9 \left[\frac{Nm^2}{Cb^2}\right] \frac{1.6 \times 10^{-19}[Cb]}{2.1 \times 10^{-10}[m]} \qquad \textbf{(41)}$$

$$\Rightarrow \quad V = 6.86 \ V$$

Solution part (b): The electric potential energy follows from the charge and the potential:

$$E_{el} = qV = -1.6 \times 10^{-19}[Cb] \ 6.86[V]$$

$$\textbf{(42)}$$

$$\Rightarrow \quad E_{el} = -1.1 \times 10^{-18} \ J$$

The negative sign is due to opposite signs of the interacting charges; electron and proton attract each other.

Solution part (c): The result in part (b) applies roughly to a hydrogen atom since this atom consists of a proton (forming its nucleus) and a single electron (to guarantee electric neutrality). The distance between the charges given in this problem is a typical value reported for the radius of the hydrogen atom.

Solution part (d): As the electron comes closer to the proton the electric potential energy resumes an even more negative value than calculated in Eq. (42). Since the electron and proton attract each other, this is the same situation as we saw before for gravity, where two masses always attract each other and the gravitational potential energy is lowered when the masses approach each other (i.e., when objects fall toward the surface of the Earth). In a classical sense, the electron does not crash into the proton for the same reason the Moon doesn't fall down onto Earth: the circular motion (Moon around Earth or electron around proton) leads to an apparent centrifugal effect balancing the attractive force.

Problem 9.15
(a) For the arrangement of charges in Fig. 9.34, calculate the electric potential at point P. Use q = 1.0 nCb and a = 1.0 m, and assume that V = 0 V at infinite distance.
(b) If a charge − 2q is brought to point P, what is the electric energy of this charge? Assume again that the electric potential energy is zero at infinite distance.

Solution part (a): Note that we have chosen the same arrangement of charges as in problem P–9.6 to illustrate the difference in calculation procedure for the potential, which is a scalar, and the electric field, which is a vector. It is useful to compare both problems once the current one is done.

The potential for a given point P in the vicinity of a single point charge is given in Eq. (9.59). If there are more than one fixed point charge, the potential is calculated as the sum of all potential contributions due to the single point charges in the arrangement. We used this approach in Example 9.13 for two fixed point charges (forming a dipole) and we will use it in the current case for the three point charges in Fig. 9.34.

For the potential, Eq. (9.59) indicates that we need not to worry about the direction in which the fixed charges lie relative to the point P. The only information needed is the distance between the point and the point charge.

The distance from each of the three charges to the point P in Fig. 9.34 is $a/\sqrt{2}$, as we already discussed in the solution to problem P–9.6. Thus, we find for the potential:

$$V = \frac{1}{4\pi\epsilon_0} \sum_{i=1}^{3} \frac{q_i}{|r_i|} =$$

$$\frac{1}{4\pi\epsilon_0}\left(\frac{q}{\frac{a}{\sqrt{2}}} + \frac{q}{\frac{a}{\sqrt{2}}} + \frac{2q}{\frac{a}{\sqrt{2}}} \right) = \frac{\sqrt{2}\,q}{\pi\epsilon_0 a} \qquad \textbf{(43)}$$

Substitution of the numerical values given in the problem text into Eq. (43) yields:

$$V = \frac{\sqrt{2}\ 1\times10^{-9}[Cb]}{\pi\ 8.85\times10^{-12}\left[\dfrac{Cb}{Vm}\right]\ 1.0[m]} \qquad \textbf{(44)}$$

$$\Rightarrow \quad V = 50.9\ V$$

Solution part (b): Once the potential is known at a given point, the potential energy for a specific charge brought to that point is obtained from Eq. (9.57):

$$E_{el} = q_{test}\ V = (-2\times10^{-9}[Cb])\ 50.9[V]$$

$$\Rightarrow \quad V = -1.02 \times 10^{-7}\ J \qquad \textbf{(45)}$$

in which we note that the unit Volt [V] is equal to the unit [J/Cb].

Problem 9.16

We study the three point charges shown in Fig. 9.37. The point charges are held at fixed positions of distance $l = 0.2$ m by forces that are not shown. What is *the electric potential energy of the system of 3 point charges*? Use for the three charges: $q_1 = + 2Q$, $q_2 = - 3Q$ and $q_3 = + Q$ where Q = 100 nCb.

Hint: The solution is done in steps. Assume that you bring first one of the point charges from a very large (infinite) distance to its position. Then repeat this procedure for the second, and lastly for the third point charge.

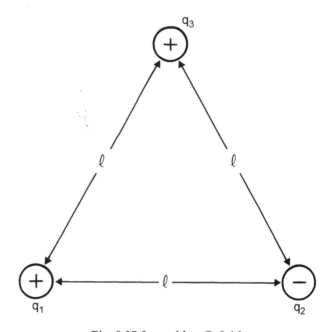

Fig. 9.37 for problem P–9.16.

Solution: Following the hint given with the problem text, we built the system of charges by moving one after the other from a place where they are all at infinite distance to each other. Since the electric force decreases rapidly with distance, a distance equivalent to an infinite distance might actually be a rather short distance. In vacuum this distance would still be quite appreciable based on the best possible precision of a measurement, however, in a solution a few micrometers is an infinite distance due to screening effects (Debye–Hückel model in electrochemistry). Based on Eq. (9.53) the electric energy of the system is $E_{el} = 0$ J while the charges are at infinite distance to each other, i.e., while they do not interact with each other.

While we bring the first charge, q_1, to its final

position, the electric energy remains zero, i.e., $E_{el} = 0$ J, since the charge still does not interact with any other charge.

In the second step we bring charge q_2 to its final position, which is at a distance d from charge q_1. In this process the change in the electric potential energy is given as:

$$\Delta E_{el,\,12} = \frac{1}{4\pi\epsilon_0}\frac{q_1 q_2}{d} \qquad (46)$$

In the last step we bring the third charge, q_3, to its final position at the distance d to either of the other two charges. The work associated with this step is equal to the sum of the work to bring the charge q_3 to a distance d from q_1 *and* the work to bring q_3 to a distance d from q_2:

$$W_{13} + W_{23} = \Delta E_{el,\,13} + \Delta E_{el,\,23} =$$

$$\frac{1}{4\pi\epsilon_0}\frac{q_1 q_3}{d} + \frac{1}{4\pi\epsilon_0}\frac{q_2 q_3}{d} \qquad (47)$$

The total change of the electric potential energy is the sum of the contributions due to each of the three steps toward the final charge arrangement:

$$E_{el} = \Delta E_{el,\,12} + \Delta E_{el,\,13} + \Delta E_{el,\,23} =$$

$$\frac{1}{4\pi\epsilon_0}\left[\frac{2Q\,(-3Q)}{d} + \frac{2Q\,Q}{d} + \frac{(-3Q)\,Q}{d}\right] \qquad (48)$$

This yields:

$$E_{el} = -\frac{7Q^2}{4\pi\epsilon_0 d} \qquad (49)$$

substituting the given values in the last formula leads to the final result:

$$E_{el} = -9\times10^9 \left[\frac{Nm^2}{Cb^2}\right]\frac{7\,(100\times10^{-9}[Cb])^2}{0.2[m]} \qquad (50)$$

$$\Rightarrow \quad E_{el} = -3.2 \times 10^{-3}\ J$$

Since the work calculated in Eq. (50) is negative, we know that the source of an external force has to do this amount of work to *disassemble* the structure of charges as shown in Fig. 9.37. In turn, creating the arrangement of charges shown in Fig. 9.37 by starting with the three charges infinitely separated releases 3.2 mJ of energy.

CHAPTER X

A second look at water: static fluids

Problem 10.1

The sphere is the shape with the smallest surface for a given volume. To prove this statement properly requires variational analysis. Here we only want to confirm this result for a selection of highly symmetric shapes by calculating the ratio of surface and volume. Find these ratios for (a) sphere, (b) cylinder, (c) cube, (d) pyramid, (e) tetrahedron, and (f) cone. Does the statement hold for these six shapes?

Solution: We use a sphere of radius r, a cylinder of height h and radius r with h = r, a cube of side length h, a pyramid of base length h with four equilateral triangles, a tetrahedron of side length h, a cone with base radius r and height h with r = h, and an octahedron which is a double–pyramid. For these bodies Table 10.2 shows a sketch, the formula for the volume, the value for r or h when the volume is V = 1 m³, the formula for the surface and the total surface area in [m²]. Note that the sphere indeed has the smallest surface of all of these bodies of equal volume.

Problem 10.2

A diver thinks that if a typical snorkel tube of 25 cm length works, a tube of length 7.0 m should also work. When trying to use such a tube, what is the pressure difference between the external pressure on the diver's chest and the air pressure in the lungs of the diver?
For those interested: what happens to the diver if this new snorkel were tested?

Solution: First we consider the diver at a depth of 7.0 m below the water surface without the snorkel tube. The external pressure on the diver's body is given by Pascal's law. If we assume a fresh water lake with water which has a density of $\rho = 1.0$ g/cm³, then:

$$p = p_0 + \rho g h =$$

$$p_0 + 1.0 \times 10^3 \left[\frac{kg}{m^3}\right] 9.8 \left[\frac{m}{s^2}\right] 7.0[m] \quad (1)$$

which yields:

$$p = p_0 + 6.9 \times 10^4 \ Pa \quad (2)$$

Note that we did not identify a value for the air pressure p_0 in this equation.

While diving to this depth, the diver's body adjusts to the pressure p of Eq. (2) by being slightly compressed until the internal pressure is in equilibrium with the external water pressure. This includes an increase in the gas pressure in the lung and an increase in the blood pressure.

If the diver now tries to use a 7 m long snorkel to connect to the air above the water surface in order to breathe, the pressurized air in the lung gets expelled upward through the tube to the lower pressure air space, which causes the pressure in the lung to drop to the air pressure p_0. That leads to a pressure difference between the inside of the lung and the water outside the diver's chest of:

$$\Delta p = p - p_0 = \rho g h$$

$$\Rightarrow \quad \Delta p = 6.9 \times 10^4 \ Pa \quad (3)$$

This difference corresponds roughly to 70 % of the atmospheric pressure, which is sufficient to collapse the lung and force the still pressurized blood into the lungs. This is called a "lung squeeze" and is not a nice way to die!

Problem 10.3

A scuba diver takes a deep breath from an air–filled tank at depth L, then abandons the tank. During the subsequent ascent to the surface the diver fails to exhale. When reaching the surface, the pressure difference between the external pressure and the pressure in the lung is 76 torr. From what depth did the diver start?
For those interested: what potentially lethal danger does the diver face?

Solution: This is an example of a possible diving accident when scuba diving. _Scuba_ stands for "self–contained under water breathing apparatus", a technique developed by Jacques–Yves Cousteau in 1943.

Body	Sketch	Volume Formula	r, h for V = 1	Surface Formula	Surface for V = 1
sphere		$\frac{4}{3}\pi r^3$	0.6204	$4\pi r^2$	4.8
cylinder (r = h)		$r^2\pi h$	0.6828	$2r\pi(r+h)$	5.9
cube		h^3	1.0	$6h^2$	6.0
pyramid		$\frac{h^3}{3\sqrt{2}}$	1.6189	$h^2(1+\sqrt{3})$	5.4
tetrahedron		$\frac{h^3}{12}\sqrt{2}$	2.0396	$h^2\sqrt{3}$	7.2
cone (r = h)		$\frac{r^2}{3}\pi h$	0.9847	$r\pi(r+\sqrt{r^2+h^2})$	7.4
octahedron		$\frac{h^3}{3}\sqrt{2}$	1.2849	$2h^2\sqrt{3}$	5.7

Table 10.2

When filling the lungs at depth L, the external pressure on the body and, correspondingly, the gas pressure in the lungs is again given by Pascal's law, i.e., $p = p_0 + \rho gL$.

As the diver ascends, the external pressure decreases until it reaches the atmospheric pressure p_0 at the surface. At the same time the blood pressure decreases to its normal (out of the water) value. But the gas pressure in the lungs remains at the value it was at depth L since the diver doesn't exhale. Therefore, the pressure difference between the lungs and the outside pressure on the chest at the surface is:

$$\Delta p = p - p_0 = \rho gL \qquad (4)$$

and the depth L is given by:

$$L = \frac{\Delta p}{\rho g} = \frac{76[torr]\ 133.32\left[\frac{Pa}{torr}\right]}{1.0\times10^3\left[\frac{kg}{m^3}\right]\ 9.8\left[\frac{m}{s^2}\right]} \qquad (5)$$

$$\Rightarrow\quad L = 1.03\ m$$

in which we used the pressure conversion of 1 torr = 133.32 Pa. Thus, surfacing from about a 1 meter depth without exhaling in this case leads to 76 torr pressure difference, which is about 10 % of the atmospheric pressure. It is still enough to rupture the lung and force air from the higher pressure lung into the lower pressure blood. This air may be carried to the heart and kill the diver. Another ugly way to die!

Problem 10.4

The U–shaped glass tube in Fig. 10.19 contains two liquids in mechanical equilibrium: water of density $\rho_w = 1.0$ kg/l, and an unknown liquid of density ρ_l. The unknown liquid is in the left tube, floating on top of the water with a clearly visible interface. Use $h_1 = 150$ mm and $h_2 = 15$ mm with the heights as labelled in Fig. 10.19. What is the density ρ_l?

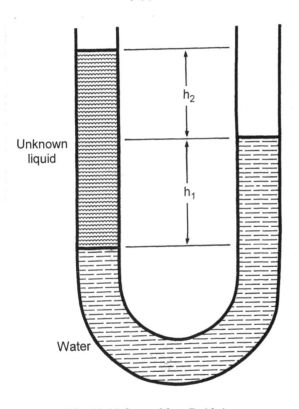

Unknown
liquid

h_2

h_1

Water

Fig. 10.19 for problem P–10.4.

Solution: We focus on the interface between the water (index w) and the unknown liquid (index l) on the left side. Since that interface must be in mechanical equilibrium as it is not moving up or down, the forces from above the interface must equal the forces from below the interface. Note that we are not interested in the forces on the interface, but the pressure contributions at the interface. The pressure at the interface is due to the water below the interface and in the right column as well as the

air above the water surface in the right column. This interface pressure is, therefore, given by:

$$p_{below\ interface} = p_{atm} + \rho_w\, g\, h_1 \qquad (6)$$

The first term on the right hand side of Eq. (6) is due to the air which rests on the open right column and the second term is due to the weight of the excess water in the right hand column (i.e., the amount of water in that column which is not balanced by water in the left hand column).

The pressure at the interface due to the liquid and the air above the interface in the left column is given by:

$$p_{above\ interface} = p_{atm} + \rho_l\, g\, (h_1 + h_2) \qquad (7)$$

in which the first term again is due to the air column resting above the liquid, this time in the left hand column. The second term is due to the weight of the unknown liquid column above the interface.

That the interface is in mechanical equilibrium implies that the pressure terms at the interface in Eq. (6) and Eq. (7) are equal:

$$p_{atm} + \rho_w\, g\, h_1 = p_{atm} + \rho_l\, g\, (h_1 + h_2)$$

$$\Rightarrow \quad \rho_l = \rho_w\, \frac{h_1}{h_1 + h_2} \qquad (8)$$

Note that this result is independent of the actual air pressure and also does not depend on g. Thus, the same experiment done on the moon would result in the same value for the density of the unknown liquid.

To obtain a quantitative result, we substitute the values given in the problem into Eq. (8):

$$\rho_l = 1.0 \left[\frac{kg}{l} \right] \frac{150[mm]}{(150+15)[mm]} = 0.91\, \frac{kg}{l} \qquad (9)$$

Note that there is another way of solving this problem. We can arrive alternatively at Eq. (8) by comparing the pressure at the height h_1 below the water surface in the right column. On the left hand side this is the pressure at the interface, on the right hand side we can calculate the pressure from Pascal's law, i.e., expressing it as the atmospheric pressure and a second term due to the height of the water column above the point of interest.

Problem 10.5

What is the pressure increase in the fluid in a syringe when a force of 50 N is applied to the circular piston of the syringe, which has a radius 1.25 cm?

Solution: The pressure increase equals the applied force divided by the area. Note that the direction of the force is in this case perpendicular to the piston surface, and thus, the pressure definition p = F/A is appropriate. The area of a piston sealing the opening of a cylinder is a circular disc with $A = r^2\pi$ where r is the inner radius of the cylinder. Thus:

$$p = \frac{F}{A} = \frac{F}{r^2\pi} = \frac{50[N]}{\pi(0.0125[m])^2} \quad \textbf{(10)}$$

$$\Rightarrow \quad p = 1.02 \times 10^5 \ Pa$$

Problem 10.6

We often say the tip of an iceberg when we want to refer to a small visible fraction of something that is otherwise hidden. For a real iceberg, what is that fraction? The density of ice is $\rho_{ice} = 917 \ kg/m^3$ and the average density of seawater is $\rho_w = 1.025 \ g/cm^3$.

Solution: For this problem we use the Archimedes principle. The magnitude of the weight of an iceberg of total volume V_{tot} is given by:

$$W_{tot} = m_{ice} \ g = \rho_{ice} \ V_{tot} \ g \quad \textbf{(11)}$$

The magnitude of the weight of the displaced sea water is equal to the magnitude of the buoyancy force acting on the iceberg, F_b:

$$W_{dis. \ w} = F_b = m_w \ g = \rho_w \ V_{dis. \ w} \ g \quad \textbf{(12)}$$

Fig. 10.23: Free–body–diagram for a floating iceberg.

in which $V_{dis. \ w}$ is equal to the volume of the iceberg below the surface of the sea.

The iceberg is in mechanical equilibrium when it floats, i.e., the weight of the iceberg and the buoyant force must cancel each other, as illustrated in the free–body–diagram in Fig. 10.23. Using Newton's first law we write for the balance of forces in the vertical direction:

$$\rho_w \ V_{disp. \ w} \ g - \rho_{ice} \ V_{tot} \ g = 0$$

$$\Rightarrow \quad \frac{\rho_{ice}}{\rho_w} = \frac{V_{disp. \ w}}{V_{tot}} \quad \textbf{(13)}$$

This provides us with a formula for the ratio of the volume of the displaced water to the total volume of the iceberg.

We now express the quantity sought in the problem. The question is about the fraction of the volume of the iceberg which reaches above the sea level, i.e.,

$$\frac{V_{tot} - V_{disp. \ w}}{V_{tot}} = 1 - \frac{V_{disp. \ w}}{V_{tot}} \quad \textbf{(14)}$$

We use Eq. (13) to replace the second term on the right hand side of Eq. (14):

$$1 - \frac{V_{disp. \ w}}{V_{tot}} = 1 - \frac{\rho_{ice}}{\rho_w} = $$

$$\quad \textbf{(15)}$$

$$1 - \frac{0.917[kg/l]}{1.025[kg/l]} = 0.105$$

For a real iceberg in the North–Atlantic off Newfoundland just over 10 % reaches out of the sea water.

Problem 10.7

To suck water up a straw to a maximum height of 10 cm, what minimum gauge pressure must be produced in the lungs? Note: the gauge pressure is defined as the pressure relative to atmospheric pressure, $p_{gauge} = p - p_{atm}$.

Solution: This problem is solved using Pascal's law. Using the definition of the gauge pressure from the problem text, $p_{gauge} = p - p_{atm}$, Pascal's law is rewritten in terms of the gauge pressure:

$$p_{gauge} = p - p_{atm} = -\rho g h \qquad (16)$$

in which the negative sign in front of the ρgh–term indicates that the pressure in the lung is lower than the atmospheric pressure during the sucking. Substituting the numerical values in Eq. (16) yields:

$$p_{gauge} = -\frac{1.0\times10^3\left[\dfrac{kg}{m^3}\right]9.8\left[\dfrac{m}{s^2}\right]0.1[m]}{1.01\times10^5\left[\dfrac{Pa}{atm}\right]} \qquad (17)$$

$$\Rightarrow \quad p_{gauge} = -9.7 \times 10^{-3}\ atm$$

The denominator in Eq. (17) allows us to convert to the non–standard unit [atm]. Of course, the best way to answer the question would be to provide an answer in the standard unit [Pa]; however, non–standard pressure units are still quite often used. For the conversion between these pressure units see the General Appendix of the textbook.

Problem 10.8
Collapsible plastic bags are used in hospitals for infusions. We want to use such a bag to infuse a electrolyte solution into the artery of a patient. For this we mount

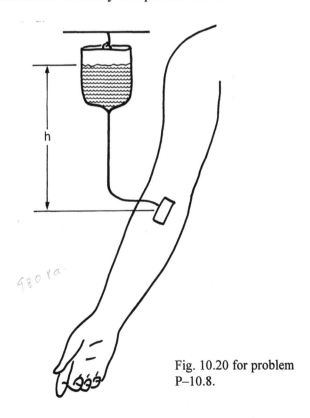

98 Pa

Fig. 10.20 for problem P–10.8.

the bag at a height h above the arm of the patient, as shown in Fig. 10.20. Assuming that the average gauge pressure in the artery is 13.3 kPa and the density of the electrolyte solution is 1.03 g/cm³, what is the minimum height h in order for the infusion to work?

Solution: The minimum gauge pressure in the fluid in the needle is equal to the gauge pressure of the blood in the artery, where the needle is entered into the vessel. Otherwise, blood would be pushed into the needle, which is desirable when donating blood but not when an infusion is attempted. We use Pascal's law to express the gauge pressure of the fluid in the needle:

$$p_{gauge} = p - p_{atm} = \rho g h$$

$$\Rightarrow \quad p_{gauge} = 1.33 \times 10^4\ Pa \qquad (18)$$

in which h is the vertical distance between the height of the liquid surface in the collapsible bag and the height of the needle. The density of the liquid is given in the problem text, thus, the height h can be calculated from Eq. (18):

$$h = \frac{p_{gauge}}{\rho g} = \frac{1.33\times10^4[Pa]}{1.03\times10^3\left[\dfrac{kg}{m^3}\right]9.8\left[\dfrac{m}{s^2}\right]} \qquad (19)$$

$$\Rightarrow \quad h = 1.32\ m$$

This result provides you with the reason why such fluid bags are always mounted more than a meter above the patient, despite the inconvenience this arrangement represents for the handling by nurses.

Problem 10.9
A helium–filled blimp cruises slowly at a low altitude. Its maximum useful payload, including crew and cargo, is 1500 kg. How much more payload can be carried if the blimp were filled with hydrogen? Use for the volume of the gas–filled interior space a value of 6000 m³. The density of helium gas is 0.16 kg/m³ and the density of hydrogen gas is 0.08 kg/m³.

Solution: This problem is an application of Archimedes' principle. We start with the blimp and its initial cargo when the gas filling is helium. We use $\rho_{He} = 0.16$ kg/m³ for the density of helium. The net force due to the He gas filling is:

97

$$F_{net, He} = W_{displaced\ air} - W_{blimp}$$
$$= \left(\rho_{air} - \rho_{He}\right) V g \qquad (20)$$

Now we consider a gas exchange: the helium filling is replaced by a hydrogen gas filling. This introduces hydrogen with $\rho_{H2} = 0.08$ kg/m³. The new net force due to the gas filling is now:

$$F_{net, H_2} = W_{displaced\ air} - W_{modif.\ blimp}$$
$$= \left(\rho_{air} - \rho_{H_2}\right) V g \qquad (21)$$

The weight of the *additional* cargo ΔW the blimp can carry after the gas exchange is due to the reduction in the weight of the gas in the blimp, which in turn increases the net upward force as we proceed from Eq. (20) to Eq. (21). The weight difference provides for the additional upward buoyant force F_b to offset the additional weight ΔW pulling the blimp down (i.e., the free–body–diagram of Fig. 10.23 applies here as well).

The requirement of mechanical equilibrium before and after the gas exchange and the loading of the additional cargo is written in the form:

$$\Delta W = m_{He} g - m_{H_2} g = \left(\rho_{He} - \rho_{H_2}\right) V g =$$

$$\left(0.16\left[\frac{kg}{m^3}\right] - 0.08\left[\frac{kg}{m^3}\right]\right) 6000[m^3] 9.8\left[\frac{m}{s^2}\right] \qquad (22)$$

$$\Rightarrow \quad \Delta W = 4.7 \times 10^3\ N$$

We obtain a mass for the additional cargo $m_{cargo} = 480$ kg by using the relation $\Delta W = m_{cargo} g$. Note that the original mass of the blimp, i.e., 1500 kg, was not used in the calculation, but allows us now to express the additional payload as accounting roughly for 30 % of the original mass.

Problem 10.10
Water is transported upwards in plants through xylem tissue, which consists of cells of 1 mm length and a species dependent diameter between 40 μm and 400 μm. The xylem cells are attached to each other to form a channel. To what maximum height can water rise in these xylem channels due to the capillarity effect?
Hint: the surface tension of water is $\sigma = 0.073$ N/m at 20°C.

Note: if you only believe what you can see, cut and split the stem of a flower with white petals (e.g. a dahlia or a carnation) and place one half of the stem in a glass with dilute red ink and the other half in a glass with dilute blue ink. After several hours the flower will be half red and half blue.

Solution: The role identified for the xylem tissue in the question, i.e., transport of liquids throughout the body of the plant, assigns the same purpose as blood vessels are assigned in animals. thus, the xylem tissue is called the vascular system of the plant.

The height to which water can rise in the xylem system due to capillarity is calculated from Eq. (10.43). For simplicity we treat the liquid transported in the xylem system as pure water, which is only a satisfactory assumption for some plants in temperate climates.

Note that we are asked to calculate the maximum height to which water can rise by capillarity in the xylem channels. The term "maximum" allows us to circumvent the need to know the contact angle to be substituted into Eq. (10.43). The term $\cos\theta$ resumes a maximum value at $\cos\theta = 1$, which corresponds to $\theta = 0°$. Any larger contact angle will lead to a lesser height. With the given surface tension of water and $\cos\theta = 1$, we find:

$$h = \frac{2\sigma_{H2O}}{r\,\rho_{H2O}\,g} =$$

$$\frac{2 \cdot 0.073\left[\frac{N}{m}\right]}{2 \times 10^{-5}[m]\ 1 \times 10^3\left[\frac{kg}{m^3}\right] 9.8\left[\frac{m}{s^2}\right]} \qquad (23)$$

Thus, the maximum height reached in the most narrow xylem channels ($r = 20$ μm) is 0.75 m. As a consequence, capillarity alone is not a sufficient explanation of the rise of liquids in trees, some, e.g. the Eucalyptus tree, reaching heights of 150 m.

Problem 10.11
(a) Fig. 10.21(a) shows a wooden sphere with a diameter of $d = 10$ cm (density $\rho = 0.9$ g/cm³) held under water by a string. What is the tension in the string?
(b) Fig. 10.21(b) shows a sphere of radius $r = 10$ cm and density of $\rho = 2.0$ g/cm³ suspended in water. What is the tension in the sting?
Hint: draw the free–body–diagram in each case.

a)   b)

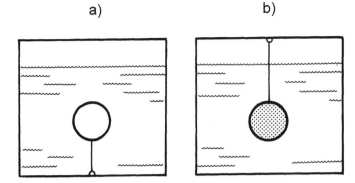

Fig. 10.21 for problem P–10.11.

Solution part (a): An object which floats at a given depth below the surface of a fluid must be in mechanical equilibrium. For the three cases we considered in the context of Fig. 10.6, this was discussed as case (II). In Fig. 10.6, such a mechanical equilibrium is based on two forces acting on the block B: the weight and the buoyant force. The situation in Fig. 10.21 is different is so far as in both cases an additional tension force acts on the object. Thus, without the string, neither case 10.21(a) nor case 10.21(b) would be in a mechanical equilibrium; it is the additional tension which establishes this equilibrium. Consequently, the free–body–diagram in each case must be based on three forces.

The free–body–diagram for the wooden sphere in case (a) is shown in Fig. 10.24(a). The buoyant force is drawn with a larger magnitude than the weight because we know from experience that the wooden sphere, if released, would buoy to the surface. To establish mechanical equilibrium, therefore, a second downwards directed force is needed. This force is provided by the tension in the string. Using Newton's first law, we write:

a)   b)

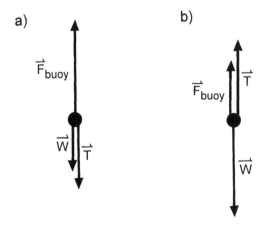

Fig. 10.24: (a) Free–body–diagram for a wooden sphere, held by a string below the surface of water. (b) Free–body–diagram for a heavy sphere suspended on a string below the surface of water.

$$F_{buoy} - T - W = 0 \qquad (24)$$

Of the three forces in Eq. (24) we can quantify two: the weight and the buoyant force of the wooden sphere:

$$W = m_{wood}g = V\rho_{wood}g = \frac{4}{3}\pi r^3 g \rho_{wood} \qquad (25)$$

$$F_{buoy} = V_{H2O}\rho_{H2O}g = \frac{4}{3}\pi r^3 g \rho_{H2O}$$

in which the volume of the wooden sphere and the volume of the displaced water are the same, with the radius $r = d/2 = 5$ cm. Substituting Eq. (25) into Eq. (24) and solving Eq. (24) for the tension T, we obtain:

$$T = F_{buoy} - W = \frac{4}{3}\pi r^3 g(\rho_{H2O} - \rho_{wood}) \qquad (26)$$

Substituting the given values into Eq. (26), we find:

$$T = \frac{4}{3}\pi(0.05[m])^3 9.8\left[\frac{m}{s^2}\right](1.0-0.9)\left[\frac{g}{cm^3}\right] \qquad (27)$$

$$\Rightarrow \quad T = 0.51 \ N$$

in which the value for the difference in densities has to be converted to SI units to obtain the shown result.

Solution part (b): The free–body–diagram for the heavy sphere from Fig. 10.21(b) is shown in Fig. 10.24(b). This time the buoyant force is drawn with a smaller magnitude than the weight because we know from experience that a heavy sphere would sink to the bottom of the beaker if not held by the string. The string provides for a mechanical equilibrium. The tension associated with the sting is calculated from applying Newton's first law to Fig. 10.24(b):

$$F_{buoy} + T - W = 0 \qquad (28)$$

Note that this equation differs from Eq. (24) for case (a) only in the sign of the tension as the string is now directed upwards. Again, the buoyant force and the weight of the heavy sphere can be calculated; the formulas are identical to those shown in Eq. (25) if we replace the label "wood" by "heavy sphere". Note that the radius of the sphere is given in part (b) instead of the diameter.

Substituting Eq. (25) into Eq. (28) and solving Eq. (28) for the tension T, we obtain:

$$T = W - F_{buoy} = \frac{4}{3}\pi r^3 g\left(\rho_{heavy} - \rho_{H2O}\right) \quad (29)$$

Numerically, this corresponds to:

$$T = \frac{4}{3}\pi(0.1[m])^3 9.8\left[\frac{m}{s^2}\right](2.0-1.0)\left[\frac{g}{cm^3}\right] \quad (30)$$

$$\Rightarrow \quad T = 41.05 \ N$$

in which the value for the difference in densities was again converted to SI units before the result was calculated.

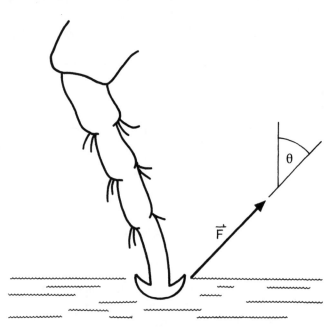

Fig. 10.22 for problem P–10.12.

Problem 10.12

Surface tension supports insects such as water–striders on the water surface. Assume that an insect's foot is spherical as shown in Fig. 10.22 and that the insect stands with all of its 6 feet on the water. Each foot presses the water surface down while the surface tension of the water produces upwards forces to restore the nor-

mal flat shape of the water surface. As a result a characteristic profile of the water surface results as shown in the figure. The mass of the insect is 15 mg and the diameter of the insect's foot is 250 μm. Find the angle θ as indicated in the figure.

Hint: the definition of the surface tension provides for a

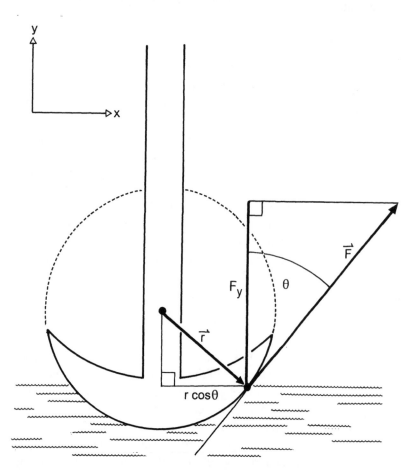

Fig. 10.25: Geometric details of the foot of an insect resting on a water surface.

tangential force along the depressed surface of the water, shown as force **F** in the figure. The surface tension of water at 20°C is σ = 0.073 N/m.

Solution: The definition of surface tension used for this problem is given in Eq. (10.32). Note that the force in that formula is directed _tangential_ to the depressed water surface, as properly indicated in Fig. 10.22. The length l_x in Eq. (10.32) represents the length of the contact line along which the force of magnitude F acts. In the case of the insect's foot, this line is the circumference of the foot where it touches the surface of the water. This circumference is determined from the given diameter of the insect's foot by using Fig. 10.25. The figure is a detailed view of the geometric relations of the force and spatial parameters relevant to this problem. We note that the circumference of the foot at the water line is given by $2\pi r \cos\theta$ in which r is the radius of the foot. We label this circumference l_x.

Using the value for l_x, we find from Eq. (10.32) the magnitude of the force **F** exerted by the water surface, as illustrated in Figs. 10.22 and 10.25:

$$F = \sigma \, l_x = \sigma \, 2\pi \, r \, \cos\theta \qquad (31)$$

Next we use Newton's first law to describe the mechanical equilibrium of the insect. Of interest is only the vertical direction as the symmetry of the foot provides automatically for a compensation of the x–directional components of the forces acting on the foot. The equilibrium must exist as the insect neither accelerates downwards (and drowns) or accelerates upwards (while not intentionally flying away). Since an insect has six legs and usually rests with all of them on the water surface, Newton's law contains seven contributions: one force in the positive y–direction due to the force **F** acting on each leg, and one force downwards due to the weight of the insect:

$$-W_{insect} + 6 \left(\sigma \, 2\pi r \cos\theta\right) \cos\theta = 0 \qquad (32)$$

in which the extra $\cos\theta$ term is introduced by using the y–component of the force **F** in Fig. 10.25. We solve Eq. (32) for $\cos\theta$:

$$\cos^2\theta = \frac{mg}{12\pi r \sigma} =$$

$$\frac{1.5\times10^{-5}[kg] \; 9.8\left[\dfrac{m}{s^2}\right]}{12\pi \; 1.25\times10^{-4}[m] \; 0.073\left[\dfrac{N}{m}\right]} = 0.427 \qquad (33)$$

in which m is the mass of the insect. Thus, we obtain $\cos\theta = 0.653$ which corresponds to an angle $\theta = 49°$. This illustrates that contrary to our intuition the depression of the water is rather steep, with a 41° angle between the flat water surface and the edge of the foot.

CHAPTER XI

Cardiovascular system: fluid flow

Problem 11.1

During flight, air flows over the top of an air plane wing of area A with speed v_t, and past the underside of the wing with speed v_u. Show that Bernoulli's law predicts that the magnitude F of the upward lift–force on the wing is given by:

$$F = \frac{1}{2} \rho A \left(v_t^2 - v_u^2 \right) \qquad (1)$$

with ρ the density of the air.

Solution: Air passes above and below an in–flight airplane wing with different speeds, as illustrated in Fig. 11.26. Bernoulli's equation relates the parameters of the air moving above and below the wing:

$$p_t + \frac{1}{2}\rho v_t^2 = p_u + \frac{1}{2}\rho v_u^2 \qquad (2)$$

The force acting on the wing is equal to the difference between the pressure above and below the wing multiplied by the area of the wing:

$$F_{wing} = A\left(p_u - p_t\right) = \frac{1}{2}\rho A\left(v_t^2 - v_u^2\right) \qquad (3)$$

This is the formula that we were asked to derive.

Problem 11.2

The instrument shown in Fig. 11.8 (Venturi–meter) is used to measure the flow speed v of a fluid in a pipe of

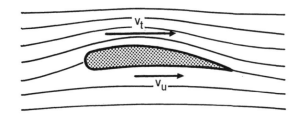

cross–sectional area A. This is done by integrating the instrument into the tube with the entry and exit cross–sectional areas identical to the primary tube. Between the entry and exit points, the fluid flows through a narrow constriction of cross–sectional area *a*. At the constriction the speed of the fluid is v_{con}. A manometer tube, connecting the wider and narrower portions, shows a difference Δh in the liquid levels in its two arms.

(a) Using Bernoulli's law and the Equation of continuity, show that:

$$v = \sqrt{\frac{2\,a^2\,g\,\Delta h}{(A^2 - a^2)}\,\frac{\rho_{liquid}}{\rho_{fluid}}} \qquad (4)$$

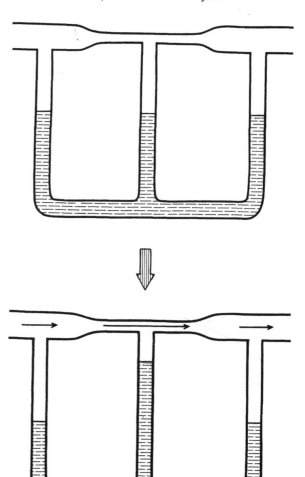

Fig. 11.26: Flow lines of air past an airplane wing during flight. The differences in air speed above and below the wing are highlighted.

Fig. 11.8: The Venturi–meter measures the speed of a fluid in a horizontal tube.

(b) What is the volume flow rate $\Delta V/\Delta t$ if we use water for the fluid in the pipe? The pipe diameter is 0.8 m, the diameter of the constriction is 20 cm, and the pressure difference is 15 kPa.

Solution part (a): We use the equation of continuity in the form:

$$A \, v = a \, v_{con} \qquad (5)$$

in which the index _con_ refers to the constricted section of the pipe. The second equation we use is Bernoulli's equation in the form:

$$p + \frac{1}{2}\rho_{fluid}v^2 = p_{con} + \frac{1}{2}\rho_{fluid}v_{con}^2 \qquad (6)$$

We combine both equations by isolating the speed of the fluid in the constriction, v_{con}, in Eq. (5), i.e., $v_{con} = Av/a$, and substitute this term into Eq. (6):

$$p + \frac{1}{2}\rho_{fluid}v^2 = p_{con} + \frac{1}{2}\rho_{fluid}\left(\frac{A^2v^2}{a^2}\right) \qquad (7)$$

We solve this equation for the speed v. We begin by abbreviating the pressure difference as $\Delta p = p - p_{con}$ and by combining the terms which contain v on the right hand side of the equation:

$$\Delta p = \frac{1}{2}\rho_{fluid}\left(\frac{A^2}{a^2} - 1\right)v^2 \qquad (8)$$

Now the speed v is isolated:

$$v = \sqrt{\frac{2\Delta p}{\rho_{fluid}}\left(\frac{a^2}{A^2 - a^2}\right)} \qquad (9)$$

The pressure difference Δp in Eq. (9), in turn, is related

to the height difference of the liquid in the center and left glass tubes by Pascal's law, $\Delta p = \rho_{liquid}g\Delta h$. Thus, we find:

$$v = \sqrt{\frac{2\rho_{liquid}g\Delta h}{\rho_{fluid}}\left(\frac{a^2}{A^2 - a^2}\right)} \qquad (10)$$

which is the formula that we were asked to derive.

Solution part (b): Note that we do not use Eq. (10), but Eq. (9) to solve this problem. Eq. (9) is rewritten for the volume flow rate $\Delta V/\Delta t$ using the definition of the volume flow rate $\Delta V/\Delta t = A \, v$:

$$\frac{\Delta V}{\Delta t} = A\sqrt{\frac{2\Delta p}{\rho_{fluid}}\left(\frac{a^2}{A^2 - a^2}\right)} = $$
$$= R^2\pi\sqrt{\frac{2\Delta p}{\rho_{fluid}}\left(\frac{r^4}{R^4 - r^4}\right)} \qquad (11)$$

in which we used $A = R^2\pi$ and $a = r^2\pi$. We neglect the r^4–term in the denominator of the last bracket in Eq. (11) since $R^4 \gg r^4$ and simplify the equation to:

$$\frac{\Delta V}{\Delta t} = \pi R^2\sqrt{\frac{2\Delta p}{\rho_{fluid}}\frac{r^4}{R^4}} = \pi r^2\sqrt{\frac{2\Delta p}{\rho_{fluid}}} \qquad (12)$$

substituting the numerical values in Eq. (12), we obtain:

$$\frac{\Delta V}{\Delta t} = \pi(0.1[m])^2\sqrt{\frac{2 \cdot 1.5\times10^4[Pa]}{1.0\times10^3[kg/m^3]}} \qquad (13)$$

$$\Rightarrow \quad \frac{\Delta V}{\Delta t} = 0.17\,\frac{m^3}{s}$$

Table 11.2: Length, radius, individual and cumulative flow resistance for vessels of type (I) arterioles, (II) aorta and (III) capillaries. The arterioles contribute most to the flow resistance in the cardiovascular system.

Vessel type	length [m]	radius [m]	R_{single} [Pa s/m³]	R_{total} [Pa s/m³]
Arterioles	2.5×10^{-3}	8.0×10^{-6}	3.9×10^{15}	2.4×10^{7}
Aorta	3.4×10^{-1}	1.1×10^{-2}	1.5×10^{5}	1.5×10^{5}
Capillaries	8.5×10^{-4}	3.5×10^{-6}	3.6×10^{16}	7.2×10^{6}

Problem 11.3

Confirm the data shown in Table 11.2 for the average length, radius, individual and total flow resistance in (a) arterioles, (b) the aorta and (c) capillaries.

Hint: use $\eta = 2.5 \times 10^{-3}$ Ns/m² as an average value for the blood viscosity coefficient from Table 11.1 at 37°C.

Solution part (a): For arterioles, we calculate the average length from the total volume value of V = 125 cm³ and the total cross–sectional area A = 500 cm² obtained from Fig. 11.5:

$$<l> = \frac{V_{total}}{A_{total}} = \frac{125[cm^3]}{500[cm^2]} = 0.25 \ cm \quad (14)$$

The average radius of the arterioles in Fig. 11.5 is the outer value. For the relevant inner value, a wall thickness of 2 μm is deducted: $\varnothing/2 = 0.001$ cm = 10 μm becomes r = 8 μm. Using the blood viscosity provided in the problem text, we substitute these values into Eq. (11.29) for the flow resistance:

$$R = \frac{8 \cdot 2.5 \times 10^{-3}[m]}{\pi \ (8 \times 10^{-6}[m])^4} \ 2.5 \times 10^{-3}\left[\frac{Ns}{m^2}\right] \quad (15)$$

$$\Rightarrow \quad R = 3.9 \times 10^{15} \ \frac{Pa \ s}{m^3}$$

We assume that all arterioles are in parallel to each other. In the case of flow through parallel tubes the individual flow resistances have to be added inversely. The total flow resistance for all $N_{arterioles} = 1.6 \times 10^8$ arterioles is therefore:

$$\frac{1}{R_{arterioles}} = \sum_{i=1}^{N_{arterioles}} \frac{1}{R_{i, \ single}} = \frac{N_{arterioles}}{R_{single}} \quad (16)$$

$$R_{arterioles} = \frac{3.9 \times 10^{15}}{1.6 \times 10^8} = 2.4 \times 10^7 \ \frac{Pa \ s}{m^3}$$

Solution part (b): Using Fig. 11.5 again, we find for the length of the aorta:

$$l = \frac{V}{A} = \frac{180[cm^3]}{5.3[cm^2]} = 34 \ cm \quad (17)$$

in which l is not an average value in this case since there

is only one aorta in a human body. Combined with an inner radius of 1.1 cm, we find for the flow resistance in Eq. (11.29):

$$R = \frac{8 \cdot 3.4 \times 10^{-1}[m]}{\pi \ (1.1 \times 10^{-2}[m])^4} \ 2.5 \times 10^{-3}\left[\frac{Ns}{m^2}\right] \quad (18)$$

$$R_{single} = R_{aorta} = 1.5 \times 10^5 \ \frac{Pa \ s}{m^3}$$

Solution part (c): Finally we calculate the same values for capillaries. Again based on Fig. 11.5 we find for the average length:

$$<l> = \frac{V}{A} = \frac{300[cm^3]}{3500[cm^2]} = 0.085 \ cm \quad (19)$$

The average inner radius is 3.5 μm. For the flow resistance of a single capillary we get:

$$R = \frac{8 \cdot 8.5 \times 10^{-4}[m]}{\pi \ (3.5 \times 10^{-6}[m])^4} \ 2.5 \times 10^{-3}\left[\frac{Ns}{m^2}\right] \quad (20)$$

$$\Rightarrow \quad R = 3.6 \times 10^{16} \ \frac{Pa \ s}{m^3}$$

and for the combined flow resistance of all capillaries, with $N_{capillaries} = 5 \times 10^9$ blood vessels:

$$\frac{1}{R_{capillaries}} = \sum_{i=1}^{N_{capillaries}} \frac{1}{R_{i, \ single}} = \frac{N_{capillaries}}{R_{single}} \quad (21)$$

$$R_{capillaries} = \frac{3.6 \times 10^{16}}{5 \times 10^9} = 7.2 \times 10^6 \ \frac{Pa \ s}{m^3}$$

Thus, the calculations show that the arterioles do indeed dominate the total flow resistance of the human blood circulation system.

When comparing the results of this problem and Table 11.2 with the second diagram in Fig. 11.4, the flow resistance of the arterioles appears to be overestimated in the current calculation. This is indeed the case since we made two oversimplifying assumptions, (i) that all arterioles are completely parallel to each other, and (ii) that all arterioles have the average length. In reality the blood vessels are still branching in the arterioles stage and their lengths vary across the human body.

104

Problem 11.4
(a) In a person with advanced arteriosclerosis (artery constriction due to accumulated plaque on the inner walls, as shown in Fig. 11.24), the Bernoulli effect produces a symptom called vascular flutter. To maintain a constant volume flow rate in this situation, the blood must travel faster than normal through the constriction. At a sufficiently high blood speed, the artery starts to collapse and then immediately reopen, leading to a repeated temporary interruption of the blood flow which can be heard with a stethoscope. Why does this vascular flutter occur?

(b) An aneurysm is a weakened spot of an artery where the artery walls balloon outward. Blood flows more slowly through this region, resulting in an increase in pressure at the aneurysm relative to the pressure in neighboring parts of the artery. This condition is dangerous because the increased pressure can cause the artery to rupture (see for a detailed discussion of aneurysms in Chapter 15). Why does the blood flow slow down at an aneurysm?

Solution part (a): The artery collapses since the high speed of the blood inside the vessel lowers the pressure in the blood stream relative to the pressure in the stationary extracellular fluid. This is due to Bernoulli's equation, $p + \frac{1}{2}\rho v^2 = $ const. In this formula, a high value for the speed, v, leads to a low value of the pressure, p. Once the pressure difference is large enough to close the artery, the blood flow stops momentarily. When this happens the blood upstream from the clogged vessel causes a pressure increase that is sufficiently large to open the artery again. The closing and reopening of the artery usually continues in a cyclic manner.

Solution part (b) : The cross–sectional area of a blood vessel and the speed of blood in the vessel are linked due to the equation of continuity. Thus, the speed of the blood flow decreases at any point along the blood vessel where the cross–section of the blood vessel increases.

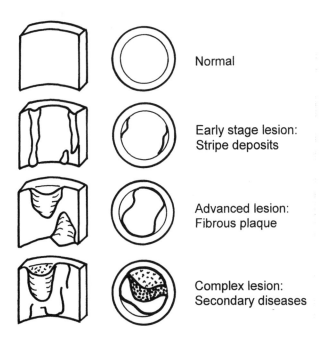

Normal

Early stage lesion: Stripe deposits

Advanced lesion: Fibrous plaque

Complex lesion: Secondary diseases

Fig. 11.24 for problem P–11.4.

Problem 11.5
The hypodermic syringe in Fig. 11.25 contains water. The barrel of the syringe has a cross–sectional area $A_1 = 30$ mm². The pressure is 1.0 atm everywhere while no force is exerted on the plunger. When the force $\mathbf{F}_{ext}$ of magnitude 2.0 N is exerted on the plunger, the water squirts from the needle. Determine the water's flow speed through the needle, v_2. Assume that the pressure in the needle remains at a value of $p_2 = 1.0$ atm and that the syringe is held horizontal. The final speed of the water in the barrel is negligible.

Solution: We first calculate the pressure of the water in the syringe's barrel, p_1. This value is determined from the mechanical equilibrium of forces that act on the plunger. A mechanical equilibrium must exist since the question asks for a flow speed of the water, implying that there is no acceleration of the plunger involved. In the equilibrium the pressure inside the barrel is equal to the two components acting on the plunger from outside, the atmospheric pressure and the pressure related to the exerted force:

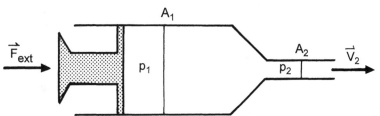

Fig. 11.25 for problem P–11.5.

$$p_1 = \frac{|F_{ext}|}{A_1} + p_{atm} =$$

$$\frac{2.0[N]}{3 \times 10^{-5}[m^2]} + 1.01 \times 10^5 [Pa] \quad \text{(22)}$$

$$\Rightarrow \quad p_1 = 1.68 \times 10^5 \ Pa$$

Now we apply Bernoulli's equation across the needle of the syringe:

$$p_1 + \frac{\rho_{H_2O}}{2} v_{barrel}^2 = p_2 + \frac{\rho_{H_2O}}{2} v_2^2 \quad \text{(23)}$$

in which we use for the speed of the water in the barrel $v_{barrel} \cong 0$ m/s as an approximation, and further that $p_2 = 1$ atm for the pressure in the needle. With these values we obtain for the speed of the water in the needle:

$$\frac{\rho_{H_2O}}{2} v_2^2 = p_1 - p_{atm}$$

$$\Rightarrow \quad v_2 = \sqrt{\frac{2(p_1 - p_{atm})}{\rho_{H_2O}}} \quad \text{(24)}$$

Substituting the values given in the problem, we find for the flow speed in the needle:

$$v_2 = \sqrt{\frac{2(1.68 \times 10^5 [Pa] - 1.01 \times 10^5 [Pa])}{1.0 \times 10^3 [kg/m^3]}} \quad \text{(25)}$$

$$\Rightarrow \quad v_2 = 11.6 \ \frac{m}{s}$$

Problem 11.6
A hypodermic needle is 4.0 cm long and has an inner diameter of 0.25 mm. What excess pressure is required along the needle so that the flow rate of water through it is 1.0 g/s? Use 1.0×10^{-3} Ns/m² for the viscosity coefficient of water.

Solution: Poiseuille's law is used to express the amount of water flowing through the needle per time unit. Poiseuille's law is first rewritten with the pressure dif-

ference along the needle as the independent variable:

$$\Delta p = \frac{(\Delta V / \Delta t) \ 8\eta l}{\pi r^4} \quad \text{(26)}$$

To use Eq. (26), we convert the flow rate of 1.0 g/s to a value with unit [m³/s], which is the proper unit to substitute for the volume flow rate $\Delta V / \Delta t$:

$$\frac{\Delta V}{\Delta t} = \frac{1}{\rho} \frac{m}{t} = \frac{1}{1.0 \times 10^3 \left[\frac{kg}{m^3}\right]} 1.0 \times 10^{-3} \left[\frac{kg}{s}\right] \quad \text{(27)}$$

$$\Rightarrow \quad \frac{\Delta V}{\Delta t} = 1.0 \times 10^{-6} \ \frac{m^3}{s}$$

Therefore,

$$\Delta p = \frac{8 \cdot 1 \times 10^{-6} \left[\frac{m^3}{s}\right] 1 \times 10^{-3} \left[\frac{Ns}{m^2}\right] 0.04[m]}{\pi \left(1.25 \times 10^{-4}[m]\right)^4} \quad \text{(28)}$$

$$\Rightarrow \quad \Delta p = 4.2 \times 10^5 \ Pa$$

CHAPTER XII

Blood and air: mixed phases

Problem 12.1

The osmotic effect is often used to determine the molar mass of macromolecules. This problem illustrates how this is done. The apparatus used is shown in Fig. 12.15: it consists of two chambers which are separated by a semipermeable membrane. One tube is filled with a dilute solution of the macromolecules and the other tube is filled with pure solvent. Additional tubes are mounted vertically on each chamber to measure the osmotic pressure (using Pascal's law).

Assume that the experiment is done at 25°C. We use van't Hoff's law from Eq. (12.20) as $\Pi = (RT/M)c$, where c is the concentration of the macromolecule in the solution (in [kg/m³]), M is the molar mass (in [kg/mol]) of the macromolecule and Π is the osmotic pressure, as measured with the apparatus in Fig. 12.15. Since van't Hoff's law applies exactly only for very dilute solutions, several measurements are taken for various dilute solutions (i.e., several different values of c) and are then extrapolated. For the extrapolation, we plot Π/c vs. c and obtain the value for Π/c at c = 0 from the plot.

Using the data from Table 12.6 for the osmotic pressure of polyisobutylene in benzene and cyclohexane
(a) plot Π/c versus c for both solutions,
(b) find the extrapolation value of Π/c at c = 0 for each curve,
(c) use van't Hoff's law in the form $\Pi = (RT/M)c$ to determine the molar mass of polyisobutylene.

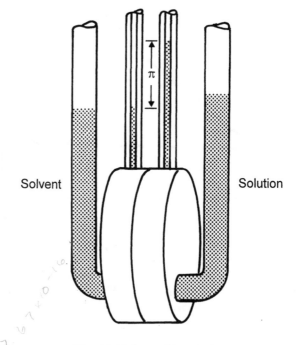

Fig. 12.15 for problem P–12.1

Solution part (a): The best way to prepare the plot for Π/c vs. c is to add a column to Table 12.6 to provide the term Π/c. This is done in Table 12.7.

With the data in Table 12.7 the plot in Fig. 12.16 is obtained.

Solution part (b): The plot illustrates that both curves indeed converge when extrapolated to c = 0 g/cm³. This

Table 12.6: Polyisobutylene data for two solutions

concentration [g/cm³]	osmotic pressure Π [atm]	
	in benzene	in cyclohexane
0.020	0.0021	0.0122
0.015	0.00153	0.0068
0.010	0.0010	0.0031
0.005	0.0005	0.0009

Table 12.7: Supplementary data for Π/c vs. C plot

c [g/cm³]	Π/c [atm cm³/g]	
	benzene	cyclohexane
0.0200	0.105	0.61
0.0150	0.102	0.453
0.0100	0.1	0.31
0.0050	0.1	0.18

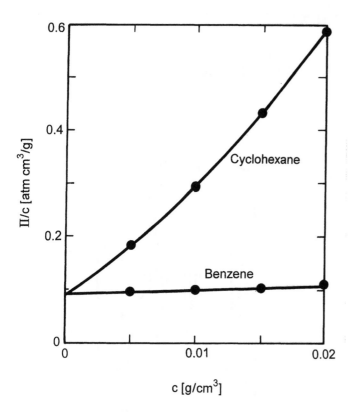

c [g/cm³]

Fig. 12.16: Plot of the ratio of osmotic pressure and concentration versus the concentration of dilute solutions of a macromolecule in two solvents.

establishes the validity of the current approach. We read the extrapolated value for Π/c from Fig. 12.16 (alternatively, numerical extrapolation methods may be used by entering the data of Table 12.7 in a computer):

$$\lim_{c \to 0}\left(\frac{\Pi}{c}\right) = 0.097 \left[\frac{atm \ cm^3}{g}\right] \qquad (1)$$

This is a convenient point to convert into standard units:

$$\lim_{c \to 0}\left(\frac{\Pi}{c}\right) = 0.097 \left[\frac{atm \ cm^3}{g}\right] \cdot \ ...$$

$$... \cdot 1.013 \times 10^5 \left[\frac{Pa}{atm}\right] 10^{-6}\left[\frac{m^3}{cm^3}\right] 10^3 \left[\frac{g}{kg}\right] \qquad (2)$$

$$\Rightarrow \quad \lim_{c \to 0}\left(\frac{\Pi}{c}\right) = 9.83 \left[\frac{Pa \ m^3}{kg}\right]$$

Solution part (c): We first confirm that the relation given for van't Hoff's law in this problem is indeed equivalent

to Eq. (12.20). For this we rewrite the mole fraction in Eq. (12.20) using Eq. (12.4):

$$\Pi = \frac{RT}{V_1^0}\frac{n_2}{n_{total}} = RT\frac{n_2}{V_1^0} \qquad (3)$$

where the second equality results because the total number of moles in the system is $n_{total} = 1.0$ mol since van't Hoff's law is derived for one mole of solution. We replace the number of moles of the dissolved macromolecule in Eq. (3) with its concentration, using:

$$c_2 = \frac{n_2 \ M_2}{V} \cong \frac{n_2 \ M_2}{V_1^0} \qquad (4)$$

in which we assume for the last equality that the total volume and the volume of solvent component 1 are essentially identical since we are dealing with a very dilute solution. Now we substitute Eq. (4) into Eq. (3) and find:

$$\Pi = RT\frac{n_2}{V_1^0} = RT\frac{c_2}{M_2} \qquad (5)$$

To obtain the molar mass of the macromolecule we rewrite Eq. (5), taking into account that the formula applies in the limit of a very dilute solution:

$$M_2 = RT\left[\lim_{c_2 \to 0}\left(\frac{\Pi}{c_2}\right)\right]^{-1} =$$

$$\frac{8.314\left[\dfrac{J}{K \ mol}\right] 298[K]}{9.83\left[\dfrac{Pa \ m^3}{kg}\right]} \qquad (6)$$

The result is a molar mass of about 252 kg/mol which is usually expressed in unit [g/mol] as $M_2 = 252,000$ g/mol.

Problem 12.2
We mix 0.174 g hydrogen gas (H_2) and 1.365 g nitrogen gas (N_2) in a container of 2.83 liters at 0 °C. Assuming that both gases behave ideally, what are (a) the partial pressure of hydrogen,
(b) the partial pressure of nitrogen, and
(c) the total pressure in the container?
Hint: the molar mass of hydrogen is 2.016 g/mol and the

molar mass of nitrogen is 28.014 g/mol.

Solution part (a): As discussed in section 12.2, the partial pressure of a component is equal to the pressure we would measure in the container if all other gas components were removed from the container.

We use Eq. (12.3) to express the partial pressure of the hydrogen component, which acts like an ideal gas:

$$p_{H_2} = \frac{n_{H_2} RT}{V} \qquad (7)$$

To substitute the given values in Eq. (7) we need to determine the number of moles of hydrogen gas in the container:

$$n_{H_2} = \frac{m_{H_2}}{M_{H_2}} = \frac{0.174[g]}{2.016\left[\dfrac{g}{mol}\right]} = 0.086 \; mol \qquad (8)$$

This yields for the partial pressure of hydrogen:

$$p_{H_2} = \frac{0.086[mol] \; 8.314\left[\dfrac{J}{K\,mol}\right] \; 273[K]}{2.83\times10^{-3}[m^3]} \qquad (9)$$

$$\Rightarrow \quad p_{H_2} = 6.9 \times 10^4 \; Pa$$

Solution part (b): The calculation for the nitrogen component is done in an analogous fashion. For the number of moles of nitrogen we find:

$$n_{N_2} = \frac{m_{N_2}}{M_{N_2}} = \frac{1.365[g]}{28.014\left[\dfrac{g}{mol}\right]} = 0.049 \; mol \qquad (10)$$

and therefore, the partial pressure of nitrogen is:

$$p_{N_2} = \frac{0.049[mol] \; 8.314\left[\dfrac{J}{K\,mol}\right] \; 273[K]}{2.83\times10^{-3}[m^3]} \qquad (11)$$

$$\Rightarrow \quad p_{N_2} = 3.9 \times 10^4 \; Pa$$

Solution part (c): The total pressure of the system follows from the single partial pressures, as described in Eq. (12.2):

$$p = p_{N_2} + p_{H_2} =$$

$$= 3.9\times10^4[Pa] + 6.9\times10^4[Pa] \qquad (12)$$

$$\Rightarrow \quad p = 1.08 \times 10^5 \; Pa$$

Problem 12.3

Most extracellular fluids in the human body and the cytoplasm of most human cells have a concentration of osmotically active components of 0.29 mol/kg, e.g. dissolved sugar or dissolved ions such as potassium, sodium and chlorine.

(a) If the body loses water (dehydration) or has a too large intake of salt, both of which affect the extracellular fluid, what consequence does this have on the body cells?

(b) What would happen if, instead, a human body were to lose too much salt from the extracellular fluid?

Solution part (a): We first consider the case in which the concentration of the active osmotic components in the extracellular fluid is higher than in the cells. As a consequence, water diffuses from inside the cell toward the extracellular space. The reason for this diffusion is given in Eqs. (12.19) and (12.20):

$$\Pi = p_{mix} - p_{pure} = \frac{RT}{V_1^0} x_2 \qquad (13)$$

This formula applies at both sides of the membrane, and thus, establishes a pressure gradient for the solvent across the membrane. An increase in the salt concentration outside the cell membrane means that a larger pressure difference is required for diffusive equilibrium. Since the extracellular pressure does not change, the cytoplasm pressure must decrease, which is achieved by water diffusion out of the cell. This dehydration of the cell leads to cell shrinkage which is potentially non–reversible, i.e., leads to permanent damage to the cell.

Solution part (b): This is the opposite situation. In this case, Eq. (13) predicts a smaller pressure difference in diffusive equilibrium. Thus, water diffuses from the extracellular space into the cell, leading to cell swelling. This may cause the cell to burst, which is a form of permanent tissue damage.

Problem 12.4
Which is lighter under otherwise equal conditions (i.e., same pressure, temperature, volume): humid air or dry air?

Solution: Dry air consists mostly of nitrogen and oxygen molecules with respective molar masses of 28 g/mol and 32 g/mol. In humid air of otherwise identical parameters, some of the nitrogen and oxygen molecules are displaced by water molecules with a molar mass of 18 g/mol. Thus, in humid air, lighter molecules replace heavier ones, and therefore, the humid air is lighter than the same amount of dry air.

Note that this applies only as long as the air remains a single phase. Once phase separation occurs, e.g., in clouds where water condensation on dust particles leads to levitating water droplets in the air, the argument remains no longer valid as each phase develops separately. In particular, the denser liquid water phase undergoes a ripening process until droplets are large enough to fall toward the ground (rain).

Problem 12.5
In 1965, a French team led by Jacques–Yves Cousteau lived for 28 days in the deep sea station Conshelf III at 108 m below the sea surface. They breathed an oxygen/ helium mixture (called helox) instead of air.
(a) Would you agree with their claim that breathing this mixture is easier than breathing air?
(b) Can you think of another reason why they used helox instead of air?
Note: One member of the team reported that among other adverse effects of this exercise the taste is irritated, and he could no longer distinguish caviar from chicken. This, of course, is a disastrous effect for a Frenchman!

Solution part (a): As discussed in section 11.4, Reynolds numbers exceeding 2000 indicate the transition toward turbulent flow in straight cylindrical tubes. Reynolds numbers vary widely for various pipe geometries, however, leading to significantly lower numbers for curved, cylindrical tubes. This is the reason why the blood flow in the aortic arch is often turbulent.

Eq. (11.42) illustrates further that the Reynolds number depends also on the gas density ρ and inversely on the gas viscosity η. The gas density is reduced when the inert component of air (nitrogen) is replaced by helium, which is another inert gas. The benefit of this gas exchange is a reduction of the likelihood that the gas mixture flows turbulently through the trachea, thus, making breathing easier.

Solution part (b): The original reason for the exchange of helium for nitrogen was _nitrogen narcosis_. In earlier deep sea diving experiments, Cousteau's team had noted that a dangerous narcotic effect occurs at depths below 45 meters due to the high partial pressure of nitrogen. For example, Cousteau reported that this effect caused one team member to offer his mouth–piece to fishes passing–by. Replacing nitrogen with helium eliminated this effect.

Besides the irritation of taste, there are other interesting changes taking place when helox is used instead of air:
(I) A funny change in the sound of the human voice takes place, causing everyone to sound like Mickey Mouse. This effect is also sometimes used by entertainers at children parties. It was considered an undesirable effect when the Cousteau team went on a life TV presentation. Therefore, on that occasion, helox was replaced by an expensive neon/oxygen mixture.
(II) When the Cousteau team celebrated on _Conshelf II_ at 12 meters below the sea surface in 1963, they used Champagne (sparkling wine). Unfortunately, it tasted flat as the high pressure in the cabin did not allow the bubbles to escape the wine.
(III) There are also some more serious dangers of helox. For example, the heat loss of the human body is increased by a factor of 70 in comparison to air.

CHAPTER XIII

Nerves: the flow of charges

Problem 13.1

We study some capacitor arrangements.

(a) An air–filled parallel plate capacitor has a plate separation of b = 1.5 mm and an area A = 4.0 cm². Find its capacitance.

(b) A capacitor with capacitance of C = 4.5 μF is connected to a 9 V battery. What is the amount of charge on each plate of the capacitor?

Solution part (a): The capacitance is obtained from Eq. (13.21):

$$C = \epsilon_0 \frac{A}{b} = 8.85 \times 10^{-12} \left[\frac{Cb^2}{Nm^2} \right] \frac{4 \times 10^{-4}[m^2]}{1.5 \times 10^{-3}[m]} \quad (1)$$

$$\Rightarrow \quad C = 2.36 \times 10^{-12} \ F = 2.36 \ pF$$

Solution part (b): The charge follows from Eq. (13.20):

$$q = C\Delta V = 4.5 \times 10^{-6}[F] \ 9[V]$$

$$\Rightarrow \quad q = 4.05 \times 10^{-5} \ Cb = 40.5 \ \mu Cb \quad (2)$$

Problem 13.2

The plates of a parallel plate capacitor are 3 cm wide and 4 cm long. The plates are separated by a 1.5 mm thick layer of paper.

(a) Calculate the capacitance of the device using the dielectric constant of paper from Table 13.3.

(b) Any dielectric material other than vacuum has a maximum electric field that can be produced in the dielectric material before it physically or chemically breaks down and begins to conduct. This maximum electric field is called *dielectric strength*. The dielectric strength for paper is reached at a value of 15×10^6 V/m. Calculate the maximum charge that can be placed on the capacitor at this dielectric strength.

Table 13.3: Dielectric constants at room temperature

Material	Dielectric constant κ
Vacuum	1.0
Air at 1.0 atm	1.00054
Polystyrene	2.6
Paper	3.5
Pyrex glass	4.7
Porcelain	6.5
Nerve membrane	7.0
Silicon	12.0
Ethanol	25.0
Water	78.5

Solution part (a): The formula for the capacitance, Eq. (13.21), is modified for a dielectric material other than vacuum as shown e.g. in Eq. (13.26). With the dielectric constant of paper $\kappa_{paper} = 3.5$ (see Table 13.3), we obtain:

$$C = \kappa_{paper} \epsilon_0 \frac{A}{b} =$$

$$= 3.5 \cdot 8.85 \times 10^{-12} \left[\frac{Cb^2}{Nm^2} \right] \frac{12 \times 10^{-4}[m^2]}{1.5 \times 10^{-3}[m]} \quad (3)$$

$$\Rightarrow \quad C = 2.5 \times 10^{-11} \ F = 25 \ pF$$

Solution part (b): We calculate first the maximum potential difference from the given dielectric strength using Eq. (9.58):

$$\Delta V_{max} = |E_{max}| \ b =$$

$$= 15 \times 10^6 \left[\frac{V}{m} \right] 1.5 \times 10^{-3} \ [m] \quad (4)$$

$$\Rightarrow \quad \Delta V_{max} = 2.3 \times 10^4 \ V$$

This is the maximum potential which can be applied before an electric breakdown occurs. With the result in Eq.

(4) the maximum charge is calculated which can be placed on the capacitor plates, using Eq. (13.20):

$$q_{max} = C\Delta V_{max} = 2.5\times10^{-11}[F]\ 2.3\times10^{4}[V]$$

$$\Rightarrow \quad q_{max} = 5.8 \times 10^{-7}\ Cb = 0.58\ \mu Cb \tag{5}$$

Problem 13.3

An air–filled parallel plate capacitor has a capacitance of 60 pF.
(a) What is the separation of the plates if each plate has an area of 0.5 m²?
(b) If the region between the plates is filled with a material with $\kappa = 4.5$, what is the final capacitance?

Solution part (a): A capacitor with a vacuum between its conducting plates is rare. For any other material between the capacitor plates, the formulation of the capacitance shown in Eq. (13.26) has to replace Eq. (13.21) as the dielectric constant differs from unity, $\kappa > 1$. If the capacitor is air–filled, however, it is justified to make the approximation $\kappa = 1$ as Table 13.3 suggests. We make this assumption in the present case.

Using Eq. (13.21), we solve for the gap spacing of the capacitor, b:

$$b = \epsilon_0 \frac{A}{C} = 8.85\times10^{-12}\left[\frac{Cb^2}{Nm^2}\right]\frac{0.5[m^2]}{60\times10^{-12}[F]} \tag{6}$$

$$\Rightarrow \quad b = 7.4 \times 10^{-2}\ m = 7.4\ cm$$

Solution part (b): Instead of rewriting the same formulas, we choose a relative approach to express the result. From Eq. (13.26) we know that $C \propto \kappa$, thus:

$$C_{new\ mat} = C_{air}\frac{\kappa_{new}}{\kappa_{air}} = 60\times10^{-12}[F]\frac{4.5}{1.0} \tag{7}$$

$$\Rightarrow C_{new\ mat} = 270 \times 10^{-12}\ F = 270\ pF$$

Problem 13.4

A simplified model for an erythrocyte is a spherical capacitor with a positively charged liquid interior of surface area A. The interior fluid is separated by a membrane of thickness b from the surrounding, negatively charged plasma fluid. The potential difference across the membrane is 100 mV and the thickness of the membrane is about 100 nm with a dielectric constant of $\kappa = 5.0$.
(a) Calculate the volume of the blood cell assuming that an average erythrocyte has a mass 1×10^{-12} kg. From the volume determine the surface area of the erythrocyte.
(b) Calculate the capacitance of the blood cell. For this calculation model the membrane as a parallel plate capacitor with the area found in part (a).
(c) Calculate the charge on the surface of the membrane. How many elementary charges does this represent? Hint: use the density of blood as 1.06 g/cm³.

Solution part (a): The first part of the question serves as a preparation step to obtain some necessary parameters to quantify later the electric properties.

The volume of the blood cell is calculated from the mass of the blood cell and the density of blood. The density of blood is a sufficiently good approximation of the density of the blood cell as the blood cells float in the whole blood. Archimedes' principle predicts for a body floating fully immersed in a fluid that both have the same density. The density of blood has been given as $\rho = 1.06$ g/cm³. We find for the volume:

$$V = \frac{1\times10^{-12}[kg]}{1.06\times10^3\left[\dfrac{kg}{m^3}\right]} = 9.4 \times 10^{-16}\ m^3 \tag{8}$$

Assuming a spherical shape of the blood cell we know that the volume is given as $V = 4\pi r^3/3$ and the surface as $A = 4\pi r^2$. From the volume formula and the value found in Eq. (8) we determine the radius of the blood cell to be $r = 6.1 \times 10^{-6}$ m. Thus, the surface area is:

$$A = 4\pi r^2 = 4.7 \times 10^{-10}\ m^2 \tag{9}$$

Solution part (b): Treating the membrane as a parallel plate capacitor we find from Eqs. (13.21) and (13.26):

$$C = \kappa\,\epsilon_0\,\frac{A}{b} =$$

$$5.0 \times 8.85\cdot10^{-12}\left[\frac{F}{m}\right]\frac{4.7\times10^{-10}[m^2]}{100\times10^{-9}[m]} \tag{10}$$

$$\Rightarrow \quad C = 2.08 \times 10^{-13}\ F$$

Solution part (c): Using Eq. (13.20) in the form $q = C\Delta V$ we find with the result of part (b) for the charge:

$$q = 2.08 \times 10^{-13}[F] \ 100 \times 10^{-3}[V]$$

$$\Rightarrow \quad q = 2.08 \times 10^{-14} \ Cb \tag{11}$$

Dividing the charge found in Eq. (11) by the elementary charge e allows us to calculate the number of elementary charges on the surface membrane of the blood cell:

$$N = \frac{q}{e} = \frac{2.08 \cdot 10^{-14}[Cb]}{1.6 \cdot 10^{-19}[Cb]} = 130,000 \tag{12}$$

which is a large number, considering that we neglect electric effects in the discussion of blood flow.

Problem 13.5

All electric devices have identifying plates specifying their electrical characteristics. E.g., a typical household device may be specified for a current of 6.0 A when connected to a 120 V source. What is the resistance of this device?

Solution: This is the first problem associated with the concept of an electric current. We use Ohm's law in the form of Eq. (13.42) to find the resistance:

$$R = \frac{\Delta V}{I} = \frac{120 \ [V]}{6 \ [A]} = 20 \ \Omega \tag{13}$$

Problem 13.6

A person notices a mild shock if the current along a path through the thumb and index finger of one hand exceeds 80 µA. Compare the respective maximum allowable potential for the hand with
(a) dry skin with a resistance of $R = 4.0 \times 10^5 \ \Omega$, and
(b) wet skin with a resistance of $R = 2000 \ \Omega$.

Solution part (a): With Ohm's law, we find:

$$\Delta V_{max} = R \ I = 4 \times 10^5 [\Omega] \ 8 \times 10^{-5}[A]$$

$$\Rightarrow \quad \Delta V_{max} = 32 \ V \tag{14}$$

Solution part (b): For the lower resistance of wet skin we find:

$$\Delta V_{max} = R \ I = 2 \times 10^3 [\Omega] \ 8 \times 10^{-5}[A]$$

$$\Rightarrow \quad \Delta V_{max} = 0.16 \ V \tag{15}$$

Thus, the danger of shock is much greater when a person's skin is wet.

Problem 13.7

A rectangular piece of copper is 2 cm long, 2 cm wide and 10 cm deep.
(a) What is the resistance of the copper piece as measured between the two square ends? (Use the resistivity of copper from Table 13.4.)
(b) What is the resistance between two opposite rectangular faces?

Solution part (a): Each square end of the copper block has an area of $A_a = (2 \times 10^{-2} \ m)^2 = 4 \times 10^{-4} \ m^2$. Using Eq. (13.42) to relate the resistance and resistivity with a length of the block of $l_a = 0.1$ m, we get:

$$R = \frac{\rho l_a}{A_a} = \frac{1.7 \times 10^{-8}[\Omega m] \ 0.1[m]}{4 \times 10^{-4}[m^2]}$$

$$\Rightarrow \quad R = 4.25 \times 10^{-6} \ \Omega = 4.25 \ \mu\Omega \tag{16}$$

Solution part (b): All four rectangular faces of the copper block have the same area, $A_b = 2 \times 10^{-2} \ m \cdot 0.1 \ m = 2 \times 10^{-3} \ m^2$. Using the same formula as in part (a) with the length of the block now $l_b = 2 \times 10^{-2}$ m we find:

Table 13.4: Resistivity values for various materials

Material	Resistivity [Ωm]
Insulators and semiconductors:	
Yellow sulfur	2.0×10^{15}
Artificial lipid membrane	1.0×10^{13}
Quartz	1.0×10^{13}
Nerve membrane	1.6×10^7
Silicon	2.5×10^3
Axoplasm	1.1×10^0
Germanium	5.0×10^{-1}
Metals:	
Mercury	1.0×10^{-6}
Iron	1.0×10^{-7}
Gold	2.4×10^{-8}
Copper	1.7×10^{-8}

$$R = \frac{\rho l_b}{A_b} = \frac{1.7 \times 10^{-8}[\Omega m]\ 2 \times 10^{-2}[m]}{2 \times 10^{-3}[m^2]} \quad \textbf{(17)}$$

$$\Rightarrow \quad R = 1.7 \times 10^{-7}\ \Omega = 0.17\ \mu\Omega$$

Note that the rather significant difference between the resistances in parts (a) and (b) is entirely due to the change in geometry.

Problem 13.8
A current of 6.0 A flows through a 20 Ω resistor for t = 3 minutes. What total amount of charge passes through any cross–section of the resistor in this time?
(a) Express your result in unit [Cb].
(b) Express your result as the number of electrons passing the cross–sectional area.

Solution part (a): The charge passing through any cross–sectional area follows from Eq. (13.31):

$$Q = It = 6.0[A]\ 180[s] = 1080\ Cb \quad \textbf{(18)}$$

Solution part (b): The number of electrons, which this amount of charge represents, follows from dividing the total charge by the charge per electron, which is the elementary charge e:

$$N = \frac{Q}{e} = \frac{1080[Cb]}{1.6 \times 10^{-19}[Cb]} = 6.8 \times 10^{21} \quad \textbf{(19)}$$

This corresponds to 1 % of a mole of electrons.

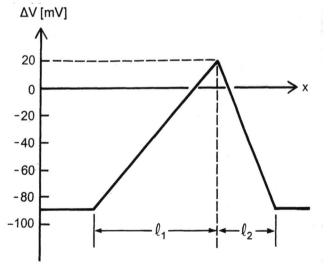

Fig. 13.29 for problem P–13.10.

Problem 13.9
A conducting, cylindrical wire has a 1.0 mm diameter, a 1.67 m length and a 50 m Ω resistance. What is the resistivity of the material? Identify the material of which this conductor is made by using Table 13.4.

Solution: We use Eq. (13.42) to determine the resistivity of the material of the wire. The cross–sectional area A of the wire is A = $r^2\pi$ = $\pi(0.5 \times 10^{-3}$ m$)^2$ = 7.85×10^{-7} m², where we once more converted the given diameter to a radius. Thus:

$$\rho = \frac{RA}{l} = \frac{50 \times 10^{-3}[\Omega]\ 7.85 \times 10^{-7}[m^2]}{1.67[m]} \quad \textbf{(20)}$$

$$\Rightarrow \quad \rho = 2.35 \times 10^{-8}\ \Omega m$$

Comparing with the tabulated values of resistivities, this value comes closest to the value of gold (Au).

Problem 13.10
The potential along an axon is shown in Fig. 13.29 at a given time instant. The axon radius is 8 μm, the resistivity of the axoplasm is taken from Table 13.4. What is the longitudinal current in the axon as a function of position? Use for the lengths the values $l_1 = 0.8$ mm and $l_2 = 0.4$ mm.

Solution: The potential versus position curve is redrawn in Fig. 13.30 to introduce the three points A, B and C. We evaluate the interval A to B first. Between the points at A and B is a potential difference of $\Delta V = 110$ mV. With the distance between A and B given as $l_1 = 0.8$ mm, and using the cross–sectional area A = πr^2, we find from Ohm's law:

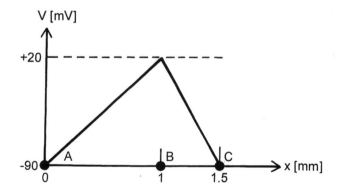

Fig. 13.30: Potential profile along the nerve, subdivided into sections by points A, B and C.

114

$$I_{AB} = \frac{\Delta V_{AB}}{R_{AB}} = \frac{\Delta V_{AB}\, A}{\rho\, l_1} =$$

$$\frac{110 \times 10^{-3}[V]\ \pi\ \left(8 \times 10^{-6}[m]\right)^2}{1.1[\Omega m]\ 0.8 \times 10^{-3}[m]} = 25\ nA \qquad (21)$$

In the same fashion, we calculate for the current between points B and C:

$$I_{BC} = \frac{\Delta V_{BC}}{R_{BC}} = \frac{\Delta V_{BC}\, A}{\rho\, l_2} =$$

$$\frac{110 \times 10^{-3}[V]\ \pi\ \left(8 \times 10^{-6}[m]\right)^2}{1.1[\Omega m]\ 0.4 \times 10^{-3}[m]} = 50\ nA \qquad (22)$$

Although the current is a scalar, it is possible to determine the direction in which the charges flow (representing a current density which is a vector quantity). From the discussion of nerves in the text we know that it is primarily positive ions (sodium and potassium) which are moving during an impulse passes. Positive charges flow toward negatively charged zones, i.e., between points A and B in Fig. 13.30 the positive charges move toward the left (to point A). Between B and C the positive charges move toward the right (to point C). Comparing this flow of charges with the currents identified in Figs. 13.19 and 13.24 we find that the current problem describes the situation *inside* of the axon, i.e. in the axoplasm and not in the extracellular fluid (interstitium).

This justifies after the fact that we used the resistivity of the axoplasm to calculate the currents. Note the physiological importance of this result.

Problem 13.11

A current density of 0.8×10^{-4} A/cm² stimulates a membrane for 150 µs. How much does this change the potential across the membrane?
Hint: Use a nerve membrane thickness of 6 nm and the dielectric constant for the nerve membrane from Table 13.3.

Solution: Eqs. (13.49) and (13.50) connect the current across the membrane, I_m, with the capacity of the membrane and the rate of change of the potential. We rewrite those equations in the form:

$$|I_m| = C\,\frac{\Delta V}{\Delta t}$$

$$\Rightarrow\quad \Delta V = \frac{|I_m|\,\Delta t}{C} = \frac{J_m\, A\, \Delta t}{C} \qquad (23)$$

Between the first and second line in Eq. (23) we replaced the current by the current density since the current density is given in the problem text. Now we substitute the capacitance in the form of Eq. (13.26) and enter the numerical values, including the dielectric constant of the nerve membrane from Table 13.3 and the current density $J_m = 0.8 \times 10^{-4}$ A/cm², which is the same as 0.8 A/m²:

$$\Delta V = \frac{J_m\, A\, \Delta t}{\kappa \epsilon_0\, \dfrac{A}{b}} = \frac{J_m\, b\, \Delta t}{\kappa \epsilon_0} =$$

$$\frac{0.8\left[\dfrac{A}{m^2}\right]\ 6 \times 10^{-9}[m]\ 150 \times 10^{-6}[s]}{7.0\ \cdot\ 8.85 \times 10^{-12}\left[\dfrac{Cb^2}{Nm^2}\right]} \qquad (24)$$

$$\Rightarrow\quad \Delta V = 0.012\ V = 12\ mV$$

Problem 13.12

For the myelinated nerve the axon radius is 10 µm, the membrane resistivity is $\rho_m = 1.0 \times 10^7$ Ωm, the axoplasm resistivity is $\rho_{ax} = 0.5$ Ωm and the myelin sheath thickness is related to the axon radius as given in Eq. (13.74). (a) What is the electrotonus spread decay length λ for this nerve?
(b) Using Eq. (13.74) for the distance between nodes of Ranvier for this nerve, how many nodes of Ranvier fire along the nerve as a result of a certain node being stimulated. Use a potential difference of $\Delta V = 100$ mV for the maximum potential change in the node which fires initially, and allow other nodes of Ranvier to fire if electrotonus spread causes at their site at least a change from -70 mV to -60 mV.

Solution part (a): We substitute the given values in Eq. (13.76):

$$\lambda = \sqrt{\frac{ab}{2} \frac{\rho_m}{\rho_{ax}}} =$$

$$\sqrt{\frac{10[\mu m] \ 4[\mu m] \ 1 \times 10^7[\Omega m]}{2 \cdot 0.5[\Omega m]}} \qquad \textbf{(25)}$$

$$\Rightarrow \quad \lambda = 2 \times 10^{-2} \ m = 2.0 \ cm$$

Solution part (b): The calculation for this part is analogous to the calculations leading to Eq. (13.78). The threshold condition for a potential perturbation relative to the maximum potential difference during a Hodgkin–Huxley impulse of 100 mV is:

$$\frac{\Delta V}{\Delta V_{HH}} = \frac{10[mV]}{100[mV]} = 0.1 \qquad \textbf{(26)}$$

Thus, we use Eq. (13.59) with $x = nD$ where n is a number indicating how many intervals between nodes of Ranvier with a distance D are included. We know further from Eq. (13.77) that D is related to the radius of the axon, a, as $D = 280a$. Thus:

$$0.1 = \exp\left(-\frac{x}{\lambda}\right) = \exp\left(-\frac{280 \ na}{\lambda}\right)$$

$$\qquad \textbf{(27)}$$

$$\Rightarrow \quad n = -\frac{\lambda}{280 \ a} \ln 0.1 = 16.45$$

Since only an integer number of nodes of Ranvier can be triggered, we conclude that the next 16 nodes will fire.

Problem 13.13
Confirm both relations in Eq. (13.73) graphically by using Fig. 13.27.

Solution: We start with unmyelinated nerves. Fig. 13.31 shows a particular choice of two points in the double–logarithmic graph of Fig. 13.27 for the data analysis. The data read off the figure are listed in Table 13.6.

Table 13.6: Data from Fig. 13.31 for unmyelinated nerves.

a [μm]	lna	v [m/s]	lnv
0.1	− 2.303	0.51	− 0.67
1.0	0.0	1.75	+ 0.56

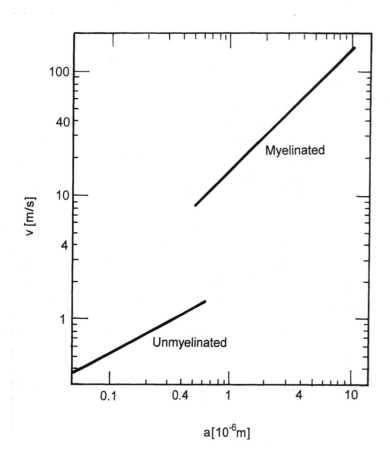

Fig. 13.27: Double–logarithmic plot of the impulse speed in myelinated and unmyelinated nerves versus the axon radius.

116

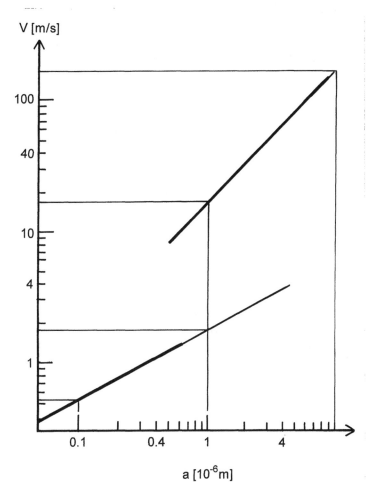

V [m/s]

100

40

10

4

1

0.1   0.4   1   4

a [10^{-6}m]

Fig. 13.31: Double–logarithmic plot of the signal speed in myelinated and unmyelinated nerves as a function of axon radius.

We write the general power law relation between the radius of the axon and the impulse speed in the form:

$$v\left[\frac{m}{s}\right] = c_2 \left(a\,[\mu m]\right)^{c_1}$$

(28)

$$\Rightarrow \quad \ln v = \ln c_2 + c_1 \ln a$$

In this formula we need only to evaluate the constant c_1 since Eq. (13.73) does predict a power law coefficient, but no prefactor. For the data in Table 13.6 we find:

$$c_1 = \frac{\Delta \ln v}{\Delta \ln a} = \frac{1.23}{2.303} = 0.53$$

(29)

This value is consistent with $c_1 = ½$ for the unmyelinated nerves based on the error margins analyzing the given data.

Table 13.7: Two data point pairs from Fig. 13.31 for the myelinated nerve (upper curve).

a [µm]	lna	v [m/s]	lnv
1.0	0.0	16.1	+ 2.78
10.0	+ 2.303	160.0	+ 5.08

Next we analyze the data for the myelinated nerve in Fig. 13.27. Fig. 13.31 shows a choice of data points to quantify the power–law behavior. The data are listed in Table 13.7. Using again Eq. (28), we find for the power law coefficient for myelinated nerves:

$$c_1 = \frac{\Delta \ln v}{\Delta \ln a} = \frac{2.3}{2.303} = 1.0$$

(30)

Both exponents are consistent with the models discussed in the text.

Problem 13.14

Table 13.5 provides approximate values for the intracellular and extracellular concentrations in unit [mmol/ l] for sodium, potassium and chlorine ions in a frog muscle with resting potential of – 98 mV and for the squid axon with a resting potential – 70 mV. Calculate the equilibrium potential for each ion species at 20^0C.

Solution: This problem is solved in a similar fashion as Eqs. (13.67) to (13.70) were derived. Note that the temperature is now 20^0C = 293 K. We determine first the equilibrium potentials for the resting nerve of a frog with a potential of – 98 mV. In analogy to Eq. (13.68) we find for the sodium balance two values, at an intracellular concentration of 9 mmol/l:

Table 13.5: Intracellular and extracellular ion concentrations for frogs and squids in [mmol/l].

Ion species	intracellular	extracellular
1. Frog muscle		
Na$^+$	9.0 – 13.0	120.0
K$^+$	140.0	2.5
Cl$^-$	3.5	120.0
2. Squid axon		
Na$^+$	50.0	440.0
K$^+$	400.0	20.0
Cl$^-$	40.0 – 100.0	560.0

117

$$\Delta V_{Na^+} = \frac{kT}{e} \ln\left(\frac{c_{Na^+,\ out}}{c_{Na^+,\ ax}}\right) =$$

$$\frac{1.38\times10^{-23}\left[\frac{J}{K}\right]293[K]}{1.6\times10^{-19}[Cb]}\ln\left(\frac{120}{9}\right) \qquad (31)$$

$$\Rightarrow \quad \Delta V_{Na^+} = 0.065\ V = +\ 65\ mV$$

and at an intracellular concentration of 13 mmol/*l* a value of $\Delta V_{Na+} = +\ 56$ mV.

For potassium, Table 13.5 provides only for one ratio for the frog's nerves, and thus, we find the equilibrium potential as:

$$\Delta V_{K^+} = \frac{kT}{e} \ln\left(\frac{c_{K^+,\ out}}{c_{K^+,\ ax}}\right) =$$

$$\frac{1.38\times10^{-23}\left[\frac{J}{K}\right]293[K]}{1.6\times10^{-19}[Cb]}\ln\left(\frac{2.5}{140}\right) \qquad (32)$$

$$\Rightarrow \quad \Delta V_{K^+} = -\ 0.102\ V = -\ 102\ mV$$

Note that this value is only slightly more negative than the resting potential.

For chlorine we need to include a further negative sign due to the negative charge of the ion. Thus, we find for the frog's nerve:

$$\Delta V_{Cl^-} = \frac{kT}{e} \ln\left(\frac{c_{Cl^-,\ out}}{c_{Cl^-,\ ax}}\right) =$$

$$\frac{1.38\times10^{-23}\left[\frac{J}{K}\right]293[K]}{-\ 1.6\times10^{-19}[Cb]}\ln\left(\frac{120}{3.5}\right) \qquad (33)$$

$$\Rightarrow \quad \Delta V_{Cl^-} = -\ 0.089\ V = -\ 89\ mV$$

In the same way the values for the squid's nerves are found. For the squid, $\Delta V_{Na+} = +\ 55$ mV and $\Delta V_{K+} = -\ 76$ mV and for the negative Cl ions $\Delta V_{Cl-} = -\ 44$ mV to $-\ 67$ mV.

CHAPTER XIV

Electrocardiography: electric phenomena of the heart

There are no problems with this chapter.

CHAPTER XV

Elastic tissue: elasticity and vibrations

Problem 15.1

For the graph in Fig. 15.1, express the force (in % of the maximum force) as a mathematical function of the sarcomere length (in μm) for the linear segments
(a) in the interval 2.2 μm ≤ l ≤ 3.2 μm,
(b) in the interval 2.0 μm ≤ l ≤ 2.2 μm, and
(c) in the interval 1.4 μm ≤ l ≤ 1.65 μm.

Solution part (a): The general mathematical formula to describe a linear dependence of a dependent variable y on an independent variable x is:

$$y = a\,x + b \qquad (1)$$

in which a (the slope) and b (the intercept of the y–axis) are constant. Two pairs of values for l and $F(l)$ are need-

ed to identify the two constants (see also the discussion in the General Appendix). The two values for l should be chosen as far apart as possible to minimize the uncertainty in the values calculated for the constants.

From the graph in Fig. 15.1 we choose for the segment in the interval 2.2 μm ≤ l ≤ 3.2 μm the data pairs $l_1 = 2.2$ μm with $F(l_1) = 100$ % and $l_2 = 3.2$ μm with $F(l_2) = 32$ %. Writing the linear formula in the form

$$F\,[\%] = a\,l\,[\mu m] + b \qquad (2)$$

we find:

(I)	100 = a 2.2 + b
(II)	32 = a 3.2 + b

(I) – (II)	68 = – 1.0 a

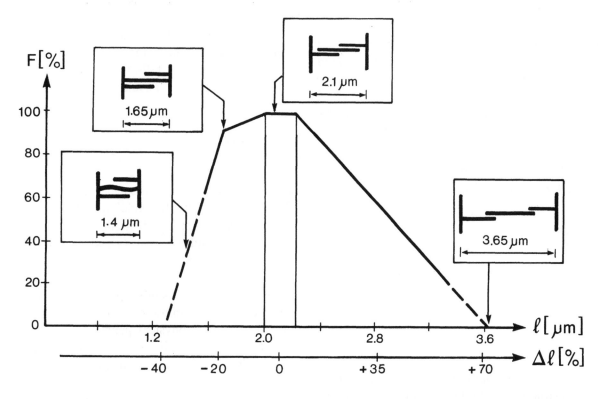

Fig. 15.1: The active muscle force is shown as a function of the sarcomere length. The force is given as a fraction of the maximum force a muscle can exert when it is at its average length of 2.1 μm. The sarcomere length is given as an absolute value l [μm] (top abscissa) and as a length change relative to the average length Δl [%] (bottom abscissa). For several specific sarcomere lengths the overlap of the myosin and actin filaments is illustrated in the inserted boxes. These insets indicate the origin of loss of active muscle force when the muscle is stretched too far (too weak overlap between actin and myosin filaments) and when the muscle tries to contract too far (myosin filaments collide with Z discs).

Thus, a = −68 %/μm. Substituting this result in either (I) or (II) we obtain b = 250 %.

Solution part (b): Since the line segment in the length interval of 2.0 μm ≤ l ≤ 2.2 μm is horizontal, we find without calculation that a = 0 %/μm and b = 100 %.

Solution part (c): This part is solved analogous to part (a). The following two data pairs are obtained from Fig. 15.1 for the interval 1.4 μm ≤ l ≤ 1.65 μm: l_1 = 1.65 μm with $F(l_1)$ = 92.5 % and l_2 = 1.3 μm with $F(l_2)$ = 0 %. This leads to a slope of a = +265 %/μm and an offset of b = −344.5 %.

Note: The values for b should be checked graphically by extrapolating the curve to l = 0 μm. In Fig. 15.1 you have to be careful when doing this as the ordinate intersects the x–axis not at l = 0 μm, but at a value of l = 0.4 μm!

Problem 15.2
Assume a leg contains a 1.2 m long bone with an average cross–sectional area of 3 cm². By how much does the bone shorten when the entire body weight of the person (use 700 N) is supported by the leg? Use for Young's modulus of the bone Y = 1.8×10^{10} Pa.

Solution: This is an application of Eq. (15.1) in which the force in the stress term F/A is given by the weight of the person. We are asked to calculate the absolute change in length, Δl, which is part of the strain term $\Delta l/l$, in which l is the initial length of the bone. Using the given value for Young's modulus Y, we find:

$$\Delta l = \frac{l\,F}{A\,Y} = \frac{1.2[m]\ 700[N]}{3 \times 10^{-4}[m^2]\ 1.8 \times 10^{10}[Pa]} \quad (3)$$

which yields:

$$\Delta l = 1.5 \times 10^{-4}\ m = 0.15\ mm \quad (4)$$

This is a tiny change in length!

Problem 15.3
We determine an upper limit of the maximum height of building construction on Earth. This limit is due to the maximum stress in the building material prior to rupture. For steel of density ρ = 7.9 g/cm³ the maximum stress is σ = 2.0×10^8 Pa.
Hint: The pressure in the steel at the ground level may not exceed the maximum stress.

Solution: The hint suggests to compare the pressure at ground level with the maximum stress with the condition p ≤ σ. The pressure is given by the force per unit area, with the force acting at the ground level of the building given by its weight. The weight in turn is given as the mass (obtained from the density and the volume), multiplied with g. Using h for the height of the building with h = V/A, in which V is the volume of the building and A its horizontal cross–sectional area, we find:

$$p = \frac{W}{A} = \frac{\rho V g}{A} = \rho h g \leq \sigma$$

$$\Rightarrow \quad h \leq \frac{\sigma}{\rho g} \quad (5)$$

We substitute the given values in Eq. (5):

$$h \leq \frac{\sigma}{\rho g} = \frac{2 \times 10^8 [Pa]}{7.9 \times 10^3 \left[\dfrac{kg}{m^3}\right]\ 9.8 \left[\dfrac{m}{s^2}\right]} \quad (6)$$

$$\Rightarrow \quad h \leq 2580\ m$$

The tallest free–standing structure is the CN Tower in Toronto, Canada, which was built in 1975 and is 554 m high. Since 1996, the tallest office building stands in Kuala Lumpur, Malaysia, and is 452 m high.

Problem 15.4
We suspend a uniform rod of length L and let it swing as a physical pendulum.
(a) What is the period of the pendulum if L = 2.0 m?
(b) If we want a simple pendulum with an object at the end of a massless string of length l to have the same period as the pendulum in part (a), what must the length l be?

Solution part (a): We study a physical pendulum which consists of a uniform rod pivoted at the upper end. The period of such a physical pendulum is given in Eq. (15.68). Substituting the length of the rod, which is the only variable in this case, leads to:

$$T = 2\pi \sqrt{\frac{2L}{3g}} = 2\pi \sqrt{\frac{2 \cdot 2[m]}{3 \cdot 9.8[m/s^2]}} \quad (7)$$

$$\Rightarrow \quad T = 2.3\ s$$

Solution part (b): This part is based on the comparison of two formulas, Eq. (15.68) for the physical pendulum and Eq. (15.67) for the simple pendulum. For consistency with the problem text, the length in Eq. (15.67) has to be relabelled as l.

One way to answer the question is to substitute the period from Eq. (7) into Eq. (15.67). It is more elegant, and more general because solving part (a) is not required, to use the two equations to express the result first in form of a function, and then substitute the numerical values in the last step.

Following the second approach, we isolate l as the unknown variable in the formula for the period in Eq. (15.67):

$$l = g \left(\frac{T}{2\pi} \right)^2 \qquad (8)$$

and substitute Eq. (15.68) for the period T:

$$l = g \left(\frac{2\pi\sqrt{2L/3g}}{2\pi} \right)^2 = \frac{2}{3} L \qquad (9)$$

i.e., the length of the string of the simple pendulum has to be $l = 1.33$ m.

Problem 15.5

If you have no meter stick but a precise clock, you can measure the height of structures by attaching an object to the end of a massless string, with the string pivoted at the top of the structure of which you want to measure the height and the object at the bottom of the structure.
(a) If the object swings 10 times back and forth in 110 s, what is the height of the structure?
(b) If you change the object on the string to one with double the mass, how does the answer given in part (a) change?

Solution part (a): We use a simple pendulum for which its length equals the height of the structure. We isolate the length of the string in Eq. (15.67) as the unknown variable:

$$L = \frac{g\, T^2}{4\pi^2} \qquad (10)$$

In this formula we substitute $T = 110[s]/10 = 11$ s since swinging once back and forth corresponds to a full period. Thus, $L = 30.0$ m.

Solution part (b): Since the mass of the object attached to the string does not enter Eq. (10), varying the mass has no effect on the outcome of the experiment.

Problem 15.6

An object has a mass of m = 0.7 kg. It is attached to a spring which has a spring constant of value k = 80 N/m. At time t = 0 the object is pulled to a distance of 10 cm from its equilibrium position (which you may choose conveniently at x = 0). The surface on which the object moves is frictionless.
(a) What force does the spring exert on the object just before it is released?
(b) What are the angular frequency, the frequency and the period of the oscillation?
(c) What is the amplitude of the oscillation?
(d) What is the maximum speed of the object?
(e) What is the phase angle ϕ of the motion?

Solution part (a): We proceed with the assumption that the force acting on an object attached to the spring in this problem is elastic, i.e., follows Hooke's law as given in Eq. (15.29). Without this assumption we could not proceed as we have not developed any other form in which the force can depend on the displacement of a mass attached to a spring. Note that the problem text does not state explicitly to use Hooke's law, however, this can be concluded implicitly when a spring constant value k is given.

Hooke's law, as given in Eq. (15.29), is used in one of two ways: either both the equilibrium position and the actual position of the attached point mass are given or are of interest. In this case x and x_{eq} must be determined separately. Often, however, this is not necessary as we are only interested in the displacement from the equilibrium position, given as $\Delta x = x - x_{eq}$. In the latter case we can treat the displacement Δx as a single parameter.

In the current problem, the equilibrium position is identified explicitly at the origin, meaning that both ways to read Hooke's law are identical with $\Delta x = x_m$. Substituting the values given in the problem into Eq. (15.29) yields the restoring force at Δx:

$$|F| = k\, \Delta x = 80 \left[\frac{N}{m} \right] 0.1[m] = 8.0\ N \qquad (11)$$

Eq. (11) gives the magnitude of the force. This force acts along the line between the equilibrium position and the actual position of the object, i.e., along the x–axis in the current problem. The x–component of the force is $F_x = -|F| = -8.0$ N, which is negative since the force is a restoring force acting in the direction toward the equilibrium position of the spring.

Solution part (b): The parameters sought in this part of the problem are all characteristic values for the motion of an object attached to a specific spring. For the angular frequency ω we use Eq. (15.49):

$$\omega = \sqrt{\frac{k}{m}} = \sqrt{\frac{80[N/m]}{0.7[kg]}} = 10.7 \frac{rad}{s} \quad (12)$$

We use Eq. (15.50) for the frequency f:

$$f = \frac{\omega}{2\pi} = \frac{10.7[rad/s]}{2\pi} = 1.70 \ Hz \quad (13)$$

and for the period, using also Eq. (15.50):

$$T = \frac{1}{f} = \frac{1}{1.70 \ [Hz]} = 0.59 \ s \quad (14)$$

Solution part (c): The amplitude is obtained by finding the maximum displacement of the point mass from the equilibrium position. Since the point mass starts from rest, the position x(t = 0) represents the amplitude A of the vibration, i.e., A = 10 cm.

Solution part (d): The maximum speed is found at the time when the point mass passes through the equilibrium position as given in Eq. (15.46):

$$v_{max} = \pm\sqrt{\frac{k}{m}} \cdot A = \pm \omega \Delta x = \quad (15)$$

$$10.7\left[\frac{rad}{s}\right] 0.1[m] = 1.07 \frac{m}{s}$$

Solution part (e): The phase angle is determined by using Eq. (15.48) for the actual motion described in the problem. At the instant of releasing the point mass we define t = 0. At that instant, the displacement of the point mass is maximum, Δx = A. Substituting these values into Eq. (15.48), we find:

$$\Delta x = A = A\cos\phi \quad \Rightarrow \quad \phi = 0 \quad (16)$$

Problem 15.7
(a) What is the total energy of the system in P–15.6?
(b) What is the elastic potential energy of this system when the object is halfway between the equilibrium position and its turning point?

Solution part (a): We obtain the total energy from Eq. (15.42):

$$E_{total} = \frac{1}{2}kA^2 = \frac{1}{2} 80\left[\frac{N}{m}\right] (0.1[m])^2 \quad (17)$$

$$\Rightarrow \quad E_{total} = 0.4 \ J$$

Solution part (b): The elastic potential energy at any given displacement from the equilibrium position Δx follows from Eq. (15.36). Substituting the position at the halfway point, Δx = A/2, we find:

$$E_{elast} = \frac{1}{2}k\Delta x^2 = \frac{1}{2}k\left(\frac{A}{2}\right)^2 = \frac{k}{8}A^2 \quad (18)$$

$$\Rightarrow \quad \frac{1}{4}E_{total} = 0.1 \ J$$

The kinetic energy at the same point is the difference between the total energy and the elastic potential energy:

$$E_{kin} = E_{total} - E_{elast} = 0.3 \ J \quad (19)$$

Problem 15.8
An object undergoes a simple harmonic motion. During that motion the object needs 0.4 s to reach one point of zero velocity from the previous such point. If the distance between those points is 50 cm, calculate
(a) the period,
(b) the frequency, and
(c) the amplitude of the motion.

Solution part (a): The period T is the time elapsing between a given point of zero velocity and the second subsequent passing of such a point. The period is therefore T = 2 · 0.4 s = 0.8 s.

Solution part (b): We use Eq. (15.50) to calculate from the period the frequency, f = 1/T = 1.25 Hz.

Solution part (c): The amplitude is one half of the distance between two successive points of zero velocity since the point mass oscillates between − A and + A. Thus, A = ½ 50 cm = 25 cm.

Problem 15.9
An object has a mass of 250 g. It undergoes a simple harmonic motion. The amplitude of that motion is 10 cm and the period is 0.5 s.
(a) What is the spring constant (assuming that the spring obeys Hooke's law)?
(b) What is the maximum magnitude of the force which acts on the object?

Solution part (a): We use again a combination of Eqs. (15.49) and (15.50) to relate the spring constant to the period of the vibrational motion:

$$T = \frac{1}{f} = \frac{2\pi}{\omega} = 2\pi\sqrt{\frac{m}{k}} \qquad (20)$$

Isolating the parameter k we obtain:

$$k = m\left(\frac{2\pi}{T}\right)^2 = 0.25[kg]\left(\frac{2\pi}{0.5[s]}\right)^2 \qquad (21)$$

which leads to a value of k = 40 N/m.

Solution part (b): The maximum force acts on the point mass when the point mass is at the largest displacement from the equilibrium position (which you conclude from Eq. (15.29)), i.e., when the point mass is at a distance from the equilibrium position equal to A, $\Delta x = A$. At that point we find with the spring constant obtained in part (a):

$$F_{max} = k\,A = 40\left[\frac{N}{m}\right]0.1[m] \qquad (22)$$

$$\Rightarrow \quad F_{max} = 4\ N$$

Problem 15.10
An object is attached to an ideal spring. It undergoes a simple harmonic motion with a total energy of E = 1.0 J. The amplitude of the motion is 15.0 cm and the maximum speed of the object is 1.2 m/s. Find
(a) the spring constant,
(b) the mass of the object, and
(c) the frequency of the oscillation.

Solution part (a): Eq. (15.42) describes the total energy of a point mass on a spring at the instant when the point mass reaches its maximum displacement at the amplitude A. Eq. (15.45) describes the total energy at the instant when the point mass passes through the equilibrium position:

$$at\ \Delta x = A : \quad E_{total} = E_{elast} = \frac{1}{2}kA^2$$
$$\qquad (23)$$
$$at\ \Delta x = 0 : \quad E_{total} = E_{kin} = \frac{1}{2}mv_{max}^2$$

The first formula in Eq. (23) allows us to calculate the spring constant:

$$k = \frac{2E_{total}}{A^2} = \frac{2\cdot 1.0[J]}{(0.15[m])^2} = 90\ \frac{N}{m} \qquad (24)$$

Solution part (b): The second formula in Eq. (23) allows us to determine the mass of the object:

$$m = \frac{2E_{total}}{v_{max}^2} = \frac{2\cdot 1.0[J]}{(1.2[m/s])^2} = 1.39\ kg \qquad (25)$$

Solution part (c): The frequency of the oscillation is obtained from these data as follows: we begin with Eq. (15.46). In that equation, the square–root term is replaced by the angular frequency, using Eq. (15.49):

$$v_{max} = \omega\,A \qquad (26)$$

The frequency is then introduced by replacing the angular frequency with Eq. (15.50):

$$v_{max} = 2\pi\,f\,A \qquad (27)$$

Isolating the frequency and substituting the given values yields:

$$f = \frac{v_{max}}{2\pi A} = \frac{1.2[m/s]}{2\pi\,0.15[m]} = 1.3\ Hz \qquad (28)$$

Problem 15.11
Fig. 15.29 shows a simplified model of an insect moving its wings during flight. The wing is pivoted about the

outer chitin capsule. The end of the wing lies 0.5 mm inside the insect's body and moves up and down by a distance of 0.3 mm from its position of equilibrium. We use an effective spring constant of k = 0.74 N/m for the elastic tissue in the insect's body surrounding the end of the wing, and we use m = 0.3 mg as the effective mass of the wing which is moved up and down. The motion of the wing corresponds in this model to the vibration of the end of the wing attached to a spring (elastic tissue).
(a) With what frequency flap the wings of the insect during flight?
(b) What is the maximum speed of the inner end of the wing?
(c) What is the maximum speed of the outer tip of the wing if the wing is treated as a rigid body?
Use l_2 = 1.4 cm.

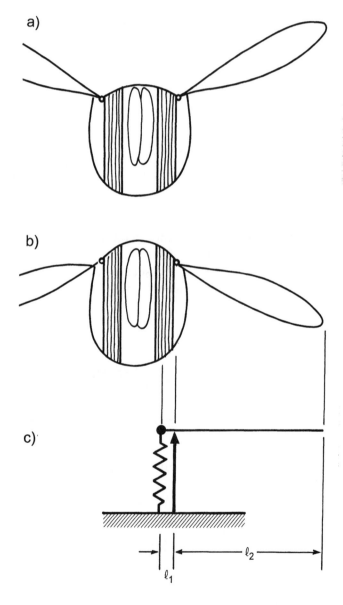

Fig. 15.29 for problem P–15.11.

Solution part (a): The motion of the wing is described as a simple harmonic motion. This is an acceptable approximation when we keep in mind that the concept of harmonic motion applies *not* only to a natural, passive vibration of the muscles which hold together the two chitin capsules of the insect (i.e., the concepts developed in section 15.3.1), but applies also to a forced vibration due to active muscle action (i.e., the concepts developed in the next chapter in section 16.3.3). The insect chooses an external frequency close to the natural vibration frequency of the passive muscles as this allows the animal to fly with the least effort due to the resonance phenomenon illustrated later in Fig. 16.18.

We use Eq. (20) from P–15.9 to calculate the natural, passive vibration frequency which is also the resonant frequency:

$$f = \frac{1}{2\pi}\sqrt{\frac{k}{m}} = \frac{1}{2\pi}\sqrt{\frac{0.74[N/m]}{0.3\times10^{-6}[kg]}} \quad \textbf{(29)}$$

$$\Rightarrow \quad f = 250 \ Hz$$

This value is a good approximation for many insects, e.g. honey bees flap their wings with a frequency of about 250 Hz and mosquitos with a frequency higher than 500 Hz. The range of frequencies observed in nature is rather wide, with 4 Hz for butterflies and up to 1000 Hz for some gnats.

Solution part (b): Using Eq. (15.46) we find for the maximum speed of the tip of the inner end of the wing, which has a vertical amplitude of 0.3 mm:

$$v_{max} = \sqrt{\frac{k}{m}} \ A =$$

$$\sqrt{\frac{0.74[N/m]}{0.3\times10^{-6}[kg]}} \ 0.3\times10^{-3}[m] \quad \textbf{(30)}$$

$$\Rightarrow \quad v_{max} = 0.5 \ \frac{m}{s}$$

Solution part (c): We treat the wing as a rigid body rotating about the pivot point. Fig. 15.30 allows us to relate the maximum speed of the inner end of the wing with the maximum speed at the outer tip geometrically:

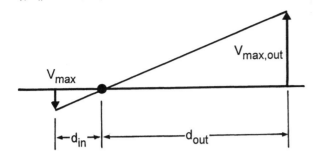

Fig. 15.30: Geometrical relation of the two ends of the wing of an insect relative to the pivot point.

$$\frac{|v_{max,\,in}|}{|v_{max,\,out}|} = \frac{l_1}{l_2} = \frac{0.5[mm]}{14[mm]}$$

(31)

$$\Rightarrow \quad |v_{max,\,out}| = 14 \frac{m}{s}$$

It is interesting to note in this context that bumble bees are among the few insects which can control their body temperature by shivering with their flight muscles. This enables these animals to live at northern latitudes and in alpine altitudes where the colder climate prevents the presence of most other insects.

Problem 15.12
The vibration frequencies of atoms in solids at room temperature are of the order of 10^{13} Hz, i.e. similar to the values shown in Table 15.3. Using a simplified model for a solid in which the atoms are connected by ideal springs we want to study how a single atom in a piece of copper vibrates with this frequency relative to surrounding atoms, which we assume are at rest.
(a) Calculate the (effective) spring constant, using the weight of 1 mol of copper from the General Appendix (Chapter 24).

Table 15.3: Vibration frequencies for various chemical bonds in organic molecules.

Bond	f [Hz]
H–O	$1.05 \times 10^{14} - 1.11 \times 10^{14}$
H–N	$9.9 \times 10^{13} - 1.05 \times 10^{14}$
H–C	$8.64 \times 10^{13} - 9.09 \times 10^{13}$
C=C	$4.8 \times 10^{13} - 5.04 \times 10^{13}$
C≡C	$6.6 \times 10^{13} - 6.78 \times 10^{13}$
C=O	$4.98 \times 10^{13} - 5.61 \times 10^{13}$

(b) What is the ratio of the (effective) spring constant of a gold atom in a piece of gold and the (effective) spring constant of the copper atom of part (a)?

Solution part (a): We start with the second formula in Eq. (15.51), writing for the spring constant k_{eff}:

$$k_{eff} = 4\pi^2 f^2 m$$

(32)

This yields:

$$k_{eff} = 4\pi^2 (1 \times 10^{13}[Hz])^2 \frac{0.06355\left[\frac{kg}{mol}\right]}{6 \times 10^{23}[mol^{-1}]}$$

(33)

$$\Rightarrow \quad k_{eff} = 420 \frac{N}{m}$$

in which we divided the atomic mass of copper by the Avogadro number to obtain the mass of a single copper atom.

It is useful to compare the value with those provided in Table 15.2 in spite of the fact that our estimate for the vibrational frequency is very coarse and that the values in Table 15.2 are given for non–metallic chemical bonds. The value we found still lies in the range of typical values for single covalent bonds.

Solution part (b): We write Eq. (32) twice, once for Au and once for Cu. Then we calculate the ratio of the two effective spring constants:

Table 15.2: Spring constants for various chemical bonds. R stands for "rest", i.e., an organic extension of the functional group.

Bond	Molecule	k [N/m]
H–Cl	HCl	484
H–O	H_2O	780
H–C	CH_3R	470 – 500
C–C		450 – 560
C=C		950 – 990
C≡C		1560 – 1700
N–N		350 – 550
C–O		500 – 580
C=O		1180 – 1340

$$\frac{k_{eff}(Au)}{k_{eff}(Cu)} = \frac{4\pi^2 f^2 \dfrac{M_{Au}}{N_A}}{4\pi^2 f^2 \dfrac{M_{Cu}}{N_A}} = \frac{M_{Au}}{M_{Cu}} \qquad \textbf{(34)}$$

substituting the molar mass for Au and Cu from the General Appendix, we find from Eq. (34):

$$\frac{k_{eff}(Au)}{k_{eff}(Cu)} = \frac{197.0[g/mol]}{63.55[g/mol]} = 3.1 \qquad \textbf{(35)}$$

CHAPTER XVI

Ear and communication: longitudinal waves

Problem 16.1

A wave with frequency 5.0 Hz and amplitude 40 mm moves in the positive x–direction with speed 6.5 m/s. What are (a) the wavelength, (b) the period, (c) the angular frequency? (d) Write a formula for the wave.

Solution part (a): The wavelength is obtained from the relation of the speed of the wave, the wavelength and the frequency given in Eq. (16.1):

$$v_{wave} = \lambda f \quad \Rightarrow \quad \lambda = \frac{v_{wave}}{f} \tag{1}$$

$$\lambda = \frac{6.5[m/s]}{5.0[1/s]} = 1.3 \ m$$

Solution part (b): The relation between period and frequency, as defined in Eq. (15.50), remains applicable to waves:

$$T = \frac{1}{f} = \frac{1}{5.0[1/s]} = 0.2 \ s \tag{2}$$

Solution part (c): Eq. (15.50) also remains applicable for the relation between the frequency and the angular frequency:

$$\omega = 2\pi f = 2\pi \ 5.0[Hz] = 10.0 \ \pi \ \frac{rad}{s} \tag{3}$$

Solution part (d): The general wave function is given in Eq. (16.14). The amplitude is given in the problem text. The angular frequency has been calculated previously in part (c). Thus, we are missing the wave number, which we determine from $\kappa = 2\pi/\lambda$ with the wavelength taken from the result in part (a):

$$\kappa = \frac{2\pi}{\lambda} = \frac{2\pi}{1.3[m]} = 1.54 \ \pi \ \frac{1}{m} \tag{4}$$

This allows us to write the wave function, using Eq. (16.14):

$$\xi = 0.04 \ \sin(10.0\pi t - 1.54\pi x) \ [m] \tag{5}$$

in which the displacement ξ is given in unit [m] and the time t must be entered in unit [s]. The two π–factors in Eq. (5) could have been entered as a numeral, writing the angular frequency as $\omega = 31.4$ rad/s and the wave number as $\kappa = 4.84$ m^{-1}. However, the notation given in Eq. (5) is beneficial when substituting specific values for time and position.

Problem 16.2

The best way to measure the compressibility of liquids or solids is to measure the speed of sound in the material. If such a measurement for water yields c = 1.4 km/s (which is about four times the value in air!), what is the compressibility of water?

Solution: The formula connecting the speed of sound in a medium and the compressibility of the medium is derived from Eq. (16.7). Noting that the compressibility is the inverse value of the bulk modulus B, we find for water from Eq. (16.7):

$$B = \rho c^2 = 1000\left[\frac{kg}{m^3}\right]\left(1400\left[\frac{m}{s}\right]\right)^2 \tag{6}$$

$$B = 2 \times 10^9 \ \frac{kg}{m \ s^2}$$

in which the unit of the bulk modulus is [Pa]. The compressibility is then the inverse value of the bulk modulus, i.e., 5×10^{-10} 1/Pa.

Problem 16.3

The range of frequencies heard by the healthy human ear stretches from about 16 Hz to 16 kHz. What are the corresponding wavelengths of sound waves at these frequencies?

Table 16.1: Speed of sound in various materials.

Material	Speed of sound [m/s]	Temperature [K]
Gases:		
Air	331	273
Air	343	293
Air	386	373
Liquids:		
Water	1400	273
Water	1490	298
Seawater (3.5% salt)	1530	298
Solids and soft matter:		
Steel	5940	
Granite	6000	
Human body tissue	1540	310
Vulcanized rubber	55	

Solution: The problem contains an implicit assumption that the hearing process takes place in air of pressure 1 atm at typical environmental temperature conditions. Using T = 20⁰C (a value close to room temperature), we obtain the speed of sound in air from Table 16.1 as c = 343 m/s. We use this value and Eq. (16.1) to analyze the lower frequency of 16 Hz first:

$$\lambda = \frac{c}{f} = \frac{343 \ [m/s]}{16 \ [Hz]} = 21.5 \ m \qquad (7)$$

In analogous fashion, the wavelength for the higher frequency follows:

$$\lambda = \frac{c}{f} = \frac{343 \ [m/s]}{16 \cdot 10^3 \ [Hz]} \qquad (8)$$

$$\Rightarrow \quad \lambda = 0.0215 \ m = 2.15 \ cm$$

The first value lies in the range of wavelengths of typical radio transmissions and the second value lies just below the wavelength of a typical microwave oven (about 12 cm). So, why do we need a radio, or why do we not hear the microwave oven (what you hear are *not* the microwaves generated in the oven)? It is important to distinguish the different types of waves. Radio– and microwaves are electromagnetic waves; such waves cannot be detected by the ear (which is sensitive only to sound waves) but are detected by the eye. The eye does not operate in the microwave or radio range of the spectrum.

Problem 16.4
Bats can detect small insects whose size is about equal to the wavelength of the sound the bat makes with its echo–location system. A bat emits a chirp at a frequency of 60 kHz. Using the speed of sound in air as 340 m/s, what is the smallest insect this bat can detect?

Solution: The wavelength of the bat's chirp is calculated from Eq. (16.1), with the wavelength isolated as the independent variable:

$$\lambda = \frac{v_{sound}}{f} = \frac{340 [m/s]}{60 \times 10^3 [s^{-1}]} = 5.7 \ mm \qquad (9)$$

Insects smaller than ½ cm in size escape undetected.

Problem 16.5
The sound intensity of 1.0×10^{-12} J/(sm²) is the threshold of hearing for human beings. What is the amplitude of the motion of the air molecules? Use c = 340 m/s and the density of air as 1.2 kg/m³.

Solution: The connection of the sound intensity and the amplitude of the sound wave in the medium is given in Eq. (16.25). We rewrite this formula with the amplitude as the independent variable:

$$A = \frac{1}{\omega} \sqrt{\frac{2I}{c\rho}} = \frac{1}{2\pi f} \sqrt{\frac{2I}{c\rho}} \qquad (10)$$

Eq. (15.50) was used to rewrite the angular frequency as the frequency f in Eq. (10). To apply Eq. (10) we need a value for the frequency. The frequency is not directly given in the problem text, but can be derived from the statement that the given value of the sound intensity is the threshold of hearing. Fig. 16.34 indicates that the greatest sensitivity of the ear is to sound of 3 kHz, which is consistent with the argument in Example 16.12. Thus, we use f = 3000 Hz in Eq. (10):

$$A = \frac{1}{2\pi \ 3000[Hz]} \sqrt{\frac{2 \cdot 1.0 \times 10^{-12} \left[\frac{J}{sm^2} \right]}{340 \left[\frac{m}{s} \right] 1.2 \left[\frac{kg}{m^3} \right]}} \qquad (11)$$

$$\Rightarrow \quad A = 3.7 \times 10^{-12} \ m$$

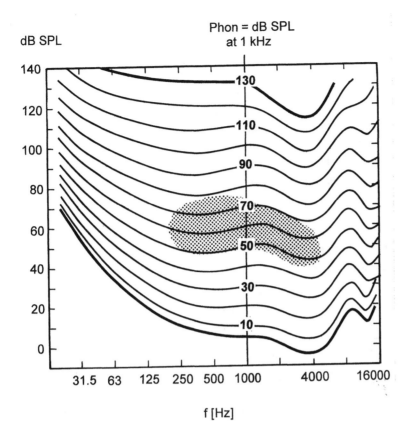

Phon = dB SPL at 1 kHz

dB SPL

f [Hz]

Fig. 16.34: The hearing range of the human ear, shown as a function of the frequency of the sound f (horizontal axis) and as a function of the sound pressure level (SPL) in [dB] (vertical axis). Each line in the plot represents sounds which are judged as equally loud. The dotted area corresponds to a normal range of conversations. The unit [phon] is defined by the dB–scale of SPL at 1 kHz.

This is an astonishing result as it represents a small fraction of the diameter of an air molecule! Hearing is indeed a technology developed by nature to its physical limits.

Problem 16.6
(a) During a 5 s time period a microphone with an area of 3 cm² receives a sound energy of 1.5×10^{-11} J. What is the intensity of the sound?
(b) Using the sound intensity from part (a), what is the variation in pressure in the sound wave, Δp?
Use T = 293 K and ρ_{air} = 1.2 kg/m³.

Solution part (a): In section 16.2.4, the intensity is defined as a measure of the amount of energy transported by a wave per time interval through a plane of unit area which is placed perpendicular to the wave's propagation direction. If we label the intensity I, the energy ΔE, the time interval Δt and the unit area A, then:

$$I = \frac{1}{A}\frac{\Delta E}{\Delta t} \qquad (12)$$

Using the quantitative values given in the problem text, we find:

$$I = \frac{1.5 \times 10^{-11}[J]}{3 \times 10^{-4}[m^2]\,5[s]} = 1 \times 10^{-6}\,\frac{J}{m^2 s} \qquad (13)$$

Solution part (b): The pressure variation Δp follows from Eq. (16.16), and the amplitude from Eq. (16.25):

$$I = \frac{1}{2}c\rho A^2\omega^2 \quad \Rightarrow \quad A = \frac{1}{\omega}\sqrt{\frac{2I}{c\rho}} \qquad (14)$$

This value is now substituted into Eq. (16.16):

$$\Delta p = c\rho\omega A = \frac{c\rho\omega}{\omega}\sqrt{\frac{2I}{c\rho}} = \sqrt{2Ic\rho} \qquad (15)$$

Eq. (15) allows us now to substitute the numerical values given in the problem and in part (a):

$$\Delta p = \sqrt{2\,1\times10^{-6}\left[\frac{J}{m^2 s}\right]343\left[\frac{m}{s}\right]1.2\left[\frac{kg}{m^3}\right]} \qquad (16)$$

$$\Rightarrow \quad \Delta p = 2.9 \times 10^{-2}\,Pa$$

The speed of sound was taken from Table 16.1, using

129

the temperature given in the problem text to select the proper value. Note once more how small these pressure variations in sound waves usually are, the value in Eq. (16) corresponds to 29 mPa!

Problem 16.7
A jet airplane has a sound intensity $I = 100$ J/(sm²) when heard at a distance of 30 m.
(a) What is the maximum sound intensity heard by a person on the ground when the airplane cruises 5000 m above the ground?
(b) What is the intensity level IL heard?

Solution part (a): We use Eq. (16.31), which illustrates the relation of sound intensity at two different distances from a point sound source:

$$I_2 = \frac{r_1^2}{r_2^2} I_1 = \left(\frac{30[m]}{5000[m]} \right)^2 100 \left[\frac{J}{m^2 s} \right] \qquad (17)$$

$$\Rightarrow \quad I_2 = 3.6 \times 10^{-3} \frac{J}{m^2 s}$$

Solution part (b): The intensity level for this sound intensity is determined from Eq. (16.27):

$$IL = 10 \log_{10} \frac{I}{I_0} =$$

$$10 \log \left(\frac{3.6 \times 10^{-3} \left[\frac{J}{m^2 s} \right]}{1 \times 10^{-12} \left[\frac{J}{m^2 s} \right]} \right) = 95.6 \ dB \qquad (18)$$

Using Fig. 16.34 and assuming that the frequencies of this sound fall well within the range audible to humans, we note that the sound of a jet engine at that large distance is still significantly louder than a normal conversation! This is one reason why commercial airplanes fly at altitudes of about 10 km when passing over land.

Problem 16.8
A certain sound has an intensity which is four times the intensity of a reference sound at the same frequency.
(a) What is the difference in the intensity level of the two sounds?
(b) If the reference sound causes a sound perception of 60 phon, what is the sound perception value of the more intense sound?

Solution part (a): We use Eq. (16.27) for the relation between sound intensity and intensity level, IL. Identifying the sound of interest by index 1 and the reference sound by index 2, we write the information given in the problem as $I_1/I_2 = 4$. We use Eq. (16.27) then to calculate the difference in the intensity levels of the two sounds:

$$IL_1 - IL_2 = 10 \left(\log_{10} \frac{I_1}{I_0} - \log_{10} \frac{I_2}{I_0} \right) = $$

$$\qquad (19)$$

$$10 \left(\log_{10} \frac{I_1}{I_2} \right) = 10 \log_{10} 4 = 6.0 \ dB$$

Thus, the difference between the two sounds amounts to 6 dB, regardless of the absolute intensity of the sounds.

Solution part (b): Answering this question is straight forward for a sound of 1 kHz, i.e., at the only frequency where the decibel scale and the phon scale are equal. At that frequency the louder sound has 66 phon. Fig. 16.34 indicates that this relation is approximately correct in the range from 200 Hz to 2000 Hz, i.e., essentially across the frequency range of the human voice during a conversation. At other frequencies, the sound perception would have to be converted to an intensity level using Fig. 16.34, and the louder sound has to be converted back to the phon scale at the same frequency.

Problem 16.9
Why is it not possible for two divers to communicate by talking under water?

Solution: Water can carry sound quite effectively. Otherwise, sea mammals such as whales and dolphins could not rely on sound for communication. However, the sound transport between media of low density (air) and high density (water) is very ineffective, as illustrated in section 16.4, where we calculated in Eq. (16.61) that only about 0.1 % of the intensity transfers. Different from the dolphin or whale, a diver must maintain an air–filled vocal tract since he/she otherwise drowns.

This is also the reason why standard microphones are useless for underwater–recording. The proper device is water–filled and is called a _hydrophone_.

Problem 16.10

Ultrasound echo–location is used by bats to enable them to fly and hunt in the dark. The ultrasound used by bats has frequencies in the range from 60 kHz to 100 kHz. We consider a bat which uses an ultrasound frequency of 90 kHz and flies with a speed of 10 m/s. What is the frequency of the echo the bat hears which is reflected off an insect which moves towards the bat with a speed of 3 m/s?

Solution: The solution is based on the same approach taken in section 16.5.3: since both the bat and the insect move, we have to combine the two separate Doppler effect cases, Eqs. (16.68) and (16.70). Different from the derivation in section 16.5.3, however, we have to take different speeds of the source (insect) and the receiver (bat) into account. Thus, we derive the combined formula, which we call the general Doppler effect, in the same fashion as Eq. (16.72) is derived, but with v_s the speed of the source and v_r the speed of the receiver. Analogous to Eq. (16.72) we find:

$$f_{rec} = f_{emit} \left(\frac{1 + v_r/c}{1 - v_s/c} \right) \qquad (20)$$

in which f_{emit} is the frequency emitted by the bat and f_{rec} is the frequency received by the bat after reflection off the insect. The + sign in the numerator of Eq. (20) is due to the motion of the receiver *toward* the source and the − sign in the denominator is due to the motion of the source *toward* the receiver. Either of the signs changes if the respective animal would move away from the other. We substitute the given values in the problem text into Eq. (20):

$$f_{rec} = 9 \cdot 10^4 [Hz] \left(\frac{1 + \dfrac{10[m/s]}{343[m/s]}}{1 - \dfrac{3[m/s]}{343[m/s]}} \right) \qquad (21)$$

$$\Rightarrow \quad f_{rec} = 93.4 \; kHz$$

in which we used 343 m/s for the speed of sound in air.

Problem 16.11

Table 16.6 presents the frequencies of the eight C keys and the neighboring D keys on a well–tuned piano. When you hit the C and D keys together, for which cases do you expect to hear a beat and what is its frequency?

Table 16.6: Frequencies of piano keys

Octave n	f [Hz]: C_n	f [Hz]: D_n
0	16.35	18.35
1	32.70	36.71
2	65.41	73.42
3	130.8	146.8
4	261.6	293.7
5	523.3	587.3
6	1046	1175
7	2093	2349
8	4186	4699

Solution: The beat effect has been discussed in section 16.5.2. A beat is heard (instead of two distinguishable sounds) if the difference in frequency is less than 15 Hz. Table 16.7 shows the beat frequency and the frequency of the single sound heart.

Table 16.7: Beat frequencies and frequencies of single sound heart for Table 16.6.

Octave n	½Δf [Hz]	f_{beat} [Hz]
0	1.0 = yes	17.35
1	2.0 = yes	34.71
2	4.0 = yes	69.41
3	8.0 = yes/no	138.8
4	16.0	
5	32.0	
6	64.5	
7	128.0	
8	256.5	

Problem 16.12

There is a hypothesis saying that the upper limit in frequency a human ear can hear can be determined by the diameter of the eardrum, which should have approximately the same diameter as the wavelength at the upper limit. If we use this hypothesis, what would be the radius of the eardrum for a person able to hear frequencies up to 18.5 kHz?

Solution: We use Eq. (16.1), relating the speed of sound, the wavelength and the frequency of the sound. With the frequency given in the problem text, the diameter of the eardrum can be determined using the speed of sound. Since the speed of sound depends on the temperature of air, we need to make an assumption regarding the tem-

131

perature of the air in the outer ear. The value lies somewhere between the environmental temperature and the body temperature. The respective speed of sound is then determined from Table 16.1 and Eq. (16.10), with the latter requiring the assumption that air is an ideal gas. Depending on your pick of temperature, you will use a value of c between 343 m/s (20^0C) and 353 m/s (37^0C). In the calculation below the speed of sound at 20 ^{0}C is used.

For the calculation we note that the problem asks for the radius of the eardrum, while the diameter is linked to the wavelength. Thus, we use $2r_{eardrum} = \lambda_{max}$:

$$r_{eardrum} = \frac{1}{2}\frac{c}{f_{max}} = \frac{1}{2}\frac{343\left[\frac{m}{s}\right]}{1.85\times10^4\left[\frac{1}{s}\right]} \quad \text{(22)}$$

$$\Rightarrow \quad r_{eardrum} = 9.3\times10^{-3}\ m = 9.3\ mm$$

Problem 16.13
Neglecting the additional delay due to the difference in sound pressure levels, we want to verify the statement made in section 16.5.1 that stereoscopic hearing is based on a delay in the time the sound travels to the farther ear. Using Fig. 16.43 for a sound source far from the person, we define d as the distance between both ears and θ as the angle between the direction of the sound source and the direction perpendicular to the line connecting both ears.
(a) Find a formula for the time delay Δt of the sound from the source at very large distance as a function of d and θ.

(b) Calculate the delay for the same sound source at $\theta = 45^0$ for d = 16 cm.

Solution part (a): The time delay Δt is derived from the extra distance the sound travels to the farther ear, and the speed of sound, c. The additional distance is determined geometrically from Fig. 16.43 as $d\sin\theta$. Thus:

$$c = \frac{d\sin\theta}{\Delta t} \quad \Rightarrow \quad \Delta t = \frac{d\sin\theta}{c} \quad \text{(23)}$$

Solution part (b): This part allows us to quantify the effect discussed in part (a). Using the speed of sound in air at 20^0C as c = 343 m/s, we find:

$$\Delta t = \frac{d\sin\theta}{c} = \frac{0.16[m]\sin45^0}{343[m/s]} \quad \text{(24)}$$

$$\Rightarrow \quad \Delta t = 3.3 \times 10^{-4}\ s = 0.33\ ms$$

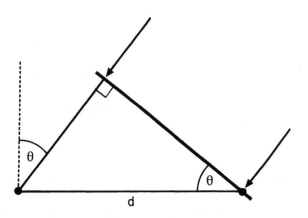

Fig. 16.43 for problem P–16.13

132

CHAPTER XVII

The eye: ray model of light (geometric optics)

Problem 17.1
When you look at your face in a small bathroom mirror from a distance of 40 cm, the upright image is twice as tall as your face. What is the focal length of the mirror?

Solution: The distance given in the text is the object distance, $p = 0.4$ m. The mirror is a spherical mirror since the only other type of mirrors we discuss in the textbook, i.e., the flat mirror, does not generate magnified images. We can use the mirror equation (Eq. (17.8)) to determine the focal length f if we can first identify the image length q. To obtain q we use the information about the magnification of the mirror: M = +2.0 since an upright image is associated with a positive magnification (based on the conventions of Table 17.1). Therefore, Eq. (17.11) yields:

$$M = -\frac{q}{p} = 2 \quad \quad \text{(1)}$$

$$\Rightarrow \quad q = -2p = -0.8 \; m$$

With this value for the image length, the mirror equation yields:

$$\frac{1}{f} = \frac{1}{p} + \frac{1}{q} = \frac{1}{0.4[m]} - \frac{1}{0.8[m]} \quad \text{(2)}$$

$$\Rightarrow \quad f = +0.8 \; m$$

The mirror is concave because the resulting value for the focal length is positive. Note that 80 cm is a rather large focal length, corresponding to a radius of curvature of the mirror of R = 1.6 m.

Problem 17.2
Optometrists use the *Snellen test* to evaluate the vision of their patients. The Snellen test consists of letters of different sizes which a person with healthy eyes can read at particular distances. The patient is 20 feet (6.1 m) from the chart and has to read the letters. If the patient's eyes are healthy, he/she will read the same line without errors, which the healthy reference group was able to read at that distance. We call this therefore 20/20 vision. A juvenile may have 20/10 vision, which means that he/she can read a line a healthy adult can only read at a distance of 10 feet (3.05 m). Vision impaired patients may score as low as 20/200, which corresponds to the single, largest letter at the top of the Snellen test. A person with healthy eyes can read that letter as far away as 200 feet (61 m) which coincides with the distance at which the eye is accommodated for vision of objects at infinite distance.

Many optometrists have offices in a mall with high rent. To keep the cost down, the examination room may only have a length of 4 meters with the patient sitting at the examination instruments near the center of the room. Suggest an appropriate set–up for the Snellen test in this room.

Solution: The easiest way, mounting the Snellen Chart 20 feet away from the person and have the patient read

Table 17.1: Sign conventions for mirrors. These conventions are used when the mirror equation is applied.

p is positive	Object is in front of mirror (real object)
p is negative	Object is in back of the mirror (virtual object)
q is positive	Image is in front of mirror (real image)
q is negative	Image is in back of mirror (virtual image)
f and R are positive	Center of curvature is in front of mirror (concave mirror)
f and R are negative	Center of curvature is in back of mirror (convex mirror)
M is positive	Image is upright
M is negative	Image is inverted

line by line, is not possible as the problem text already implies. You could diminish the size of the Snellen chart such that the letters appear as large at 2 meters distance as if the original chart were 6 meters away from the eye. However, there are differences between near and far vision and the result would not be comparable with the 20/20 group. Indeed, there exists a second Snellen chart for reading which is a similar chart but printed significantly smaller. This is used, however, for a different purpose.

A second proposal to the optometrist would be to use a mirror (and a slide projector with a slide containing the Snellen chart). This approach has two draw–backs. First, the slide would have to be a mirror–inverted photograph because a projection through a single mirror inverts the letters. Note that this is recognized by some police forces in Europe; they have printed *police* mirror–inverted on the hood of their cruisers such that people seeing them in their rear mirror recognize and respond quicker in the anticipated fashion. The more crucial draw–back for the optometrist in the small mall office can be derived from Fig. 17.7: the apparent distance of the chart for the patient is the sum of the distance of the patient to the wall with the mirror plus the distance of the projector to the wall, called d in Fig. 17.7. To arrange for the sum of these two distances to be 20 feet, or 6.1 m, limits the flexibility of placing the diagnostic instruments and the projector in the room.

Thus, in most offices you will find a projector with two mirrors at opposite walls. In this case, the projector is placed near the rear wall mirror and the distance d in Fig. 17.7 becomes the length of the room. This arrangement with two mirrors also allows the slide to carry the Snellen test without inversion of the letters.

Problem 17.3
A concave spherical mirror has a radius of curvature of 20 cm. Locate the images for object distances as given below. In each case, state whether the image is real or virtual and upright or inverted, and find the magnification.
(a) p = 10 cm
(b) p = 20 cm
(c) p = 40 cm

Solution part (a): We know from Table 17.1 that both, the radius of curvature R and the focal length f, are positive for a concave mirror. Thus, we know that the focal length f = R/2 = 10.0 cm. We answer the question for each of the three cases using the mirror equation (Eq. (17.8)) and the equation for the magnification given in Eq. (17.11): for p = 10.0 cm:

$$\frac{1}{q} = \frac{1}{f} - \frac{1}{p} = \frac{1}{0.1[m]} - \frac{1}{0.1[m]} = 0 \tag{3}$$
$$\Rightarrow \quad q = \infty$$

This means that there is no image formed in the first case. The light rays are reflected in the mirror such that they travel parallel to each other.

Solution part (b): For p = 20.0 cm:

$$\frac{1}{q} = \frac{1}{f} - \frac{1}{p} = \frac{1}{0.1[m]} - \frac{1}{0.2[m]} \tag{4}$$
$$\Rightarrow \quad q = 0.2 \ m$$

and the magnification is:

$$M = -\frac{q}{p} = -\frac{0.2[m]}{0.2[m]} = -1.0 \tag{5}$$

Thus, the image is formed 20 cm in front of the mirror; it is real and inverted and of the same size as the object.

Solution part (c): For p = 40.0 cm:

$$\frac{1}{q} = \frac{1}{f} - \frac{1}{p} = \frac{1}{0.1[m]} - \frac{1}{0.4[m]} \tag{6}$$
$$\Rightarrow \quad q = 13.33 \ cm$$

and the magnification is:

$$M = -\frac{q}{p} = -\frac{13.33[cm]}{40.0[cm]} = -0.333 \tag{7}$$

Thus, the image is formed 13.3 cm in front of the mirror; it is again real and inverted. This time the image is smaller than the object size (33 %).

Problem 17.4
Construct the images for the three objects shown in Fig. 17.31 (this figure is shown in the textbook only).

Solution: The three sketches are shown in Fig. 17.35.

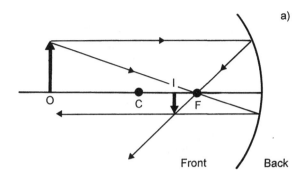

a)

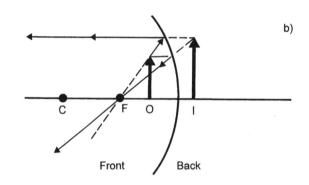

b)

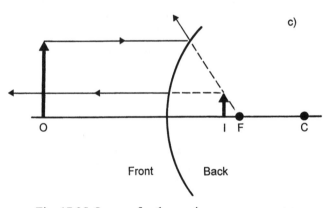

c)

Fig. 17.35: Images for three mirror arrangements.

Problem 17.5

When you look at yourself in a flat mirror, you see yourself with left and right sides switched, but not upside down. How come?

Hint: Remember that you are a three–dimensional body. Study the image of the following three vectors: (I) head to foot, (II) left to right hand and (III) nose to back of head. The remainder of the puzzle is perception of the brain!

Solution: Let's go over that image you see in the mirror

in detail. Note that what is at the left side of yours remains at the left side in the image. Further, your head is at the top in the image as it is at the top of the object. Thus, two of the three axis which define a Cartesian coordinate system did not change. The mirror image still does not represent the object in its three–dimensional form as the third direction, the direction towards the mirror, is inverted. What is in front of you towards the mirror (let's define this as the positive y–axis) is located in the direction of the negative y–axis relative to your image.

At this point our brain is unwilling to contemplate the physical facts, it goes beyond comprehension to mirror a person front to back. Thus, the brain does not accept the physically correct change. Since the fact remains that the person in the image is different, the brain must consequently interpret this difference in another way. The way chosen is the least confusing to the observer: since our body possesses essentially a middle axis plane, to which we like to refer often ("left" versus "right"), the easy way out is to interpret the image as left–right switched.

This is a first example highlighting in the discussion of optics how powerful our brain is and how crucial a role it takes in observing the world around us. It is indeed capable to dismiss the real, measured impression, as communicated by the external sensors like the eye, and replace it by something which one has to accept has all the features of a "make–belief". While voluntary alterations of the facts are a domain of psychology, involuntary alterations of facts due to the mechanisms of the brain and the brain/external sensor interfaces are a domain of psychophysics. Pointing out such phenomena is done frequently in the text and in the problem sets.

Problem 17.6

A light ray enters a layer of water at an angle of 36^0 with the vertical. What is the angle between the refracted light ray and the vertical?

Solution: We use the law of refraction as derived in Eq. (17.16). For air we use $n_1 = 1.0$ and $\alpha_1 = 36^0$. For water we use from Table 17.2 the index of refraction of $n_2 = 1.33$. Thus:

$$n_1 \sin\alpha_1 = n_2 \sin\alpha_2$$

$$\sin\alpha_2 = \frac{1.0}{1.33} \sin 36^0 \quad \Rightarrow \quad \alpha_2 = 26^0 \tag{8}$$

135

Table 17.2: Index of refraction for various materials

Material	Index of refraction
Solids at 20^0C	
Diamond (C)	2.42
Sapphire (Al_2O_3)	1.77
Fluorite (CaF_2)	1.43
Fused quartz (SiO_2)	1.46
Crown Glass	1.52
Flint Glass	1.61
Ice (H_2O, at 0^0C)	1.31
Sodium chloride (NaCl)	1.54
Liquids at 20^0C	
Benzene (C_6H_6)	1.50
Carbon tetrachloride (CCl_4)	1.46
Ethanol (C_2H_5OH)	1.36
Glycerine	1.47
Water (H_2O)	1.33
Sugar solution (30%)	1.38
Sugar solution (80%)	1.49
Gases at 20^0C and 1 atm	
Air	1.00027
Carbon dioxide (CO_2, at 0^0C)	1.00045
Vacuum	1.0

Problem 17.7

A light ray strikes the flat, L = 2.0 cm thick block of glass (n = 1.5) in Fig. 17.32 at an angle of $\theta = 30^0$ with the normal.

(a) Find the angles of incidence and refraction at each surface.
(b) Calculate the lateral shift of the light ray, d.

Solution part (a) : We use the law of refraction at the first interface from air to glass, labelling the angles of incidence and refraction with θ:

$$n_{air}\sin\theta_{air} = n_{glass}\sin\theta_{glass}$$

$$\sin\theta_{glass} = \frac{1.0}{1.5}\sin 30^0 \Rightarrow \theta_{glass} = 19.5^0 \quad\text{(9)}$$

For the second interface from glass to air, we have to read Eq. (9) backwards and find $\theta_{air} = 30^0$. This result is expected as the interface and all the parameters of the light ray exactly mirror the conditions at the first interface (compare the discussion in Example 17.2).

Solution part (b): The distance the light ray travels through the glass is obtained geometrically. Fig. 17.36 illustrates the incident beam (which is extended through the glass slab for geometric construction purposes resulting in the line AD), the refracted beam (line AC) and the direction across the glass slab perpendicular to the two parallel glass surfaces (line AB, with a length of 2.0 cm as given in the problem text). The distance h we seek is equal to the distance between points A and C. We introduce further the label α for the angle between lines AC and AD, which defines the angle α as $\alpha = \theta_1 - \theta_2$.

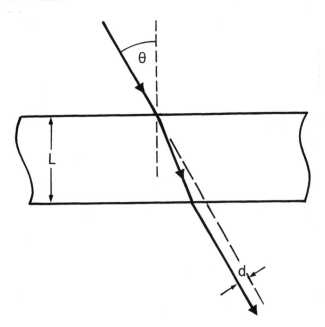

Fig. 17.32 for problem P–17.7.

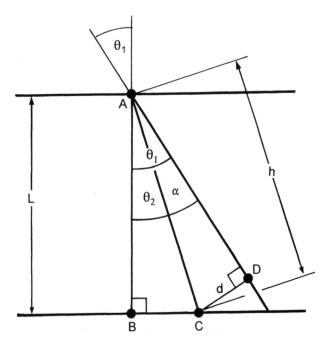

Fig. 17.36: Geometry of a refracted light ray in a transparent slab with two parallel surfaces.

136

Now we use Fig. 17.36 to quantify the length h based on the triangle ABC:

$$\cos\theta_2 = \frac{AB}{AC} = \frac{2[cm]}{h}$$

$$h = \frac{2[cm]}{\cos 19.5^0} = 2.12 \ cm \tag{10}$$

This does not answer the question, however, since the lateral shift is sought. The lateral shift d is shown in Fig. 17.36 as well. The length of d is obtained from the triangle ACD. With $\alpha = \theta_1 - \theta_2 = 30^0 - 19.5^0 = 10.5^0$ we find:

$$d = h \sin\alpha = 2.12[cm] \ \sin 10.5^0$$

$$\Rightarrow \quad d = 0.386 \ cm \tag{11}$$

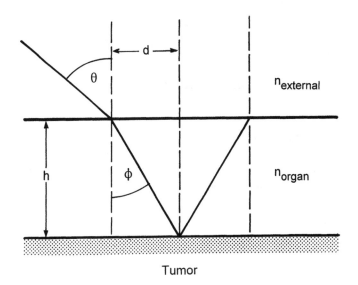

Fig. 17.37: Geometry of the incoming and reflected light rays for a tumor located below the surface of an organ.

Problem 17.8

In Fig. 17.33, an ultrasonic beam reflects off a tumor (dotted) in an organ (shaded) at $\theta = 50^0$ with a shift L = 12 cm. If the speed of the wave is 10 % less in the organ than in the medium above, determine the depth of the tumor below the organ's surface.

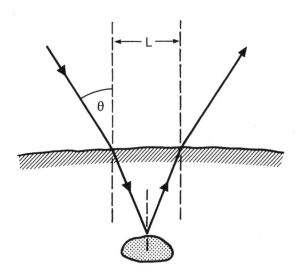

Fig. 17.33 for problem P–17.8.

Solution: The depth h of the tumor below the organ surface is calculated from the lateral displacement d of the ultrasound ray, as defined in Fig. 17.37, and the angle between the ultrasound ray and the direction perpendicular to the tumor surface, ϕ.

Fig. 17.37 defines the length d as the lateral dis-

placement of the ultrasound ray while it travels from the surface of the organ to the tumor. Due to the symmetry of the paths of the ray in the organ, the figure illustrates that the length d is one half of the total displacement L within the organ, i.e., d = 12.0 [cm]/2 = 6.0 cm. We need only to analyze the incoming ray, therefore, to solve the problem.

The angle ϕ is found from Snell's law, applied at the interface between the external medium and the organ. With the ultrasound ray incident at an angle of 50^0 with the direction perpendicular to the organ's surface, we find:

$$n_{extern} \ \sin 50^0 = n_{organ} \ \sin\phi$$

$$\Rightarrow \quad \frac{\sin\phi}{\sin 50^0} = \frac{n_{extern}}{n_{organ}} = \frac{v_{organ}}{v_{extern}} \tag{12}$$

in which the last formula is the result of applying Eq. (17.15). With the ratio of speeds of sound for the various tissue materials given in the problem text, we find:

$$\sin\phi = 0.9 \ \sin 50^0 \quad \Rightarrow \quad \phi = 43.6^0 \tag{13}$$

Combining the values for d and ϕ we obtain from Fig. 17.37 trigonometrically:

$$h = \frac{d}{\tan(43.6^0)} = 6.3 \ cm \tag{14}$$

Problem 17.9

Construct the images for the three lenses shown in Fig. 17.34 (this figure is only shown in the textbook). Note that the third case is a diverging lens.

Solution: The three sketches are shown in Fig. 17.38.

Problem 17.10

A converging lens has a focal length f = 20.0 cm. Locate the images for the object distances given below. For each case state whether the image is real or virtual and upright or inverted, and find the magnification.
(a) 40 cm
(b) 20 cm
(c) 10 cm

Solution part (a): The focal length f is positive for a converging lens as stated in Table 17.4. To solve the problem, the thin lens formula from Eq. (17.34) and the magnification from Eq. (17.29) are used, with f = + 20.0 cm. For p = 40.0 cm, we find:

$$\frac{1}{q} = \frac{1}{f} - \frac{1}{p} = \frac{1}{20[cm]} - \frac{1}{40[cm]} \quad (15)$$

$$\Rightarrow \quad q = 40.0 \ cm$$

and

$$M = -\frac{q}{p} = -\frac{40[cm]}{40[cm]} = -1.0 \quad (16)$$

The image is real and inverted. It is located 40.0 cm behind the lens. The image has the same size as the object.

Solution part (b): For p = 20.0 cm, we find:

$$\frac{1}{q} = \frac{1}{f} - \frac{1}{p} = \frac{1}{20[cm]} - \frac{1}{20[cm]} \quad (17)$$

$$\Rightarrow \quad q = \infty$$

a)

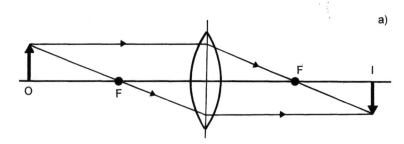

b)

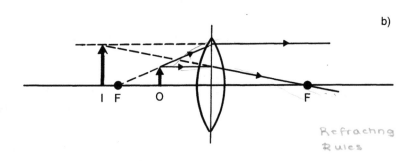

Refracting
Rules

c)

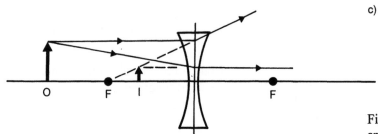

Fig. 17.38: Images for three lens arrangements.

138

Thus, no image is formed. The light rays emerging from the lens travel parallel to each other.

Solution part (c): For p = 10.0 cm, we find:

$$\frac{1}{q} = \frac{1}{f} - \frac{1}{p} = \frac{1}{20[cm]} - \frac{1}{10[cm]} \quad \textbf{(18)}$$

$$\Rightarrow \quad q = -20.0 \ [cm]$$

and

$$M = -\frac{q}{p} = -\left(\frac{-20[cm]}{10[cm]}\right) = +2.0 \quad \textbf{(19)}$$

The image is upright and virtual. It is located 20.0 cm in front of the lens. It is also twice as large as the object.

Problem 17.11
Where must an object be placed to have no magnification ($|M| = 1.0$) for a converging lens with f = 12.0 cm?

Solution: From Eq. (17.29) we note that the condition of no magnification is quantified in the form:

$$|M| = 1.0 = -\frac{q}{p} \quad \textbf{(20)}$$

Eq. (20) allows us to eliminate one of the three lengths in the thin lens formula. Eliminating q, we find:

$$\frac{1}{p} + \frac{1}{q} = \frac{1}{f} = \frac{1}{p} - \frac{1}{|M|p}$$

$$\Rightarrow \quad p = f\left(1 - \frac{1}{|M|}\right) \quad \textbf{(21)}$$

For a converging lens, the focal length is positive (see Table 17.4), i.e., f = + 12.0 cm. Since only the magnitude of the magnification is given, we distinguish two cases:
(I) if M = + 1.0 then Eq. (21) yields p = 0. This is an unreasonable solution since the object is touching the lens.
(II) if M = − 1.0 then Eq. (21) yields p = 24.0 cm. This is the solution we sought.

Problem 17.12
A person can see an object focussed only if the object is no further than 30 cm from the right eye and 50 cm from the left eye. Write a prescription for the refractive powers $\Re$ (in diopters) for the corrective lenses.

Solution: We answer the question for the right eye and the left eye separately.

For the right eye to see all objects well focussed, a lens has to be placed in front of the eye such that objects at distances larger than 30 cm from the eye are replaced with the virtual image at 30 cm or less in front of the eye. The eye then looks at the virtual image (as the eye's object) and forms a focussed image on the retina.

To quantify the prescription, we choose an object at infinite distance, p = ∞, and require the image at 30 cm in front of the prescription lens: q = − 30.0 cm (see Table 17.4). Note that we neglect in this calculation the distance between the prescription lens and the lens of the eye. We calculate the focal length of the prescription lens using the thin lens formula (Eq. (17.34)):

$$\frac{1}{f} = \frac{1}{p} + \frac{1}{q} \quad \Rightarrow \quad f = q = -30 \ cm \quad \textbf{(22)}$$

A negative focal length means that the prescription is for a diverging lens. Using the definition for the refractive power of a lens as given in Eq. (17.35) we find from Eq. (22):

Table 17.4: Sign conventions for thin lenses. These conventions are used when the thin lens formula and related relations for thin lenses are applied. Note two radii: R_1 is the radius of curvature of the front surface of the lens and R_2 is the radius of curvature of the back surface of the lens. These are used when the Lens maker's equation (introduced in the Appendix of the chapter) is applied.

p is positive	Object is in front of the lens
p is negative	Object is in back of the lens
q is positive	Image is in back of the lens
q is negative	Image is in front of the lens
R_1 and R_2 are positive	Center of curvature for each surface is in back of the lens
R_1 and R_2 are negative	Center of curvature for each surface is in front of the lens
f is positive	Converging lens
f is negative	Diverging lens

$$\Re = \frac{1}{f\,[m]} = \frac{1}{-0.3\,[m]} = -3.33\ dpt \quad (23)$$

For the left eye, the same calculations are repeated with q = – 50.0 cm. This leads to a focal length f = – 50 cm and to a refractive power of the lens of $\Re$ = – 2.0 dpt.

Problem 17.13
The near point of an eye is 100 cm. A corrective lens is to be used to allow this eye to focus clearly on objects 25 cm in front of it.
(a) What should be the focal length of the lens?
(b) What is the refractive power $\Re$ of the lens?

Solution part (a): We use the thin lens formula (Eq. (17.34)) to determine the focal length of the prescription lens. The text identifies the distance to the object as p = 25.0 cm. The prescription lens must form a virtual image at a distance q = – 100.0 cm since the image of the prescription lens serves as the object for the eye's lens. We find therefore:

$$\frac{1}{f} = \frac{1}{p} + \frac{1}{q} = \frac{1}{25\,[cm]} + \frac{1}{-100\,[cm]} \quad (24)$$
$$\Rightarrow\ f = 33.3\ cm$$

Solution part (b): We use Eq. (17.35) to convert the result in Eq. (24) into a refractive power:

$$\Re = \frac{1}{f} = \frac{1}{0.333\,[m]} = +3.0\ dpt \quad (25)$$

Problem 17.14
A person, who can see clearly when objects are between 30 cm and 1.5 m from the eye, is to be fitted with bifocals.
(a) The upper portion of the corrective glasses are designed such that the person can see distant objects clearly. What refractive power $\Re$ does that part of the glasses have?
(b) The lower portions of the glasses has to enable the person to see objects comfortably at 25 cm. What refractive power $\Re$ does that part of the glasses have?

Solution part (a): To correct nearsightedness (myopia)

we follow the arguments presented with Fig. 17.26: prescription glasses must convert an object at infinite distance, p = ∞, into a virtual image located at the farthest point the eye can see clearly. For the upper part of the prescription glasses this means q = – 1.5 m, allowing us to calculate the focal length from the thin lens formula (Eq. (17.34)):

$$\frac{1}{f} = \frac{1}{p} + \frac{1}{q} = 0 + \frac{1}{-1.5\,[m]} \quad (26)$$
$$\Rightarrow\ f = -1.5\ m$$

in which the negative value for the focal length f means that the lens must be diverging (see Table 17.4). From Eq. (26) we calculate the refractive power of the lenses, using Eq. (17.35). We obtain the value $\Re$ = – 0.67 dpt.

Solution part (b): The lower part of the lens is supposed to correct for farsightedness. This case has been discussed with Fig. 17.25 (hyperopia). Following the rationale presented there we require that objects at the desired near point of vision (p = s_0 = 25 cm) have to form a virtual image at the actual near point of the patient which is in the current case at q = – 0.30 cm. Note that this image is virtual as it must be formed on the same side of the lens where the object as located to enable the eye to look at it. With these data we use the thin lens formula again to determine the focal length of the prescription lenses:

$$\frac{1}{f} = \frac{1}{p} + \frac{1}{q} = \frac{1}{0.25\,[m]} + \frac{1}{-0.3\,[m]} \quad (27)$$
$$\Rightarrow\ f = +1.5\ m$$

The positive value of the focal length found in Eq. (27) means that the lenses are converging as shown in Table 17.4. Using Eq. (17.35) we find for the refractive power $\Re$ = + 0.67 dpt.

Problem 17.15
The near point of an eye is 75.0 cm.
(a) What should be the refractive power $\Re$ of a corrective lens prescribed to enable the patient to see an object clearly at 25.0 cm?
(b) If, using these corrective glasses, the patient can see an object clearly at 26.0 cm but not at 25.0 cm, by how many diopters did the lens grinder miss the prescription?

Solution part (a): The near point at 75.0 cm means that the person cannot see objects clearly which are closer than that distance from the eye. Reading is therefore a problem and the person will see an optometrist.

The optometrist prescribes corrective glasses such that the patient can see clearly (e.g. read a text) at a distance of 25 cm. Thus, for an object placed at object distance p = + 25.0 cm the prescribed lens must form a virtual image at q = − 75.0 cm at which the patient's eye then can look. We calculate for this situation the focal length of the prescribed lens from the thin lens formula:

$$\frac{1}{f} = \frac{1}{p} + \frac{1}{q} = \frac{1}{25[cm]} + \frac{1}{-75[cm]} \quad (28)$$

$$\Rightarrow \quad f = 37.5 \ cm$$

We calculate the refractive power from the focal length in Eq. (28) as $\Re = 1/f = 2.67$ dpt.

Solution part (b): We repeat the calculation of part (a) except that we use p = 26.0 cm for the prescription lens. Substituting this value in Eq. (28) we find for the actual focal length f = 39.8 cm and for the actual refractive power $\Re = 2.51$ dpt. Thus, the error is 0.16 dpt.

Problem 17.16
(a) Some gardeners advice against watering flowers in full sun shine to avoid burns to leaves due to the focusing effect of water droplets. Is this advice reasonable? Hint: Treat the water droplet as a sphere placed on the leaf and use the thin lens formula.
(b) For the plant scientists: do you know why it is still not a good idea to water the flowers in full sun light?

Solution part (a): Fig. 17.39 illustrates a spherical droplet of radius R on a flat leaf surface. We treat the droplet as a thin lens, and thus, use the thin lens formula, Eq. (17.34). Combined with the lens maker's equation, which we derived in the Appendix of the chapter as Eq. (17.57), the formula reads:

$$\frac{1}{f} = (n - 1)\left(\frac{1}{R_1} - \frac{1}{R_2}\right) \quad (29)$$

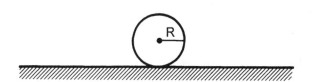

Fig. 17.39: A spherical water droplet on a flat leaf surface.

Using Fig. 17.39 we note that $- R_1 = R_2$ due to the symmetry of the two water–air interfaces of the droplet, i.e., one radius is measured behind the interface and one radius is measured in front of the interface (as defined in Table 17.4). Defining $- R_1 = R_2 = R$ and obtaining the indices of refraction from Table 17.2, we obtain:

$$\frac{1}{f} = (1.33 - 1.00)\left(\frac{2}{R}\right) \Rightarrow f = 1.5 \ R \quad (30)$$

Since we treat in this calculation the sphere as a thin lens, the focal length f is measured from the center of the spherical droplet. Thus, the sun light would only be focussed deep in the leaf with no noticeable focussing at the surface, i.e., at distance R from the center of the droplet. Thus, the alleged burning can not take place.

Solution part (b): Plant cells, like all other living cells, can get undercooled, i.e., also plants can catch a cold. The undercooling results when the water droplets on the leaf evaporate, removing for this process the latent heat of evaporation from the leaf. You can test this effect by spraying water on your skin and blowing over the skin to let the water evaporate. Where a water droplet sits on the skin you feel a cooling effect.

Problem 17.17
A contact lens is made of plastic with an index of refraction of n = 1.58. The lens has a focal length of f = +25.0 cm, and its inner surface has a radius of curvature of +18.0 mm. What is the outer radius of curvature?

Solution: This problem requires the same combination of thin lens formula and lens maker's equation we used in the previous problem to derive Eq. (29). Note that we consider the same medium on both sides of the lens (as we considered air on both sides of the water droplet in the previous problem). We substitute the given values of n = 1.58, f = + 25 cm and R_2 = + 1.8 cm into Eq. (29):

$$\frac{1}{n - 1}\left(\frac{1}{f} + (n - 1)\frac{1}{R_2}\right) = \frac{1}{R_1}$$

$$\Rightarrow \quad R_1 = \frac{(n - 1) f R_2}{(n - 1) f + R_2} \quad (31)$$

which yields:

$$R_1 = + 1.6 \ cm = + 16 \ mm \quad (32)$$

CHAPTER XVIII

The microbial world: microscopy

Problem 18.1
Two converging lenses which have focal lengths of $f_1 =$ 10.0 cm and $f_2 = 20.0$ cm are placed L = 50 cm apart. The final image is shown in Fig. 18.10.
(a) How far to the left of the first lens is the object placed if $l = 31$ cm?
(b) What is the combined magnification (not the total angular magnification in this case!) of the two lenses using the same data as in part (a)?

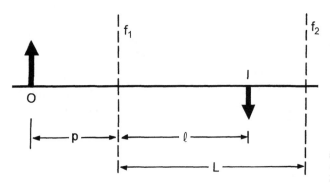

Fig. 18.10 for problem P–18.1.

Solution part (a): There are two possible paths to solve problems with combinations of two (or more) lenses: depending on the way the question is asked we start either with the first or with the last lens. Although this may sound trivial, it is important to keep this in mind when trying to work on problems like the one in this question, since it means that we have to be open to reversing the chosen approach if a solution isn't easily found.

   In the current problem it is necessary to start with the second lens and work backwards. One may anticipate this as the question asks for the position of the object in relation to the position of the first lens.

   The value of the focal length of the second lens is $f_2 = 20.0$ cm. The image distance follows withL and l from Fig. 18.10: $q_2 = -(L - l) = -(50[cm] - 31[cm]) = -19.0$ cm, where the negative sign is due to Table 17.4. "In front of the lens" in Fig. 18.10 is any position to the left of lens 2, as shown. We calculate with these values the object distance relative to lens 2, i.e., the position of the object which forms the image I at the position shown. Note that this is not the position of the object O shown in Fig. 18.10 since we are still working only with

the second lens. The object position p_2 is found with the thin lens formula:

$$\frac{1}{p_2} + \frac{1}{q_2} = \frac{1}{f_2} \qquad (1)$$

which yields:

$$\frac{1}{p_2} = \frac{1}{f_2} - \frac{1}{q_2} = \frac{1}{20[cm]} - \frac{1}{-19[cm]} \qquad (2)$$

$$\Rightarrow \quad p_2 = +9.74 \ cm$$

Now we consider the first lens. We can do this next as we now have enough information to determine the object distance p_1 sought in the problem: Besides the focal length of the first lens, given in the text as $f_1 = 10.0$ cm, we also know the image position for the first lens since it follows from the object distance for the second lens, i.e., $q_1 = L - p_2 = 50[cm] - 9.74[cm] = 40.26$ cm. Using again the thin lens formula we find:

$$\frac{1}{p_1} = \frac{1}{f_1} - \frac{1}{q_1} = \frac{1}{10[cm]} - \frac{1}{40.26[cm]} \qquad (3)$$

$$p_1 = +13.3 \ cm$$

Solution part (b): We consider both lenses separately since each may contribute to the overall magnification. Using Eq. (17.29) we find, respectively:

$$M_1 = -\frac{q_1}{p_1} = -\frac{40.26[cm]}{13.3[cm]} = -3.03 \qquad (4)$$

$$M_2 = -\frac{q_2}{p_2} = -\frac{-19[cm]}{9.74[cm]} = +1.95$$

The overall magnification is the product of the magnifications of the single lenses, i.e., for the current problem $M_{total} = M_1 M_2 = -5.91$. The final image is inverted since M_{total} is negative. The final image is also virtual, which means that it is located in front of the last lens.

Problem 18.2

A magnifying glass is used to examine the structural details of a human hair. The hair is held 3.5 cm in front of the magnifying glass, and the image is 25.0 cm from the eye.

(a) What is the focal length of the magnifying glass?

(b) What angular magnification is achieved?

Solution part (a): The text identifies both the object and image distances for the magnifying glass as $p = 3.5$ cm and $q = -25.0$ cm. The image distance must be negative since the image is located on the same side of the lens as the object. Using the thin lens formula we find for the focal length:

$$\frac{1}{f} = \frac{1}{p} + \frac{1}{q} = \frac{1}{3.5[cm]} + \frac{1}{-25.0[cm]} \quad (5)$$

$$\Rightarrow \quad f = 4.07 \; cm$$

Solution part (b): Remember that we have two formulas for the angular magnification, Eq. (18.4) for an observer with a relaxed eye (object at infinite distance) and Eq. (18.6) for an observer focussing on an object at the near point. In the current case the latter case applies since the object is at the near point of the observer. Thus, we find:

$$m = 1 + \frac{s_0}{f} = 1 + \frac{25.0[cm]}{4.07[cm]} = 7.14 \quad (6)$$

Problem 18.3

A microscope has an objective lens with $f = 16.22$ mm and an eyepiece with $f = 9.5$ mm. With the length of the microscope's barrel set at 29.0 cm, the diameter of an erythrocyte's image subtends an angle of 1.43 mrad with the eye. If the final image distance is 29.0 cm from the eyepiece, what is the actual diameter of the erythrocyte? Hint: Start with the size of the final image. Then use the thin lens formula for each lens to find their combined magnification. Use this magnification to calculate the object size in the final step.

Solution: This problem shows how calculations for multi–lens systems become sometimes more complicated. You want to recognize that the added complexity is not due to the need of more challenging mathematical skills but is due to the multi–step approach you have to take to reach a solution. These steps are associated with treating one lens after the other and determining the lo-

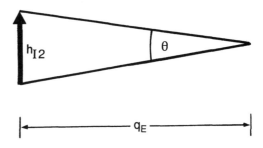

Fig. 18.11: Geometry of the relation of the angle θ, the image distance and the height of the image.

cation and magnification of intermediate images. Use the next few problems also to develop a strategy of how to tackle problems of this type.

In the current problem we start with the size of the final image which is only given as an angle of observation of $\theta = 1.43$ mrad. We use the geometrical sketch in Fig. 18.11 which illustrates the relation between θ, the height (size) of the final image, h_{I2}, and the distance between image and eyepiece, q_E, given as $q_E = 29.0$ cm in the text. Noting that θ is very small we write:

$$\sin\theta \cong \theta = 1.43 \times 10^{-3}[rad] = \frac{h_{I2}}{|q_E|} \quad (7)$$

$$\Rightarrow h_{I2} = 29[cm]1.43 \times 10^{-3} = 4.15 \times 10^{-2} \; cm$$

In the second step the thin lens formula and the formula for the magnification of a lens are used to find the magnification of each of the two lenses of the microscope. Fig. 18.12 identifies the respective object and image locations and sizes.

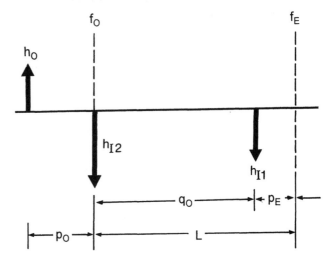

Fig. 18.12: Image and object locations and sizes for a microscope.

143

(i) for the eyepiece we determine the object distance from the thin lens formula and substitute the value in the magnification formula:

$$\frac{1}{p_E} = \frac{1}{f_E} - \frac{1}{q_E} = \frac{1}{0.95[cm]} - \frac{1}{-29[cm]}$$

$$\Rightarrow \quad p_E = 0.92 \ cm \qquad \textbf{(8)}$$

$$M_E = -\frac{q_E}{p_E} = -\frac{-29[cm]}{0.92[cm]} = 31.5$$

(ii) for the objective lens, we note $q_o = L - p_E$, as shown in Fig. 18.12. Thus, $q_o = (29.0 - 0.92)$ cm = 28.08 cm. With this value we use again the thin lens formula and the equation for the magnification as in part (i):

$$\frac{1}{p_O} = \frac{1}{f_O} - \frac{1}{q_O} = \frac{1}{1.622} - \frac{1}{-28.08}$$

$$\Rightarrow \quad p_O = 1.72 \ cm \qquad \textbf{(9)}$$

$$M_O = -\frac{q_O}{p_O} = -\frac{-28.08[cm]}{1.72[cm]} = -16.3$$

Combining the result for both lenses we find the combined magnification of the microscope:

$$M = M_E \, M_O = -16.3 \cdot 31.5 = -513.5 \quad \textbf{(10)}$$

Knowing the size of the final image, the total magnification calculated in Eq. (10) allows us to determine the size of the original object:

$$h_O = \frac{h_{I2}}{|M|} = \frac{4.15 \times 10^{-2}[cm]}{513.5} = 0.81 \ \mu m \quad \textbf{(11)}$$

CHAPTER XIX

Color vision: magnetism and electromagnetic spectrum

Problem 19.1

Two long, parallel wires are separated by a distance of $l_2 = 5$ cm, as shown in Fig. 19.34. The wires carry currents $I_1 = 4$ A and $I_2 = 3$ A in opposite directions. Find the direction and magnitude of the net magnetic field
(a) at point P_1 that is a distance $l_1 = 6$ cm to the left of the wire carrying current I_1,
(b) at point P_2 that is a distance $l_3 = 5$ cm to the right of the wire carrying current I_2.
(c) At what point is the magnitude of the magnetic field zero, $|\mathbf{B}| = 0$?

Solution: We quantify the magnetic field for each of the two wires before answering the three questions. The magnetic field as a function of distance from a current carrying wire is given in Eq. (19.2). For the wire carrying I_1 we find:

$$|\boldsymbol{B_1}| = \frac{\mu_0 I_1}{2\pi d_1} = \frac{1.26{\times}10^{-6}\left[\frac{N}{A^2}\right] 4[A]}{2\pi d_1} \quad \textbf{(1)}$$

$$\Rightarrow \quad |\boldsymbol{B_1}| = 8.0 \times 10^{-7}[T\,m]\,\frac{1}{d_1}$$

in which d_1 is the distance from wire 1. For the wire carrying I_2 we find:

$$|\boldsymbol{B_2}| = \frac{\mu_0 I_2}{2\pi d_2} = \frac{1.26{\times}10^{-6}\left[\frac{N}{A^2}\right] 3[A]}{2\pi d_2} \quad \textbf{(2)}$$

$$\Rightarrow \quad |\boldsymbol{B_2}| = 6.0 \times 10^{-7}[T\,m]\,\frac{1}{d_2}$$

in which d_2 is the distance from wire 2.

Solution part (a): We determine the net magnetic field at point P_1 as the sum of two contributions: the magnetic field at P_1 due to wire 1 and the magnetic field at P_1 due to wire 2. Even if we were not asked for the direction of the net magnetic field, the direction of each of the two contributions must be determined since we need to know whether the two contributions should be added or subtracted from each other.

The contribution at point P_1 due to wire 1 is calculated with $d_1 = l_1$:

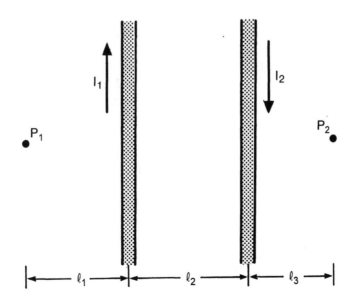

Fig. 19.34 for problem P–19.1.

$$|\boldsymbol{B_1}|(P_1) = \frac{8.0 \times 10^{-7} \ [T \ m]}{0.06 \ [m]} \qquad (3)$$

$$\Rightarrow \quad |\boldsymbol{B_1}|(P_1) = 1.33 \times 10^{-5} \ T$$

This contribution is directed out of the paper at point P_1 in Fig. 19.34 due to the right hand convention for the direction of the magnetic field for a current, as introduced in Fig. 19.9. The contribution at the same point due to wire 2 is calculated with $d_2 = l_1 + l_2$:

$$|\boldsymbol{B_2}|(P_1) = \frac{6.0 \times 10^{-7} \ [T \ m]}{0.11 \ [m]} \qquad (4)$$

$$\Rightarrow \quad |\boldsymbol{B_2}|(P_1) = 5.5 \times 10^{-6} \ T$$

This contribution is directed into the plane of the paper at point P_1 in Fig. 19.34. Thus, the net magnetic field at P_1 is $|\boldsymbol{B}|(P_1) = 7.8 \times 10^{-6}$ T, pointing out of the plane of the paper in Fig. 19.34.

Solution part (b): We determine the net magnetic field at point P_2 in the same fashion as the magnetic field at P_1. The contribution at point P_2 due to wire 1 is calculated with $d_1 = l_2 + l_3$:

$$|\boldsymbol{B_1}|(P_2) = \frac{8.0 \times 10^{-7} \ [T \ m]}{0.1 \ [m]} \qquad (5)$$

$$\Rightarrow \quad |\boldsymbol{B_1}|(P_2) = 8.0 \times 10^{-6} \ T$$

This contribution is directed into the plane of the paper at point P_2 in Fig. 19.34 due to the right hand convention for the direction of the magnetic field for a current. The contribution at the same point due to wire 2 is calculated with $d_2 = l_3$:

$$|\boldsymbol{B_2}|(P_2) = \frac{6.0 \times 10^{-7} \ [T \ m]}{0.05 \ [m]} \qquad (6)$$

$$\Rightarrow \quad |\boldsymbol{B_2}|(P_2) = 1.20 \times 10^{-5} \ T$$

This contribution is directed out of the paper at point P_2 in Fig. 19.34. Therefore, the net magnetic field at P_2 is $|\boldsymbol{B}|(P_2) = 4.0 \times 10^{-6}$ T pointing out of the plane of the paper in Fig. 19.34.

Solution part (c): From parts (a) and (b) we know that

the contributions due to the two wires have to be subtracted from each other for all points to the left or to the right of the arrangement. Thus, on either side there could be a point where the net magnetic field is indeed vanishing.

To set the problem properly up for this, we have to define two conventions:
(i) We assign a positive sign to the magnetic field value at a point where that field points out of the plane of paper in Fig. 19.34, and we assign a negative sign if the magnetic field points into the plane of the paper.
(ii) We define a x–axis perpendicular to the two wires in the plane of Fig. 19.34. The positive x–axis points toward the right and the origin (x = 0) is chosen at the position of wire 1.

With these conventions, we combine the two equations for the magnitudes of the magnetic field for wire 1 and wire 2, i.e., Eqs. (1) and (2):

$$|\boldsymbol{B}|(x) =$$

$$\left(-8 \times 10^{-7} \frac{1}{x} + 6 \times 10^{-7} \frac{1}{x - l_2} \right) T \, m \qquad (7)$$

For the x–position at which this magnitude of the magnetic field becomes zero, we set Eq. (7) equal to zero. This yields:

$$\frac{-8 \times 10^{-7} [Tm] \, (x - l_2) + 6 \times 10^{-7} [Tm] \, x}{x \, (x - l_2)} = 0 \qquad (8)$$

$$\Rightarrow \quad x = + 4 \, l_2$$

Thus, the point with zero magnetic field lies 20 cm to the right of wire 1 or 15 cm to the right of wire 2.

Problem 19.2
At what distance from a long straight conductor which carries a current of 1 A is the magnitude of the magnetic field due to the wire equal to the magnitude of the Earth's magnetic field at the surface of the Earth, which is $|\boldsymbol{B}| = 50 \ \mu T$?

Solution: Eq. (19.2) is rewritten with the distance d as the unknown variable:

$$d = \frac{\mu_0}{2\pi} \frac{I}{|\boldsymbol{B}|} \qquad (9)$$

We substitute the given current and the magnitude of the

Earth's magnetic field in Eq. (9) to find the distance d at which this particular field value is reached:

$$d = \frac{1.26\times10^{-6}\left[\frac{N}{A^2}\right]1.0[A]}{2\pi\ 5\times10^{-5}[T]} = 4.0\ mm \qquad (10)$$

Problem 19.3
A conducting wire has a mass of 10 g per meter length. The wire carries a current of 20 A and is suspended directly above a second wire of the same type which carries a current of 35 A. How far do you have to chose the separation distance between the wires so that the upper wire is balanced at rest by magnetic repulsion?

Solution: To establish mechanical equilibrium, the magnetic force per unit length of the wire, acting on the top wire, must be equal to the weight per unit length of the wire. Thus, the free–body–diagram of the system (e.g. choosing 1 meter as the unit length of the wire) contains two vertical force vectors, the weight downwards and the magnetic force upwards.

The weight per unit length is labelled |**W**|/L and its value for the wire in the present problem is given by:

$$\frac{|\mathbf{W}|}{L} = \frac{mg}{L} = \frac{10[g]}{1[m]}9.8\left[\frac{m}{s^2}\right]$$

$$\Rightarrow \quad \frac{|\mathbf{W}|}{L} = 0.098\ \frac{N}{m} \qquad (11)$$

Using Eq. (19.1) for the magnetic force per unit length of a wire, we require that:

$$\frac{|\mathbf{F}_{mag}|}{L} = \frac{\mu_0\ I_1\ I_2}{2\pi\ d} = \frac{|\mathbf{W}|}{L} \qquad (12)$$

Substituting Eq. (11) on the right hand side and then isolating for the unknown variable d, we find:

$$d = \frac{\mu_0\ I_1\ I_2}{2\pi\ 0.098[N/m]} \qquad (13)$$

Substituting the numerical values given in the problem text, this yields as a result:

$$d = \frac{1.26\times10^{-6}\left[\frac{N}{A^2}\right]20\ [A]\ 35\ [A]}{2\pi\ 0.098\left[\frac{N}{m}\right]} \qquad (14)$$

$$\Rightarrow \quad d = 1.4\ mm$$

Thus, the distance between the wires is 1.4 mm.

Problem 19.4
Two parallel conductors carry each a current of 2 A and are 6 cm apart.
(a) If the currents flow in the opposite direction, find the force per unit length exerted on either of the two conductors. Is the force attractive or repulsive?
(b) How do the results in part (a) change if the currents flow parallel to each other?

Solution part (a): Eq. (19.1) provides us with the equation for the magnetic force per unit length. Substituting the given values we find:

$$\frac{|F_{mag}|}{l} = \frac{\mu_0 I_1 I_2}{2\pi d} = \frac{1.26\times10^{-6}\left[\frac{N}{A^2}\right](2[A])^2}{2\pi\ 0.06[m]} \qquad (15)$$

$$\Rightarrow \quad \frac{|F_{mag}|}{l} = 1.34\times10^{-5}\ \frac{N}{m}$$

From Fig. 19.7 we conclude that the flow of the currents in opposite directions leads to a repelling force.

Solution part (b): With the currents flowing in the same direction, the magnitude of the force per unit length calculated in Eq. (15) remains unchanged, but the force is now an attractive force, as determined from comparison with Fig. 19.7.

Problem 19.5
Fig. 19.35 shows two parallel wires which carry currents I_1 = 100 A and I_2. The top wire is held in position, the bottom wire is prevented from moving sideways but can slide up and down without friction. If the wires have a mass of 10 g per meter of length calculate current I_2 such that the lower wire levitates at a position 4 cm below the top wire.

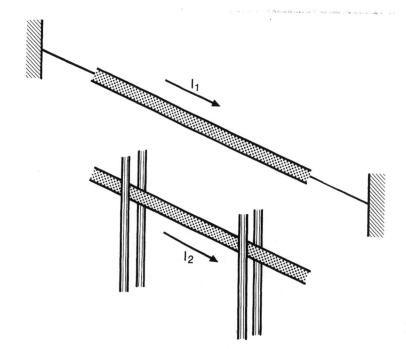

Fig. 19.35 for problem P–19.5.

Solution: The magnetic force exerted on the lower wire by the upper wire is directed upward since the currents in both wires flow in the same direction. Thus, in mechanical equilibrium, Newton's first law applies to a piece of the lower wire of length L in the form:

$$\sum_i F_{i,\,y} = 0 = \frac{\mu_0 I_1 I_2 L}{2\pi d} - mg \qquad (16)$$

in which the upwards directed force component is the magnetic force taken from Eq. (19.1) and the downwards directed force is the weight. d is the distance between the two wires in mechanical equilibrium. m is the mass of a wire segment of length L. We determine the current in the lower wire, I_2, from Eq. (16):

$$I_2 = \frac{2\pi d}{\mu_0 I_1}\frac{m}{L}\,g =$$

$$\frac{2\pi\;0.04[m]\;0.01\left[\dfrac{kg}{m}\right]\;9.8\left[\dfrac{m}{s^2}\right]}{1.26\times10^{-6}\left[\dfrac{N}{A^2}\right]\;100[A]} = 195\;A \qquad (17)$$

Problem 19.6

The index of refraction for violet light in silica flint glass is 1.66, and that for red light is 1.62. What is the angular dispersion of visible light (expressed as the angle φ) passing through the equilateral prism shown in Fig. 19.36, if the angle of incidence is 50°?

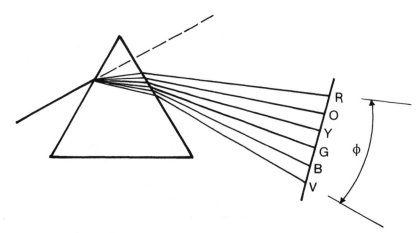

Fig. 19.36 for problem P–19.6.

148

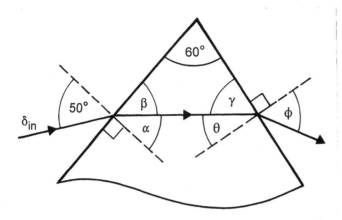

Fig. 19.39: Geometry of a light ray passing through a prism.

Solution: We establish the necessary geometrical relations in Fig. 19.39 before solving this problem. The figure defines angles α, β, γ, θ and ϕ relative to the light ray passing the prism. The given angles of 50^0 and 60^0 are shown as well. The following three relations between these angles are derived from the figure:

$$\beta = 90^0 - \alpha$$

$$\gamma + \beta + 60^0 = 180^0 \Rightarrow \gamma = 120^0 - \beta \quad (18)$$

$$\theta = 90^0 - \gamma$$

(I) We study first a red light ray, with an index of refraction of $n = 1.62$. For this light ray reads the law of refraction (Eq. (17.16)) at the first air/glass interface:

$$n_{air} \sin 50^0 = n_{glass} \sin\alpha$$

$$\sin\alpha = \frac{1.0}{1.62} \sin 50^0 \Rightarrow \alpha = 28.2^0 \quad (19)$$

We find from Eq. (19) the angle of incidence of the light ray on the second interface (glass to air) by using the geometrical relations derived from Fig. 19.39:

$$\theta = 90^0 - \gamma = 90^0 - 120^0 + \beta =$$
$$- 30^0 + 90^0 - \alpha = 60^0 - 28.2^0 = 31.8^0 \quad (20)$$

Applying the law of refraction a second time at the second interface provides for the exiting angle ϕ:

$$n_{glass} \sin\theta = n_{air} \sin\phi$$

$$\sin\phi = \frac{1.62}{1.0} \sin 31.8^0 \Rightarrow \phi_{red} = 58.6^0 \quad (21)$$

(II) We repeat the same calculations for the violet light ray with index of refraction $n = 1.66$. Replacing Eq. (19) we find:

$$\sin\alpha = \frac{1.0}{1.66} \sin 50^0 \Rightarrow \alpha = 27.5^0 \quad (22)$$

Using Eq. (20), we obtain for the violet light ray the angle of incidence on the second glass/air interface $\theta = 32.5^0$. In analogy to Eq. (21) we obtain for the angle of the exiting violet light ray:

$$\sin\phi = \frac{1.66}{1.0} \sin 32.5^0 \Rightarrow \phi_{vio} = 63.2^0 \quad (23)$$

Combining the results for the red and the violet light ray we find the angle of dispersion, $\Delta\phi$:

$$\Delta\phi = 63.2^0 - 58.6^0 = 4.6^0 \quad (24)$$

Problem 19.7
Light of wavelength λ_0 in vacuum has a wavelength of $\lambda_w = 438$ nm in water and it has a wavelength of $\lambda_b = 390$ nm in benzene.
(a) What is the wavelength λ_0 in vacuum?
(b) Using only the given information, determine the ratio of the index of refraction of benzene to that of water.

Solution part (a): To relate the speed of light in a medium to the medium's index of refraction, we combine Eq. (17.15) which connects the speed of light across an interface, and Snell's law in the form Eq. (17.14). This has been done before, e.g. in Example 17.5, where we found in Eq. (17.23) the relation: $c/v_{medium} = n_{medium}$ with c the speed of light in vacuum.

For the current problem, we want to connect this formula to the wavelength and frequency values of light of a specific color. This is done with Eq. (19.11). We use Eq. (19.11) twice:
(i) for the light in water (index w): $v_w = \lambda_w f$, and
(ii) for the light in vacuum (index 0): $c = \lambda_0 f$.
Note that we do not use an index with the frequency since the frequency of light does not change when pass-

149

ing an interface (see Eq. (19.12)).

Substituting Eq. (19.11) in the form given above into Eq. (17.23) yields:

$$n_w = \frac{\lambda_0 \, f}{\lambda_w \, f}$$

$$\Rightarrow \quad \lambda_0 = n_w \lambda_w = \quad\quad\quad\quad (25)$$

$$1.33 \cdot 438[nm] = 583 \; nm$$

Solution part (b): For the comparison with benzene we use Eq. (25) twice to calculate the ratio of the two index of refraction:

$$\frac{n_b}{n_w} = \frac{\dfrac{\lambda_0 \, f}{\lambda_b \, f}}{\dfrac{\lambda_0 \, f}{\lambda_w \, f}} = \frac{\lambda_w}{\lambda_b} = \frac{438[nm]}{390[nm]} = 1.12 \quad (26)$$

Problem 19.8

Fig. 19.37 shows that our eye is much more sensitive to absolute intensities of green light in comparison to absolute intensities of red light. Why are the green and red lights of a traffic light still looking roughly equally bright?

Solution: If a green street light would emit green light (e.g. in the 500 to 550 nm wavelength range) and if a red street light would emit red light (e.g. in the 650 nm to 700 nm wavelength range) then, indeed, the green light were about twenty times brighter than the red light.

However, actual street lights function in a different fashion. The color of a street light is the result of elimination of certain wavelength intervals from the visible range (white light). The light bulb in the street light emits white light and a filter glass eliminates part of the spectrum to create the final color impression. As an example, if molecules embedded in the filter glass absorb in the green part of the spectrum then you see the complementary color, in this case red.

As a consequence, you see all street light colors roughly equally intensive as only minor fractions of the white light are removed in each case.

Problem 19.9

Describe the color vision of an alien if the sensitivity of the three color receptors in the eye of the alien were as shown in Fig. 19.38.

Solution: Note: while the particular sensitivity spectrum in Fig. 19.38 is assigned to an alien, we have to keep in mind that color vision varies greatly throughout the animal kingdom. Even such familiar animals as dogs see everything quite differently than we do!

The particular alien's vision is characterized by non–overlapping sensitivity peaks in the spectrum of Fig. 19.38. Any wavelength interval between the shown peaks (e.g. between 480 nm and 500 nm where we see blue colors) leads to black/white (grey–tone) vision if the alien has retinal rods like in our eyes.

Objects, which emit light in an interval of wavelengths for which one of the types of retinal cones of the

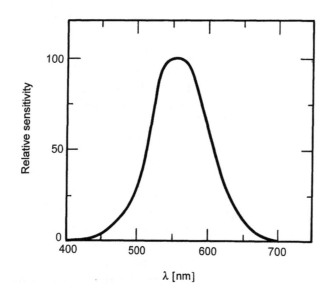

Fig. 19.37 for problem P–19.8.

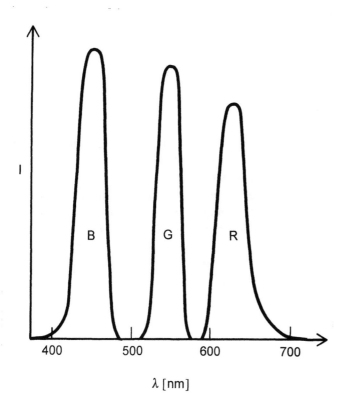

Fig. 19.38 for problem P–19.9.

alien is sensitive, are characterized by just one color. For example, the alien sees objects with wavelengths between 510 nm and 580 nm as bold green. We, in turn, distinguish light in the same range as leaf green to bright yellow. This indicates that communication with the alien could turn out difficult when trying to establish a common ground based on the obvious things we both see. The world for the alien's brain would somewhat be simpler as there are only three bold colors and grey, but no transitional colors in between.

CHAPTER XX

The human body in space: circular motion

Problem 20.1

A roller coaster ride includes a circular loop with radius R = 10 m.

(a) What minimum speed must the car have at the top to stay in contact with the tracks?

(b) What minimum speed must the car have when entering the loop to satisfy the solution in part (a)?

Solution part (a): This is a problem about the mechanics of forces, comparable to the type of problems we dealt with in Chapters 2 to 4. We follow the same approach we developed earlier: we first identify the system of interest as the car passing through the roller coaster loop. The circular track is part of the environment.

   Two forces act on the car: the weight of the car and the contact force exerted by the track. Of these two forces, only the weight is not zero at the top point when the car passes with the least possible speed. You can illustrate that to yourself swinging an object on a string in a vertical loop. The object will remain on a circular loop as long as you don't slow it down too much. As you slow it down, the effort of pulling the object down when it passes the highest point of its path (the tension force in the string, which corresponds to the contact force of the car with the roller coaster track) decreases. At the minimum speed you do not exert a force on the object while it is at the highest point.

   The free–body–diagram for this problem is trivial with a single force acting on the system straight downwards, as shown in Fig. 20.21. As discussed in the text, we apply a specific choice of coordinate system to problems including circular motion. The plane of the circular motion is defined by two coordinates attached to the system, labelled ∥ for the direction parallel to the velocity vector and ⊥ for the direction perpendicular to the velocity vector. The direction perpendicular to this plane is labelled the z–direction.

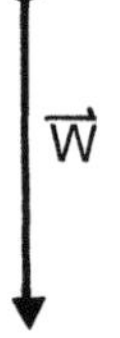

Fig. 20.21: Free–body–diagram for the roller coaster car.

Since there is no motion in the z–direction perpendicular to the plane of the loop, the respective equation can be neglected. Also, when the car is at the top of the loop, there is no force acting parallel to the velocity vector, which is tangential to the track. The only remaining equation of interest is Newton's second law in the direction perpendicular to the track, which is the direction downwards. With the positive axis pointing upwards and using the first formula in Eq. (20.17) we find:

$$\sum_i F_{i,\perp} = -mg = -m\frac{v_{top}^2}{R} \qquad (1)$$

in which R is the radius of the loop of the roller coaster track, m is the mass of the car, and v_{top} is the minimum speed of the car at the top of the track. This is indeed the minimum speed because the car would lose contact to the track at lower speed since only a fraction of the weight would be needed to provide the circular motion and the remaining fraction of the weight would cause the car to fall. Note that at higher speeds an additional force has to be added to the left hand side of Eq. (1) which is due to the normal force exerted by the track onto the car. The magnitude of this normal force can indeed be calculated from Eq. (1) if the speed of the car at the top point of the loop is known.

   Eq. (1) is solved by isolating the unknown minimum speed at the top of the loop:

$$v_{top} = \sqrt{gR} = \sqrt{9.8\left[\frac{m}{s^2}\right]10[m]} = 9.9\,\frac{m}{s} \qquad (2)$$

Note that the mass of the car was cancelled when deriving Eq. (2) from Eq. (1). Thus, the mass of the car does not change the result.

Solution part (b): We answer this part by using the concept of conservation of energy as discussed in Chapter 5. To do so, we compare two states for the system: (i) when the car is at the top of the loop, at which point we know most details about it, and (ii) when the car is at the bottom of the loop, because we are asked about the speed of the car at that point:

$$E_{total,\ top} = E_{kin,\ top} + E_{pot,\ top} =$$

$$E_{total,\ bottom} = E_{kin,\ bottom} + E_{pot,\ bottom} \tag{3}$$

Remember that we can choose the reference height y = 0 freely when writing the conservation of energy in the form of Eq. (3). In the current case, choosing the origin for the height, y = 0, at the bottom of the loop simplifies the formula and leads to the simplest form for the later quantitative analysis. With this choice we find:

$$\frac{1}{2}mv_{top}^2 + mg\,(2R) = \frac{1}{2}mv_{bottom}^2 \tag{4}$$

For the second term on the left hand side of Eq. (4) we used the fact that the highest point of the loop is twice the radius length above the lowest point.

We substitute the result from part (a) for v_{top} on the left side of Eq. (4):

$$\frac{1}{2}mgR + mg\,(2R) = \frac{1}{2}mv_{bottom}^2 \tag{5}$$

$$\Rightarrow \quad v_{bottom} = \sqrt{5gR}$$

With the given value of R, we calculate v_{bottom} = 22 m/s, which corresponds to 80 km/h.

Problem 20.2

The gravitational constant, G^*, and the gravitational acceleration on the surface of the Earth, g, can be measured in independent laboratory experiments.
(a) What other information do you need about the Earth to determine the Earth's mass?
(b) Finding this information (it is also used in the current chapter), calculate the mass of the Earth.

Solution part (a): We consider an arbitrary object with mass m. Note that we will find that we do not need to measure this mass. Therefore, our result does not depend on the precision of our knowledge of the reference mass.

When we release this test object near the surface of the Earth, we write Newton's second law in the y–direction (with the y–axis pointing downwards):

$$\sum_i F_{i,\ y} = G^* \frac{M_E\,m}{R_E^2} = ma = mg \tag{6}$$

where we used Newton's law of gravity to quantify the force acting on the test mass. We also used the gravitational constant g to specify the acceleration. We solve Eq. (6) for the mass of the Earth, M_E:

$$M_E = \frac{gR_E^2}{G^*} \tag{7}$$

Thus, the missing information besides the two constants g and G^* is the radius of the Earth.

Solution part (b): We enter R_E = 6370 km in Eq. (7):

$$M_E = \frac{9.80665\left[\dfrac{m}{s}\right]\ (6.37\times10^6[m])^2}{6.6733\times10^{-11}\left[\dfrac{Nm^2}{kg^2}\right]} \tag{8}$$

$$\Rightarrow \quad M_E = 5.96 \times 10^{24}\ kg$$

Problem 20.3

Calculate the orbital speed for the two Russian missions shown in Fig. 20.1. Use the mass and the radius of the Earth from the Examples in this chapter.

Solution: Eq. (20.35) applies to any orbiting satellite, not just the ISS. Thus, we use this formula and the values for the Earth's mass and radius used in Eq. (20.36). The height above ground for the two Russian missions shown in Fig. 20.1, Sputnik 1 (first unmanned satellite (83 kg, 58 cm diameter), launched in October 1957) and Vostok 1 (carrying Yury Gagarin into space in April 1961) can be read from the figure. Note that the scale on the figure is logarithmic. We find for Sputnik 1 that h = 946 km and for Vostok 1 h = 327 km. Note that the complete name of the Sputnik 1 mission was "Iskustvennyi Sputnik Zemli" which means "fellow world traveller of the Earth". With these heights we determine the orbiting speeds: For Sputnik 1, we then get:

$$v_{Sp.} = \sqrt{G^* \frac{M_E}{(R_E+h)}} =$$

$$\sqrt{\frac{6.67\times10^{-11}\left[\dfrac{m^3}{kgs^2}\right]\ 5.98\times10^{24}[kg]}{6.37\times10^6[m]\ +\ 9.46\times10^5[m]}} \tag{9}$$

i.e., the orbiting speed is v = 7385 m/s. In the same fashion we find for Vostok 1:

$$v_{Vo} = \sqrt{\frac{6.67 \times 10^{-11} \left[\frac{m^3}{kgs^2}\right] 5.98 \times 10^{24} [kg]}{6.37 \times 10^6 [m] + 3.27 \times 10^5 [m]}} \quad (10)$$

$$\Rightarrow \quad v_{Vo} = 7715 \frac{m}{s}$$

Comparing these two speeds with the speed of ISS at 7660 m/s, as found in Example 20.7, we notice that the absolute speeds vary little due to the relatively small variations of the spacecraft distance from the center of the Earth.

Problem 20.4
A centrifuge of radius 12 cm is used to separate a blood sample with the result shown in Fig. 12.4. The force needed to obtain sedimentation of red blood cells in a plasma solution is about 4×10^{-11} N, acting on the erythrocyte of average mass of 3×10^{-16} kg. At what number of revolutions per second must the centrifuge be operated?

Solution: We identify an arbitrary red blood cell as the system, with the plasma solvent, the glass tube and the centrifuge representing the environment. While in operation, the sedimentation in a centrifuge occurs in a horizontal direction. The vertical motion in the fluid due to gravity is negligible. Thus, we consider only one horizontal contact force which has the magnitude given in the text. The free–body–diagram is trivial with just one horizontal force.

Since this problem contains a circular motion caused by the centrifuge, the direction tangential to the velocity vector of the tube is labelled ∥ and the direction toward the rotational axis is labelled ⊥. The vertical direction, which is perpendicular to the plane of the circular motion, is called the z–direction.

Of the three equations establishing the application of Newton's laws to this problem, given in Eq. (20.17), only the first one is needed to find the rotation frequency of the centrifuge:

$$\sum_i F_{i,\perp} = F_{centri} = m \frac{v^2}{r} = mr\omega^2 \quad (11)$$

in which the last term is obtained by comparing Eqs. (20.10) and (20.12). We isolate and quantify ω in Eq.

(11):

$$\omega = \sqrt{\frac{F_{centri}}{mr}} = \sqrt{\frac{4 \times 10^{-11} [N]}{3 \times 10^{-16} [kg] \; 0.12 [m]}} \quad (12)$$

$$\Rightarrow \quad \omega = 1054 \frac{rad}{s} = 168 \frac{rev}{s}$$

In Eq. (12) the conversion 1 rev = 2π rad was used. [rev] is the non–SI unit for *revolutions*.

Problem 20.5
A proton (mass and charge are given in Table 9.1) moves with a speed of 100 km/s through the magnetic field of the Earth, which has at the particular location a magnitude of 50 µT. What is the ratio of the gravitational force and the magnetic force on the proton when the proton travels perpendicular to the magnetic field?

Solution: The magnetic force is found from Eq. (20.47):

$$f_{mag} = qvB =$$

$$= 1.6 \times 10^{-19} [Cb] \; 1 \times 10^5 \left[\frac{m}{s}\right] 5 \times 10^{-5} [T] \quad (13)$$

$$\Rightarrow \quad f_{mag} = 8 \times 10^{-19} \; N$$

As Eq. (20.48) illustrates, this is the maximum magnetic force acting on the particle when the particle's motion occurs in a direction perpendicular to the magnetic field.

The gravitational force on the proton near the surface of the Earth (i.e., its weight) is:

$$W = m_p g = 1.67 \cdot 10^{-27} [kg] \; 9.8 \left[\frac{m}{s}\right] \quad (14)$$

$$\Rightarrow \quad W = 1.6 \times 10^{-26} \; N$$

Table 9.1: Elementary particles in the atom

Particle	Mass [kg]	Charge [Cb]
Electron	9.11×10^{-31}	-1.6×10^{-19}
Proton	1.673×10^{-27}	$+1.6 \times 10^{-19}$
Neutron	1.675×10^{-27}	0

154

Thus, the ratio of both forces favors significantly the magnetic force with:

$$\frac{f_{mag}}{W} = 5 \times 10^7 \qquad (15)$$

The gravitational force can usually be neglected when discussing magnetic forces acting on atomic scale particles.

Problem 20.6

A long straight wire in a vacuum system carries a current of 1.5 A. A low–density, 20 eV electron beam is directed parallel to the wire at a distance of 0.5 cm. The electron beam travels against the direction of the current in the wire. Find
(a) the magnitude of the magnetic force acting on the electrons in the electron beam, and
(b) find the direction in which the electrons are deflected from their initial direction.

Solution part (a): The problem is illustrated in Fig. 20.22. The figure indicates the direction of the magnetic field **B** due to the current in the wire. As shown, the magnetic field at the position of the electron beam points out of the plane of the paper.

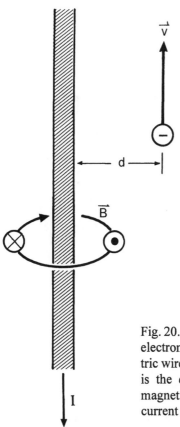

Fig. 20.22: Geometry of electron beam and electric wire. Also indicated is the direction of the magnetic field due to current in the wire.

We first use Eq. (19.2) and Eq. (20.47) to determine the magnitude of the force acting on each electron. Eq. (19.2) allows us to calculate the magnitude of the magnetic field of the current at a given distance d from the wire:

$$B = \frac{\mu_0 I}{2\pi d} = \frac{1.26\times10^{-6}\left[\frac{N}{A^2}\right] 1.5[A]}{2\pi \; 5\times10^{-3}[m]} \qquad (16)$$

$$\Rightarrow \quad B = 6 \times 10^{-5} \; T$$

With this result, we use Eq. (20.47) to determine the magnitude of the magnetic force on each electron in the beam. Eq. (20.47) contains the speed of the electrons which we calculate from the kinetic energy of 20 eV given in the problem. For the energy conversion from [eV] to [J] we use the conversions given in the General Appendix:

$$E_{kin} = 20[eV] \; 1.6\times10^{-19}\left[\frac{J}{eV}\right] = \qquad (17)$$

$$3.2 \times 10^{-18} \; [J] = \frac{1}{2}m_e v^2$$

which leads to v = 2.65 × 10^6 m/s when the mass of the electron is taken from Table 9.1. Note that it is always useful to check such a speed, calculated from an energy for a atomic or sub–atomic particle, against the speed of light. In the current case we find a speed just below 1 % of the speed of light, thus, our classical calculation (using $E_{kin} = \frac{1}{2}mv^2$) is valid. If the speed exceeds a few percent of the speed of light a relativistic correction would have to be used.

The values from Eqs. (16) and (17) are substituted into Eq. (20.47):

$$f_{mag} = 1.6\times10^{-19}[Cb] \cdot \dots$$

$$\dots \cdot 2.65\times10^6\left[\frac{m}{s}\right] 6\times10^{-5}[T] \qquad (18)$$

$$\Rightarrow \quad f_{mag} = 2.5 \times 10^{-17} \; N$$

Solution part (b): The direction of the force is determined with the right hand rule. Note that the right hand rule was used to determine the direction of the force acting on a positively charged particle in Fig. 20.15. Fig.

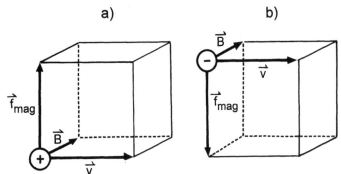

a)   b)

Fig. 20.23: Application of the right hand rule to determine the direction of the magnetic force acting on a moving charged particle in a magnetic field, (a) for a positive charge, and (b) for a negative charge.

20.23 shows a generalization of that rule for both positively and negatively charged particles. We apply Fig. 20.23(b) to the directions shown in the sketch of Fig. 20.22. With the velocity vector directed upwards and the magnetic field at the position of the electron pointing out of the plane of the paper, the force is directed toward the wire. Thus, the electron is attracted toward the wire.

Problem 20.7

We consider Aston's mass spectrometer as illustrated in Fig. 20.16. The magnitude of the electric field is given as E = 1.0 kV/m and the magnitude of the magnetic fields in both Wien filter and the mass selector is 1.0 T. Calculate the radius of the path in the mass selector for an ion with a single positive charge and with a mass of m = 2.0 × 10^{-26} kg.

Solution: The mass spectrometer in Fig. 20.16 operates in two steps: the Wien filter (crossed electric and magnetic fields) serves as a velocity selector, and the subsequent magnetic sector field serves as a mass selector.

We first calculate the speed of those ions which pass through the Wien filter along a straight line. The condition for passing is given in Eq. (20.61):

$$v = \frac{E}{B} = \frac{1\times10^3 [V/m]}{1.0[T]} = 1 \times 10^3 \frac{m}{s} \quad (19)$$

In the next step, Eq. (20.53) is used to calculate the radius of the ions in the magnetic sector field:

$$r = \frac{2\times10^{-26}[kg]\ 1\times10^3[m/s]}{1.6\times10^{-19}[Cb]\ 1.0[T]} \quad (20)$$

$$\Rightarrow \quad r = 1.25 \times 10^{-4}\ m = 0.125\ mm$$

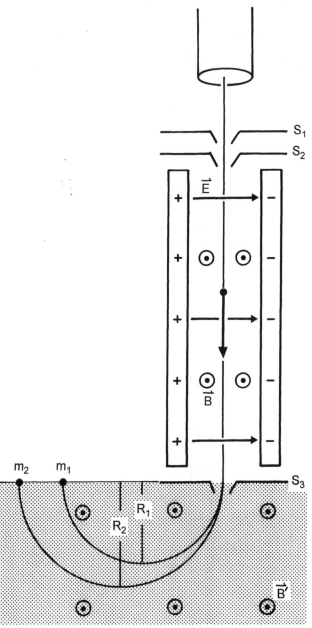

Fig. 20.16: Aston's mass spectrometer. The ions, collimated with slits S$_1$ and S$_2$, first pass through a velocity selector (Wien filter) with perpendicular electric and magnetic fields and then enter a mass selector with magnetic field **B'**.

156

Problem 20.8

A mass spectrometer as shown in Fig. 20.16 is used to separate isotopes. If the beam emerges with a speed of 250 km/s and the magnetic field in the mass selector is 2 T, what is the distance between the collectors for
(a) ^{235}U and ^{238}U, and
(b) ^{12}C and ^{14}C?

Solution part (a): We need not to quantify the properties of the Wien filter in this case because the speed of the incoming ions is given in the problem. We quantify Eq. (20.53) for each isotope separately and then calculate the difference in position for the collector. Note from Fig. 20.16 that this distance is twice the difference in radii as calculated from Eq. (20.53) since both isotopes enter the sector field at the same point and the sector field spans through an angle of 180^0.

As discussed in more detail in Chapter 22, the isotope labels allow us to determine the mass of each isotope: ^{235}U has a mass of 235 u in which u is the atomic unit as defined in the General Appendix. Therefore, the mass of ^{235}U is given as 3.902×10^{-25} kg and ^{238}U has a mass of 238 u, which is 3.952×10^{-25} kg. This leads to:

$$r_{235U} = \frac{3.902 \times 10^{-25}[kg]\ 2.5 \times 10^5 \left[\frac{m}{s}\right]}{1.6 \times 10^{-19}[Cb]\ 2.0[T]} \quad \textbf{(21)}$$

$$\Rightarrow \quad r_{235U} = 0.305\ m$$

and

$$r_{238U} = \frac{3.952 \times 10^{-25}[kg]\ 2.5 \times 10^5 \left[\frac{m}{s}\right]}{1.6 \times 10^{-19}[Cb]\ 2.0[T]} \quad \textbf{(22)}$$

$$\Rightarrow \quad r_{238U} = 0.309\ m$$

i.e., the separation is 8 mm.

Solution part (b): The analogous calculation for the two carbon isotopes leads to:

$$r_{12C} = \frac{1.993 \times 10^{-26}[kg]\ 2.5 \times 10^5 \left[\frac{m}{s}\right]}{1.6 \times 10^{-19}[Cb]\ 2.0[T]} \quad \textbf{(23)}$$

$$\Rightarrow \quad r_{12C} = 0.0156\ m$$

and

$$r_{14C} = \frac{2.325 \times 10^{-26}[kg]\ 2.5 \times 10^5 \left[\frac{m}{s}\right]}{1.6 \times 10^{-19}[Cb]\ 2.0[T]} \quad \textbf{(24)}$$

$$\Rightarrow \quad r_{14C} = 0.0182\ m$$

i.e., the separation is 5 mm. Note that a smaller magnetic field leads to a larger separation.

CHAPTER XXI

The chemical bond: atomic and molecular physics

Problem 21.1
Calculate for Bohr's atomic model the speed of the orbiting electron in the ground state.

Solution: The speed of the orbiting electron is obtained from Eq. (21.14). However, that equation requires the radius of the orbit. It is more instructive to combine Eq. (21.14) with the standing wave condition in Eq. (21.7) for the ground state (n = 1) because this allows us to eliminate the radius of the orbit from the calculation:

$$\frac{e^2}{4\pi\epsilon_0 r^2} = m\frac{v^2}{r} = \frac{v\hbar}{r^2} \tag{1}$$

$$\Rightarrow \quad v = \frac{e^2}{2\epsilon_0 h} = 2.19 \times 10^6 \ \frac{m}{s}$$

This result is interesting in that the speed of the orbiting electron is c/137 with c the speed of light in vacuum. This speed does only depend on natural constants. It is in particular independent of the mass of the electron, i.e., any other singly charged particle orbits the hydrogen nucleus with the same speed. Eq. (21.17) for Bohr's radius shows that capturing another sub–atomic particle leads, however, to another radius of the orbit, with smaller radii for heavier particles.

Problem 21.2
In the spectrum of helium ions, a series of absorption lines exists (Pickering series) for which every other line coincides with a Balmer series line of the hydrogen atom (the remaining lines fall in between the Balmer series lines). Which transitions in the helium ion are responsible for the Pickering series?

Solution: A helium ion is a helium atom which has lost one or two electrons. Only the He$^+$ ion has a spectrum since a He^{2+} is an α–particle without electrons. Thus, the electronic structure of a helium ion with a single positive charge is similar to a hydrogen atom with Z = 2 as the atomic number, as discussed at the beginning of section 21.3 and in Example 21.5. Using Eq. (21.30) to modify Eq. (21.23) for the transition energies of the helium ion spectrum, we find for He$^+$:

$$f_{He^+} = 4 \ R_H \left| \left(\frac{1}{n_{initial}^2} - \frac{1}{n_{final}^2} \right) \right| \tag{2}$$

This condition has to be compared with the Balmer series for the hydrogen atom in Eq. (21.23):

$$f_{Balmer} = R_H \left| \left(\frac{1}{n_{initial}^2} - \frac{1}{2^2} \right) \right| \tag{3}$$

The Pickering series corresponds to transitions in a He ion from quantum numbers $n_{i, He^+} = 2n_{i, Balmer}$ to $n_{f, He^+} = 4$. Thus, the even–numbered lines in the Pickering series coincide with Balmer lines, the odd–numbered Pickering lines fall between Balmer lines.

Problem 21.3
A hydrogen is in its first excited state (n = 2). Using Bohr's atomic model calculate
(a) the radius of the electron's orbit,
(b) the potential energy of the electron, and
(c) the total energy of the electron.

Solution part (a): The radius of the lowest orbit is called the Bohr radius and is given in Eq. (21.17). Using Eq. (21.16), we find that the radii of the excited states of the hydrogen atom are related in a simple fashion to the Bohr radius: $r(n) = n^2 r_{Bohr}$. Thus, we find for n = 2 the radius of $r = 2.12 \times 10^{-10}$ m = 0.212 nm.

Solution part (b): The only form of potential energy relevant in the atomic shell is the electric potential energy, given in Eq. (21.18). For n = 2 we find:

$$E_{el} = -\frac{e^2}{4\pi\epsilon_0 r} =$$

$$-9\times10^9 \left[\frac{Nm^2}{Cb^2} \right] \frac{(1.6\times10^{-19}[Cb])^2}{2.12\times10^{-10}[m]} \tag{4}$$

i.e., $E_{el} = -1.09 \times 10^{-18}$ J $= -6.8$ eV.

Solution part (c): There are two ways to calculate the total energy. Calculating the kinetic energy and adding the kinetic energy and the result of part (b) requires a longer calculation. A shorter approach is to use Eq. (21.20) which states that the total energy is ½ of the potential energy. Therefore, $E_{total} = -5.5 \times 10^{-19}$ J, which is equal to -3.4 eV.

Problem 21.4

Calculate the electric force on the electron in the ground state of the hydrogen atom.

Solution: The force acting on the electron is the Coulomb force, Eq. (9.1). Using the distance between electron and proton in the hydrogen atom from Eq. (21.17) we find:

$$|F| = \frac{1}{4\pi\epsilon_0} \frac{e^2}{r_{Bohr}^2} =$$

$$9 \times 10^9 \left[\frac{Nm^2}{Cb^2}\right] \frac{(1.6\times10^{-19}[Cb])^2}{5.29\times10^{-11}[m])^2} \quad (5)$$

i.e., $|F| = 8.2 \times 10^{-8}$ N. Note that this force is included in Table 3.2, where it is compared to other, mechanic forces.

Problem 21.5

What is the wavelength of light that can cause a transition of an electron in the hydrogen atom from the orbit with n = 3 to n = 5?

Solution: We use Eq. (21.23) first to calculate the frequency of the light photon for the given transition:

$$f_{3 \to 5} = R_H \left|\frac{1}{3^2} - \frac{1}{5^2}\right| = 2.34 \times 10^{14} \frac{1}{s} \quad (6)$$

in which the value for the Rydberg constant R_H is taken from Eq. (21.24). This transition corresponds to a photon of 0.97 eV, which is small compared to the dissociation energy for hydrogen of 13.6 eV. The photon has to be absorbed for the transition to occur since the electron is brought to an orbit with a higher quantum number.

The frequency in Eq. (6) can be converted to a wavelength in the same fashion as illustrated in Eq. (21.27) of Example 21.2:

$$\lambda_{3 \to 5} = \frac{c}{f_{3 \to 5}} = \frac{3 \times 10^8 \left[\frac{m}{s}\right]}{2.34 \times 10^{14} \left[\frac{1}{s}\right]} \quad (7)$$

$$\Rightarrow \lambda_{3 \to 5} = 1.28 \times 10^{-6} \ m = 1.28 \ \mu m$$

This transition lies in the near infrared part of the electromagnetic spectrum, as identified in Fig. 19.26.

Problem 21.6

A hydrogen atom emits a photon with wavelength $\lambda = 656$ nm. Which transition did the hydrogen atom undergo to emit this photon?

Solution: We convert the given wavelength into a photon energy since this allows us to use the values in Eq. (21.25) to find a suitable transition. With the photon energy given by E = hf and the wavelength and frequency connected by the speed of light, c = λf, we find:

$$E_{trans} = \frac{hc}{\lambda} = \frac{6.6\times10^{-34}[Js] \ 3\times10^8\left[\frac{m}{s}\right]}{6.56\times10^{-7}[m]} \quad (8)$$

$$\Rightarrow E_{trans} = 3.02 \times 10^{-19} \ J$$

in which the Planck constant and the speed of light are taken from tables in the General Appendix. For comparison with Eq. (21.25) we use the conversion from unit [J] to unit [eV]: $E_{trans} = 1.89$ eV.

In the next step we try to find a combination of two hydrogen atom energy levels in Eq. (21.25) which corresponds to $E_{trans} = 1.89$ eV. After a brief inspection of the equation we note that the transition from quantum number 2 to quantum number 3 is equal to E_{trans}. Thus, this is the sought transition.

We know further that the hydrogen atom has emitted the photon with the energy calculated in Eq. (8). Emission corresponds to a loss of energy, thus, the transition occurred from n = 3 to n = 2, i.e., the atom was excited prior to the transition (luminescence).

Problem 21.7

Calculate the wavelength of an electron in a hydrogen atom which is in the orbit with n = 3.

Solution: Note that the problem text does not refer to a transition. The question aims at the wavelength of a standing wave of the electron in the state $n = 3$, based on de Broglie's idea that an electron can be described by such a wave. The equation which connects the wave properties and particle properties of the electron is Eq. (21.4). In this equation, we need only the speed of the electron as all other terms are constants. The speed of an orbiting electron is discussed in Problem P–21.1. Note that the discussion in that problem was restricted to the ground state. Thus, we must revisit the equation we used to derive the result in P–21.1, i.e., the first line in Eq. (1). For $n > 1$, the quantum number n enters that formula, coming from Eq. (21.7) when substituting for the term mvr in Eq. (1):

$$\frac{e^2}{4\pi\epsilon_0 r^2} = m\frac{v^2}{r} = \frac{vn\hbar}{r^2}$$

$$\Rightarrow \quad v = \frac{e^2}{2\epsilon_0 nh} \tag{9}$$

We substitute v from Eq. (9) into Eq. (21.4):

$$\lambda = \frac{h}{mv} = \frac{2\epsilon_0 nh^2}{m_e e^2} =$$

$$\frac{2 \cdot 8.85\times10^{-12}\left[\frac{Cb^2}{Nm^2}\right] n \, (6.6\times10^{-34}[Js])^2}{9.1\times10^{-31}[kg]\,(1.6\times10^{-19}[Cb])^2} \tag{10}$$

which yields for $n = 3$: $\lambda = 9.9 \times 10^{-10}$ m $\cong$ 1 nm.

Problem 21.8
Identify the molecule for which Fig. 21.18 shows the linear combination of the atomic orbitals.

Solution: The easiest way to identify the molecule is to study the two atoms, shown at the left and right of Fig. 21.18. The atom at the left with a single electron is hydrogen. The atom at the right has 7 electrons in its outer shell with quantum number $n = 2$, i.e., 2 electrons in the 2s orbital and 5 electrons in the 2p orbital. We identify this atom by consulting the periodic system: fluorine has 7 electrons in the $n = 2$ orbitals, in addition to two electrons in the 1s orbital. Thus, the molecule shown in Fig. 21.18 is hydrofluoric acid, HF.

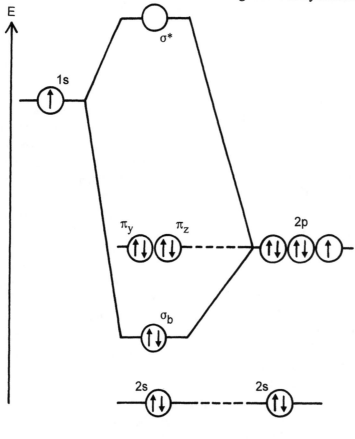

Fig. 21.18 for problem P–21.8

CHAPTER XXII

Radiation: X–rays and nuclear physics

Problem 22.1
Using the approach taken in Example 22.1, estimate the energy of K_α X–rays emitted from a gold anode.

Solution: Fig. 22.5 identifies the K_α transition as a transition of an electron from the orbital with n = 2 to a vacancy in the orbital with n = 1.

From the periodic system, we find that a gold atom has Z = 79. In the final state after the transition, one electron screens the interaction of the electron in the K–shell and the nucleus since the innermost shell is occupied by two electrons when full. The electron/nucleus interaction before the transition is also screened by one electron for the electron undergoing the transition from the L–shell. That screening electron is the single electron in the K–shell since the other electron in that shell has been kicked out to allow the X–ray causing transition. Using Eq. (21.30) we find for the initial and final state of the transition electron:

$$E_L = (Z - 1)^2 \, E_2 = 78^2 \, \frac{(-13.6[eV])}{2^2}$$

$$\Rightarrow \quad E_L = -20.69 \; keV \tag{1}$$

$$E_K = (Z - 1)^2 \, E_1 = 78^2 \, (-13.6[eV])$$

$$\Rightarrow \quad E_K = -82.74 \; keV$$

in which E_1 for the hydrogen atom is taken from Eq. (21.25) and E_2 is either taken also from Eq. (21.25) or is calculated from Eq. (21.21). For the transition we find: $\Delta E = E_{final} - E_{initial} = -62.05$ keV, which is a negative energy because that energy is lost by the system in form of an X–ray photon. Note that the minimum energy needed to kick the initial K–shell electron out of the atom is 82.74 keV, thus, an acceleration voltage of at least 82.74 kV is required. In the actual experiment a higher voltage must be used to obtain an appreciable number of X–rays since the exciting electron slows in the material of the anode.

Problem 22.2
The K–shell ionization energy of Cu is 8980 eV and the

L–shell ionization energy is 950 eV. Determine the wavelength of the K_α X–rays emission of Cu.

Solution: The K_α transition corresponds to a transfer of an electron from the L–shell to a vacancy in the K–shell. The associated energy of the transition is:

$$\Delta E = E_{final} - E_{initial} =$$
$$- 8980[eV] - (- 950[eV]) = - 8030 \; eV \tag{2}$$

which corresponds to $\Delta E = - 1.28 \times 10^{-15}$ J. This value is converted into a wavelength, using Planck's constant and the speed of light:

$$\lambda = \frac{c}{f} = \frac{hc}{|\Delta E|} = \frac{6.6 \times 10^{-34}[Js] \; 3 \times 10^8 \left[\frac{m}{s}\right]}{1.28 \times 10^{-15}[J]} \tag{3}$$

$$\Rightarrow \quad \lambda = 1.55 \times 10^{-10} \; m = 0.155 \; nm$$

Problem 22.3
The nucleus of the deuterium atom consists of one proton and one neutron. What is the binding energy of this nucleus if the mass of the deuterium nucleus is given as 2.014102 u?
Hint: 1 u = $1.6605677 \times 10^{-27}$ kg

Solution: Both the proton and neutron mass are given in Eq. (22.6) in unit [u]. The binding energy of the deuteron is provided by the difference between the deuteron nucleus mass and the combined mass of its constituents, i.e., one proton and one neutron:

$$\Delta m = m_D - m_{p^+} - m_{n^0} =$$
$$2.014102u - 1.007825u - 1.008665u \tag{4}$$

$$\Rightarrow \quad \Delta m = -2.388 \times 10^{-3} \; u$$

Using Einstein's formula, Eq. (22.7), we convert the loss of mass into an energy:

$$\Delta E = \Delta m \, c^2 =$$

$$2.388 \times 10^{-3} \, u \left(3 \times 10^8 \left[\frac{m}{s} \right] \right)^2 \qquad \textbf{(5)}$$

which yields:

$$\Delta E = 3.57 \times 10^{-13} \, J$$
$$\Delta E = 2.23 \; MeV \qquad \textbf{(6)}$$

Thus, we have established the mass to energy conversion $1 \, u = 931 \, MeV$. Comparison of the result in Eq. (6) with the result for the helium nucleus in Eq. (22.8) shows that the deuteron is much weaker bound than helium. Indeed, the largest binding energies (per nucleon) occur for the most stable nuclei which are located near iron in the periodic system.

Problem 22.4

A living organism has 16.1 ± 0.1 ^{14}C decays per minute and per gram carbon. The wood found in the Egyptian king Sneferu's grave measured 8.5 ± 0.2 decays/(min g). When was the tree cut from which this wood came?

Solution: We established Eq. (22.16) for the number of radioisotopes left in a sample after time t has elapsed. Using Eq. (22.15) for the activity, we note that the same time dependence applies to the rate of decay, or activity: since $N \propto |\Delta N/\Delta t|$, we find:

$$\left(\frac{\Delta N}{\Delta t} \right)_{t_{fin}} = \left(\frac{\Delta N}{\Delta t} \right)_{t=0} e^{-\lambda t_{fin}} =$$

$$\left(\frac{\Delta N}{\Delta t} \right)_{t=0} \exp \left\{ - \frac{ln2 \; t_{fin}}{T_{1/2}} \right\} \qquad \textbf{(7)}$$

in which we used Eq. (22.20) to replace the decay constant λ with the half–life.

For the present problem, the time elapsed since the wood was cut, t_{fin}, is the only unknown in Eq. (7). Isolating this time variable, we find:

$$t_{fin} = - \frac{T_{1/2}}{ln2} \; ln \left(\frac{(\Delta N/\Delta t)_{t_{fin}}}{(\Delta N/\Delta t)_{t=0}} \right) \qquad \textbf{(8)}$$

We substitute all given values in Eq. (8). The half–life

for ^{14}C is 5370 years. Thus:

$$t_{fin} = - \frac{5370[y]}{ln2} \; ln \left(\frac{8.5[min^{-1}g^{-1}]}{16.1[min^{-1}g^{-1}]} \right) \qquad \textbf{(9)}$$

$$\Rightarrow \quad t_{fin} = 4950 \; yrs$$

Before interpreting this result, a proper error analysis is required. This analysis consists of two parts: (i) the error margins for the natural decay rate and the decay rate in the ancient wood sample given in the problem text allow us to use mathematical error propagation methods to determine a statistical error on the calculated time. This calculation, accompanied by a general discussion of error propagation methods, is provided in the Appendix to the solution volume. It leads to:

$$\frac{\Delta t_{fin}}{t_{fin}} = 3.8 \; \% \quad \Rightarrow \quad \Delta t_{fin} = 190 \; yrs \quad \textbf{(10)}$$

(ii) We have also to take the systematic error, shown as a solid line in Fig. 22.14, into account. For a calculated time of about 5000 years, this correction is of the order of 150 to 200 years. The systematic error can be corrected for by using Fig. 22.14, the statistical error remains an error to be reported with the result: the wood for Sneferu's grave was cut in the year 2830 ± 200 BC (Assuming that the carbon–dating analysis was done in 1970).

In this case, we can use historical data to confirm our result. Sneferu (or Snofru) was a ruler during the IIIrd Dynasty. He was credited with conquering the Sinai peninsula. His rule has occurred some time between 3000 BC and 2750 BC.

Problem 22.5

Nuclear waste from power plants may contain ^{239}Pu, a plutonium isotope with a half–life of 24,000 years. How long does it take for the stored waste to decay to 10 % of its current activity level?

Solution: We use Eq. (22.20) to calculate the decay constant for the plutonium isotope:

$$\lambda = \frac{ln2}{T_{1/2}} = \frac{ln2}{24,000[y]} = 2.89 \times 10^{-5} \frac{1}{y} \quad \textbf{(11)}$$

Note that the result is given in unit [1/yrs]. Although it is always advisable to convert to SI units (here [1/s]), we find that this is not necessary for the current problem.

Next we apply Eq. (22.16) with $N(t) = 0.1\,N_0$, which corresponds to 10 % of the initial amount of radioactive plutonium:

$$0.1\,N_0 = N_0\,e^{-\lambda t}$$

$$\Rightarrow\quad t = -\frac{\ln(0.1)}{2.89 \times 10^{-5}\left[\dfrac{1}{y}\right]} = 79{,}700\ yrs \quad \textbf{(12)}$$

Just waiting isn't good enough when it comes to dealing with nuclear waste!

Problem 22.6

A small radioactive ^{210}Po source of 0.05 MBq is placed on a biological sample. This polonium isotope emits α–particles of 5.4 MeV. The range of the α–particles in the sample is 20 µm. What is the energy dose rate (per hour) absorbed by the biological sample?

Hint: Treat the source as a point source and use the density of water for the density of the sample.

Solution: We assume that the skin surface is perfectly flat. 50 % of the emitted α–particles will enter the skin, the other half is stopped in the air space above the skin without doing any damage.

The 50 % of alpha particles entering the skin affect a hemispherical volume. With the given value for the range of the α–particles, we quantify this volume:

$$V = \frac{1}{2}\frac{4}{3}\pi r^3 = \frac{2\pi}{3}(2 \times 10^{-5}[m])^3 \quad \textbf{(13)}$$

$$\Rightarrow\quad V = 1.7 \times 10^{-14}\ m^3$$

We have to convert the volume into an affected mass since all units used in dosimetry, such as [R] in Eq. (22.3), [Gy] in section 22.2 and [Sv] in section 22.5, are given per [kg]. Replacing the biological sample in the problem with water, we find for the exposed mass:

$$m = \rho V = 1000\left[\frac{kg}{m^3}\right]1.7 \times 10^{-14}[m^3] \quad \textbf{(14)}$$

$$\Rightarrow\quad m = 1.7 \times 10^{-11}\ kg$$

The energy dose rate is now determined in two steps. First, we determine the energy deposited per second in the sample, then we convert this value in an energy dose rate.

The energy deposited per second is equal to the number of α–particles entering the sample per second, multiplied by the energy each of these particles deposits when stopped. The number of particles entering the sample is ½ of the 0.05 MBq activity given in the problem text (the unit [Bq] is defined in section 22.4):

$$\frac{\Delta E}{\Delta t} = \frac{\Delta N}{\Delta t}E_\alpha =$$

$$2.5 \times 10^4\left[\frac{1}{s}\right]5.4 \times 10^6[eV]\,1.6 \times 10^{-19}\left[\frac{J}{eV}\right] \quad \textbf{(15)}$$

which equals 2.2×10^{-8} J/s.

The energy dose rate follows when the result in Eq. (15) is divided by the mass of the sample:

$$Ener.\ Dose\ rate = \frac{(\Delta E/\Delta t)}{m} =$$

$$\frac{2.2 \times 10^{-8}[J/s]}{1.7 \times 10^{-11}[kg]} = 1300\ \frac{Gy}{s} \quad \textbf{(16)}$$

This quantity is converted to unit [Gy/h] by multiplying with 3600 s/h. This leads to an energy dose rate per hour of 4.7×10^6 Gy/h.

Using a quality factor W_R of 10 for α–particles from Table 22.3, the value found in Eq. (16) corresponds to 4.7×10^7 Sv/h, which is a tremendous radiation exposure in comparison to the values listed in Table 22.4. Note, however, that the effects reported in Table 22.4 apply to whole body exposure, not a localized application as discussed in this problem. Nevertheless, this problem illustrates the great danger of open radioactive materials, a reason for the extreme measures of precaution in laboratories where such materials are handled.

Table 22.3: Quality factors W_R for the biological impact of radiation. These values are rough data, they are used in radiation protection.

Radiation type	W_R
X–ray and γ–radiation	1
β^+, β^-	1
n^0	5 – 10
α	10

Table 22.4: Medical impact of various whole body equivalent doses.

Equiv. Dose [Sv]	Pathological diagnosis
1 – 5	Serious temporary alterations of the blood count
4 – 5	50% death rate in 30 days
10 – 50	Vomiting and nausea
50 – 100	Brain and nerve damage, death in 1 week

Problem 22.7

A tracer study drug contains 11 kBq of a technetium isotope, ^{99}Tc, which has a half–life of 363 minutes. Technetium can be used as a substitute for ^{131}I in tracer studies of the thyroid gland. What is the activity of the drug when it is used after 3 hours?

Solution: We start with Eq. (7), which we derived in problem P–22.4 for the activity, $\Delta N/\Delta t$, measured in [Bq]. Substituting the values given in the problem text, with 3 h = 10,800 s and 363 min = 21,780 s, we find:

$$
\frac{\Delta N}{\Delta t} = \left(\frac{\Delta N}{\Delta t}\right)_0 \exp\left\{- \frac{ln2\ t}{T_{1/2}}\right\}
$$

$$
\frac{\Delta N}{\Delta t} = 1.1 \times 10^4 \left[\frac{1}{s}\right] \exp\left\{- \frac{ln2\ 10800[s]}{21780[s]}\right\} \tag{17}
$$

The activity after 3 hours results as $\Delta N/\Delta t = 7800$ Bq = 7.8 kBq.

CHAPTER XXIII

Magnetic resonance imaging: nuclear spin and magnetic resonance

There are no problems with this chapter.

CHAPTER XXIV

General Appendix

Problem 24.1
For the two solutions of a quadratic equation, Vieta showed:

$$(I) \quad x_1 + x_2 = -\frac{b}{a}$$

$$(II) \quad x_1 \cdot x_2 = \frac{c}{a}$$

(1)

in which we used the notations from Eq. (24.26). Show that both of Vieta's rules are correct.

Solution: If the quadratic equation is written in the form $ax^2 + bx + c = 0$, then there are a maximum of two real solutions x_1 and x_2 for which Eq. (24.26) applies:

$$x_{1,2} = \frac{-b \pm \sqrt{b^2 - 4ac}}{2a}$$

(2)

The two statements by Vieta are tested by substituting the two solutions from Eq. (2) into the two formulas in Eq. (1).

We begin with the first statement by Vieta, i.e., Formula (I) in Eq. (1):

$$x_1 + x_2 =$$

$$\frac{-b + \sqrt{b^2 - 4ac}}{2a} + \frac{-b - \sqrt{b^2 - 4ac}}{2a}$$

(3)

We combine the two terms on the right hand side of Eq. (3):

$$x_1 + x_2 = \frac{-b + \sqrt{b^2 - 4ac} + (-b) - \sqrt{b^2 - 4ac}}{2a}$$

$$\Rightarrow \quad x_1 + x_2 = \frac{-2b}{2a} = -\frac{b}{a}$$

(4)

Thus, the first statement by Vieta is correct.

For the second statement, the two solutions in Eq. (2) are multiplied with each other:

$$x_1 \cdot x_2 =$$

$$\left(\frac{-b + \sqrt{b^2 - 4ac}}{2a} \right) \left(\frac{-b - \sqrt{b^2 - 4ac}}{2a} \right)$$

(5)

We multiply on both sides with $4a^2$ and use standard algebraic methods to rewrite the brackets on the right hand side of Eq. (5):

$$4a^2 x_1 x_2 =$$

$$= \left(-b + \sqrt{b^2 - 4ac} \right) \left(-b - \sqrt{b^2 - 4ac} \right)$$

(6)

$$= b^2 - (b^2 - 4ac) = 4ac$$

Now, both sides are divided by $4a^2$:

$$x_1 x_2 = \frac{4ac}{4a^2} = \frac{c}{a}$$

(7)

This proves the second statement by Vieta.

Problem 24.2
(a) Plot in double–logarithmic representation the two functions (I) $y = 4x^2$ and (II) $y = 4x^2 + 1$ in the interval $0.1 \leq x \leq 10.0$.
(b) What draw–back of double–logarithmic plots can you identify?

Solution part (a): The plot is shown in Fig. 24.19.

Solution part (b): Double–logarithmic plots may be misleading when the function $y = f(x)$ is a sum. If the function is a sum of only two terms, as given in the current example, then one term dominates the double–logarithmic plot for large values of x and the other term dominates the plot for small values of x. At intermediate values the double–logarithmic plot is curved. You see this in Fig. 24.19. For x values in the range $4x^2 \gg 1$ (i.e., the first term in the sum is much larger than the second

165

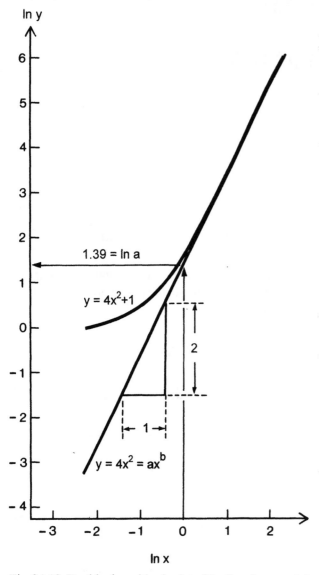

Fig. 24.19: Double–logarithmic plot of the functions $y = 4x^2$ and $y = 4x^2 + 1$ in the abscissa interval $-3 \le \ln x \le +3$.

(c) show that the slope of the logarithmic plot is 3, and
(d) show that the intercept of the logarithmic plot is $\ln 2$.

Solution parts (a) and (b): The linear plot is shown in Fig. 24.20(a) and the logarithmic plot is shown in Fig. 24.20(b).

Solution part (c): The logarithmic plot allows us to identify the constants in a straight forward manner. The prefactor 3 of the exponent in the function is found as the slope in Fig. 24.20(b): the ordinate value jumps from 0.693 to 3.693 when passing through the interval 0 to 1 along the abscissa.

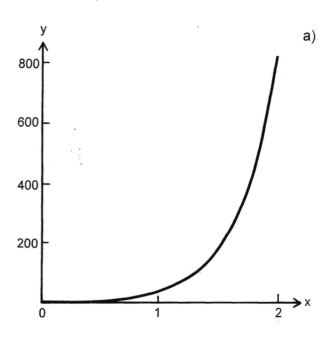

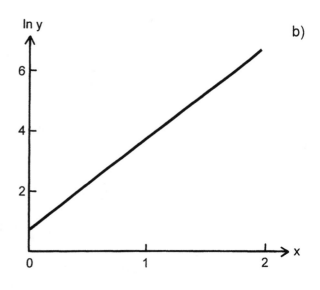

Fig. 24.20: For the function $y = 2e^{3x}$, (a) y versus x for $0 \le x \le 2$, and (b) $\ln y$ versus x for $0 \le x \le 2$.

term in the sum), the double–logarithmic plot is the same for both functions. This is the case for $x \ge 4$ (or $\ln x \ge 1$). In turn, the curve for $y = 4x^2 + 1$ levels out for $x < 0.1$ (or $\ln x < -2$), i.e., below that threshold the second term in the sum, const = 1, dominates.

In general, be careful when you find indeed a straight segment in a double–logarithmic plot. Be suspicious about this being an indication that a power law holds if the range of x–values does not stretch over several orders of magnitude!

Problem 24.3
For the function $y = 2e^{3x}$
(a) plot y versus x for $0 \le x \le 2$,
(b) plot $\ln y$ versus x for $0 \le x \le 2$,

166

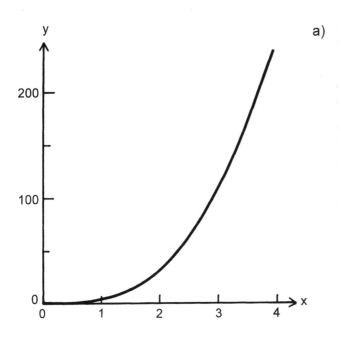

a)

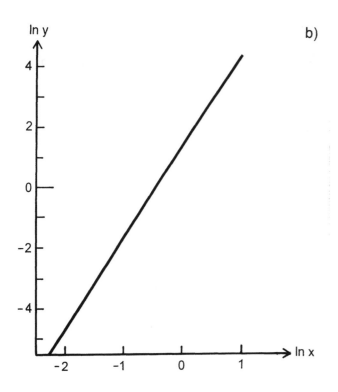

b)

Fig. 24.21: For the function $y = 4x^3$, (a) y versus x for $0 \leq x \leq 4$, and (b) lny versus lnx for $0 \leq x \leq 4$.

Solution part (d): The intercept at x = 0 in the logarithmic plot is the logarithm of the prefactor of the function, i.e., 2. Note that ln2 = 0.693.

Problem 24.4

For the function $y = 4x^3$
(a) plot y versus x for $0 \leq x \leq 4$,
(b) plot lny versus lnx for $0 \leq x \leq 4$,
(c) show that the slope of the double–logarithmic plot is 3, and
(d) show that the intercept of the double–logarithmic plot is ln 4.

Solution parts (a) and (b): The linear plot is shown in Fig. 24.21(a) and the double–logarithmic plot is shown in Fig. 24.21(b).

Solution part (c): The slope in the double–logarithmic plot represents the exponent of the function, in the current problem with a value of 3. To quantify this from the plot, any data pair can be used. Such pairs are shown in Table 24.11.

Table 24.11.

Set	ln(x)	ln(y)
#1	0.0 (x = 1.0)	1.386
#2	0.693 (x = 2.0)	3.466

The difference between the two lnx values is 0.693 and the difference between the two lny values is 2.08; the ratio 2.08/0.693 = 3.0, as expected.

Solution part (d): The intercept is read off the graph for lnx = 0, i.e., x = 1. At that value we find lny = 1.386 (see Table 24.11), which corresponds to y = 4.0.

Problem 24.5

We develop an empirical formula connecting the wing span and the mass of some species able to fly. Then we evaluate a few interesting consequences. (The first to make these considerations was Leonardo da Vinci).
(a) Use the data in Table 24.10 to draw a double–logarithmic plot lnW versus lnM where W is the wing span and M is the mass. Determine the constants a and b in a power–law relation $W = a\,M^b$.
(b) The largest animal believed ever to fly was a pterosaur species found in Texas and named Quetzalcoatlus northropi. This animal lived in the late Cretaceous 138 to 65 million years ago. It had an 11 m wing span. What is the maximum mass of this pterosaur? Note: the largest wing span of a living species is 3.6 m for the Wandering Albatross.
(c) Assume that man wishes to fly like a bird. What minimum wing span would be needed for a person of 70 kg to take off?

167

Table 24.10: Mass and wing span of various birds.

Bird	Wing span [cm]	Mass [g]
Hummingbird	7	10
Sparrow	15	50
Dove	50	400
Andean Condor	320	11500
Californian Condor	290	12000

Table 24.12: Extended data from Table 24.10.

Bird	Wing span W [cm]	lnW	Mass M [g]	lnM
Hum.	7	1.95	10	2.30
Sp.	15	2.71	50	3.91
Dove	50	3.91	400	5.99
A.C.	320	5.77	11500	9.35
C.C.	290	5.67	12000	9.39

Solution part (a): The resulting double–logarithmic plot is shown in Fig. 24.22. An organized approach to plotting these data is based on extending Table 24.10 to include the logarithm values of wing span and mass, as shown in Table 24.12.

Using these logarithmic data, the given power law $W = a M^b$, which is an application of Eq. (24.32) is rewritten in the form $\ln W = b \ln M + \ln a$, in analogy to Eq. (24.33). The constants a and b are determined from this equation in the manner described in the General Appendix. For the analysis we do not choose data pairs from Table 24.12. As the graph in Fig. 24.22 illustrates, single data points deviate from the line that best fits the data (represented by the solid line). So that the deviation of single data entries does not affect our results, the two data pairs used in the analysis are obtained from the solid line in the graph in Fig. 24.22. We choose $\ln W_1 = 2$ with $\ln M_1 = 2.6$ and $\ln W_2 = 6$ with $\ln M_2 = 9.6$. This leads to:

(I)	$2 = b\,2.6 + \ln a$
(II)	$6 = b\,9.6 + \ln a$

(I) – (II)	$4 = b\,(9.6 - 2.6)$

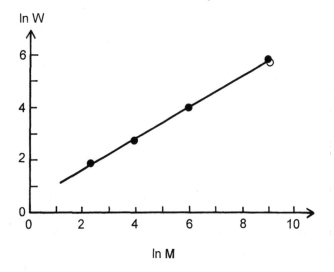

Fig. 24.22: Double–logarithmic plot of the mass and the wing span of various birds.

Thus, b = 0.57. Due to the fluctuations of the original data and the systematic errors you commit when reading data off a given plot, values in the interval $0.5 \le b \le 0.6$ may have been obtained. This variability in the results of independent data analyses is one way to determine the range of possible values for b acceptable when comparing with a model. A more convenient approach is based on a proper error analysis, which is discussed in the Appendix of the current Solutions chapter.

Substituting the value we found for b in Eq. (I) yields: $2 = 1.48 + \ln a$, i.e., $\ln a = 0.52$ which corresponds to a value of $a = 1.7$.

Solution part (b): We use the given value for the pterosaurs' wing span: W = 11 m = 1100 cm. The value has been converted to unit [cm] since that is the unit used when we developed our formula in (a). Entering this wing span in the power law relation leads to:

$$W = a M^b \quad \Rightarrow \quad M = \left(\frac{W}{a} \right)^{1/b}$$

(8)

$$M = \left(\frac{1100}{1.7} \right)^{1/0.57} = 85{,}400 \ g$$

The mass of pterosaurs did not exceed 85 kg.

Solution part (c): We use again the power law relation we found in part (a):

$$W = a M^b$$

$$\Rightarrow \quad W = 1.7 \cdot 70000^{0.57} = 580 \ cm$$

(9)

A person of mass 70 kg would need a 5.8 m wing span. Even if you allow for artificial wings of this length attached to your arms, trying to flap them wouldn't impress any of our feathered friends. For an account of their likely thoughts see Disney's "Sword in the Stone" and the comments by Archimedes (an intelligent owl) therein.

Problem 24.6
(a) What is the sum of the two vectors $\mathbf{a} = (5, 5)$ and $\mathbf{b} = (-14, 5)$?
(b) What are the magnitude and direction of $\mathbf{a} + \mathbf{b}$?
(c) What is the angle between $\mathbf{a}$ and $\mathbf{b}$?

Solution part (a): We define the vector sum as $\mathbf{r}$, that means $\mathbf{r} = \mathbf{a} + \mathbf{b}$, or, in component notation,

$$r_x = a_x + b_x = 5 + (-14) = -9$$
$$r_y = a_y + b_y = 5 + 5 = 10 \qquad (10)$$

Thus, $\mathbf{r} = (-9, 10)$. This vector is shown in Fig. 24.23.

Solution part (b): The magnitude of vector $\mathbf{r}$ is calculated from Eq. (24.36):

$$|r| = \sqrt{r_x^2 + r_y^2} = \sqrt{(-9)^2 + 10^2} = 13.5 \quad (11)$$

To fully characterize the vector $\mathbf{r}$ in polar coordinates, its angle with the positive x–axis must also be determined. This can be done geometrically, as can be seen from Fig. 24.23:

$$\tan\theta = \frac{r_y}{r_x} = -1.11 \quad \Rightarrow \quad \theta = 132^0 \quad (12)$$

Note: Your pocket calculator may show $\theta = -48^0$.

Solution part (c): The angle ϕ between two vectors is obtained from the dot product, Eq. (24.39):

$$\mathbf{a} \cdot \mathbf{b} = |a| \cdot |b| \cdot \cos\phi \qquad (13)$$

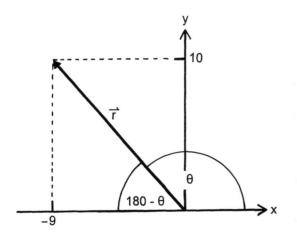

Fig. 24.23: Vector $\mathbf{r}$ shown in polar coordinates.

In Eq. (13), we determine separately the term on the left hand side and the two magnitudes on the right hand side. For the dot product, we write:

$$\mathbf{a} \cdot \mathbf{b} = a_x b_x + a_y b_y =$$
$$5 \cdot -14 + 5 \cdot 5 = -70 + 25 = -45 \qquad (14)$$

and for the magnitudes of $\mathbf{a}$ and $\mathbf{b}$:

$$|a| = \sqrt{5^2 + 5^2} = 7.1$$
$$|b| = \sqrt{(-14)^2 + 5^2} = 14.9 \qquad (15)$$

Substituting Eqs. (14) and (15) in Eq. (13), we find:

$$\cos\phi = \frac{-45}{7.1 \cdot 14.9} = -0.425$$
$$\Rightarrow \quad \phi = 115.2^0 \qquad (16)$$

Problem 24.7
If vector $\mathbf{a}$ is added to vector $\mathbf{b}$, the result is the vector $\mathbf{c} = (6, 2)$. If $\mathbf{b}$ is subtracted from $\mathbf{a}$, the result is the vector $\mathbf{d} = (-5, 8)$.
(a) What is the magnitude of vector $\mathbf{a}$?
(b) What is the magnitude of vector $\mathbf{b}$?
(c) What is the angle between $\mathbf{a}$ and $\mathbf{b}$?

Solution parts (a, b): Two equations are required:

$$(a) \quad \mathbf{a} + \mathbf{b} = \begin{pmatrix} 6 \\ 2 \end{pmatrix}$$
$$(b) \quad \mathbf{a} - \mathbf{b} = \begin{pmatrix} -5 \\ 8 \end{pmatrix} \qquad (17)$$

or, written in component form:

$$(I) \quad a_x + b_x = 6$$
$$(II) \quad a_y + b_y = 2$$
$$(III) \quad a_x - b_x = -5 \qquad (18)$$
$$(IV) \quad a_y - b_y = 8$$

Adding Eqs. (17a) and (17b), or the first and third as

well as second and fourth line of Eq. (18), leads to vector **a**:

$$2\,\boldsymbol{a} = \begin{pmatrix} 1 \\ 10 \end{pmatrix}$$

(19)

$$\Rightarrow \quad |\boldsymbol{a}| = \sqrt{0.5^2 + 5^2} = 5.0$$

Subtracting Eq. (17b) from Eq. (17a), or subtracting the third from the first and the fourth from the second line in Eq. (18), gives **b**:

$$2\,\boldsymbol{b} = \begin{pmatrix} 11 \\ -6 \end{pmatrix}$$

(20)

$$\Rightarrow \quad |\boldsymbol{b}| = \sqrt{5.5^2 + (-3)^2} = 6.3$$

Solution part (c): The angle ϕ is obtained from the dot product (Eq. 24.39):

$$\boldsymbol{a} \bullet \boldsymbol{b} = a_x b_x + a_y b_y = 0.5 \cdot 5.5 + 5.0 \cdot (-3)$$

$$= 2.75 - 15 = -12.25$$

(21)

which yields:

$$\cos\phi = \frac{-12.25}{5.03 \cdot 6.26} = -0.389$$

(22)

$$\Rightarrow \quad \phi = 112.9^0$$

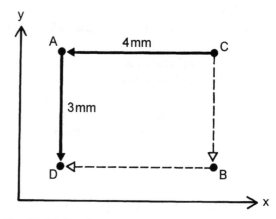

Fig. 24.24: In–plane components of the fracture of the femur.

Problem 24.8

Fig. 24.15(a) shows a shear fracture of the neck of the femur. In a shear fracture opposite fracture faces have slid past each other. Fig. 24.15(b) shows a sketch of a fracture with the net displacement AB along the fracture plane.

(a) What is the net displacement AB for a horizontal slip of 4.0 mm and a vertical slip of 3.0 mm?

(b) If the fracture plane is tilted by $\theta = 20^0$ to the plane perpendicular to the bone, by how much have the two bones moved relative to each other along the bone's axis?

Solution part (a): Fig. 24.24 shows the relative position of points A and B _in_ the fracture plane. For convenience, this plane has been chosen as the xy–plane. With this choice of coordinate system, the horizontal slip is along the x–axis, where the point A on the bone has moved to position C. The vertical slip, along the vertical y–axis,

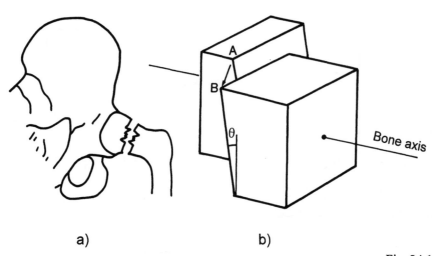

a)

b)

Fig. 24.15 for problem P–24.8.

moves the point on the bone from C to point B. To put it another way, point A slips to point B, and the horizontal slip is the x–component of the vector **AB** and the vertical component is the y–component of **AB**. Thus, the displacement from A to B can be written in vector notation:

$$\mathbf{AB} = \mathbf{AC} + \mathbf{CB} = \begin{pmatrix} -4 \\ 0 \end{pmatrix} + \begin{pmatrix} 0 \\ -3 \end{pmatrix} \quad \textbf{(23)}$$

$$|\mathbf{AB}| = \sqrt{4^2 + 3^2}\ [mm] = 5\ mm$$

The total displacement within the fracture plane is 5 mm.

Solution part (b): Of the two components of displacement considered in part (a) the horizontal displacement **AC** does not contribute to a displacement along the axis of the bone. Fig. 24.25 shows how the component of the vertical displacement of part (a), i.e., **CB**, which is equi-

valent to the displacement **AD**, relates to the displacement along the bone's axis. In Fig. 24.25 the displacement from point A to point E is the displacement along the bone's axis (and the displacement from point E to point D is the displacement perpendicular to the bone's axis). The angle of θ = 20⁰ given in the problem is the angle between the vectors **AE** and **AD**. We can calculate the length of **AE** using trigonometry:

$$|\mathbf{AE}| = |\mathbf{AD}|\ \cos 20^0 = 3[mm]\ \cos 20^0$$
$$\Rightarrow \quad |\mathbf{AE}| = 2.8\ mm \quad \textbf{(24)}$$

The displacement along the bone's axis is 2.8 mm.

In an analogous fashion it can be shown that the displacement perpendicular to the axis of the bone, i.e. the magnitude of the vector **ED**, is 1.0 mm. This is the displacement sought in the problem text.

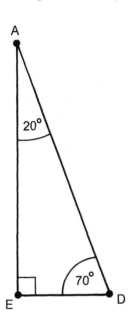

Fig. 24.25: Tilt of the plane of fracture of the femur relative to the bone.

Problem 24.9
Fig. 24.16 shows a back view of an adult male and female human body (accompanied by two children).
(a) For a typical male, the vertical distance from the bottom of the feet to the neck is d_1 = 150 cm and the distance from the neck to the hand is d_2 = 80 cm. Find the vector describing the position of the hand relative to the bottom of the feet if the angle at which the arm is held is θ = 35⁰ to the vertical.
(b) Repeat the calculation for a typical female with d_1 = 130 cm, d_2 = 65 cm and the same angle θ.

Solution part (a): We choose the origin at the bottom of the feet of the person, the x–axis horizontally toward the right and the y–axis vertically upwards. In this coordinate system we express the two vectors shown in Fig. 24.16: $\mathbf{d}_{m1}$ and $\mathbf{d}_{m2}$. Based on the given lengths (magnitudes) and the given angle we find:

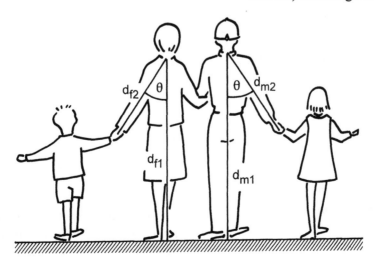

Fig. 24.16 for problem P–24.9.

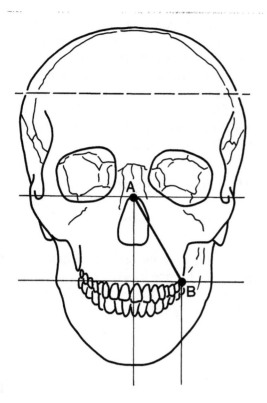
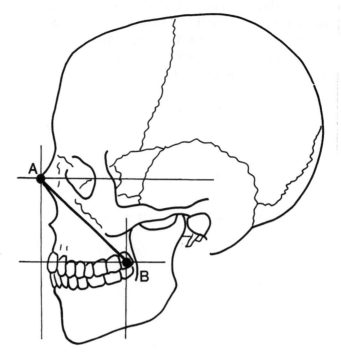

Fig. 24.17 for problem P–24.10.

$$d_{m1} = \begin{pmatrix} 0 \\ |d_{1m}| \end{pmatrix} = \begin{pmatrix} 0 \\ 150 \ [cm] \end{pmatrix}$$

$$d_{m2} = \begin{pmatrix} |d_{m2}| \ \sin\theta \\ -|d_{m2}| \ \cos\theta \end{pmatrix} = \begin{pmatrix} 45.9 \ [cm] \\ -65.5 \ [cm] \end{pmatrix}$$

(25)

Note the negative sign in the y–component of the second vector! The vector from the bottom of the feet to the hand is the sum of the two vectors in Eq. (25):

$$d_m = d_{m1} + d_{m2} = \begin{pmatrix} 45.9 \ cm \\ 84.5 \ cm \end{pmatrix}$$

(26)

Solution part (b): The calculations are analogous for the female:

$$d_{f1} = \begin{pmatrix} 0 \\ |d_{f1}| \end{pmatrix} = \begin{pmatrix} 0 \\ 130 \ [cm] \end{pmatrix}$$

$$d_{f2} = \begin{pmatrix} -|d_{f2}| \ \sin\theta \\ -|d_{f2}| \ \cos\theta \end{pmatrix} = \begin{pmatrix} -37.3 \ [cm] \\ -53.2 \ [cm] \end{pmatrix}$$

(27)

Note that both components of the second vector are ne-

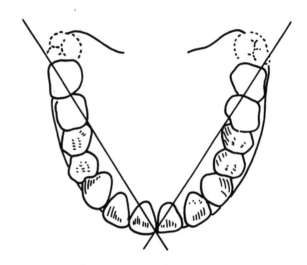

Fig. 24.18 for problem P–24.10.

gative in this case since the arm is held toward the person's left side. The resulting vector from the bottom of the feet to the hand is the sum of the two vectors in Eq. (27):

$$d_f = d_{f1} + d_{f2} = \begin{pmatrix} -37.3 \ cm \\ 76.8 \ cm \end{pmatrix}$$

(28)

Problem 24.10
Fig. 24.17 shows (top) a front view and (bottom) a side view of a human skull. Two perpendicular projections such as these are often used to determine distances and

angles in three–dimensional bodies, e.g. for focussed radiation therapy with high energy beams.

(a) Assuming that the diameter of the skull at the dashed line shown with the top skull in Fig. 24.17 is 16 cm, determine the distance from the tip of the nasal bone (point A) to the center of the last molar in the upper jaw (point B).

(b) Determine the angle between two lines connecting the point halfway between the two central maxilla incisor teeth and the last maxilla molars on either side.

(c) Compare the result in (b) with the result obtained from Fig. 24.18, which shows a top view of the permanent dentition.

Solution part (a): The distance between the two intersections of the dashed line with the skull in the top sketch measures 54 mm. This provides us with a scale for Fig. 24.17 because the problem states that the dashed line measures 16 cm for a real skull. Before analyzing the figure a coordinate system must be chosen. This is shown in Fig. 24.26 with the direction upwards chosen to be the z–direction for both sketches, the direction to the observer's right in the top sketch the x–direction and the direction towards the back of the skull in the bottom sketch the y–direction. For convenience we choose the point A to coincide with the origin of the coordinate system: A = (0,0,0).

We use the skull in the top sketch to obtain the length of the xz–projection of vector **AB** and then we use the skull in the bottom sketch to obtain the length of the yz–projection of the same vector. The vector sum of both projections yields the actual vector from A to B in the last step.

In the top sketch of Fig. 24.17 we measure for the horizontal component of the distance between A and B 12.0 mm and for the vertical component of the same distance 20.7 mm. The projection of the vector between

A and B in the top sketch is given by $\mathbf{AB_{xz}}$ = (3.56 cm, 0, − 6.13 cm) where we used the scale conversion as found at the beginning of the solution. The index "xz" identifies that this is not the final vector **AB** but only its projection into the xz–plane. The z–component is negative since the point B lies at a negative z–value.

Now we repeat the same analysis for the bottom sketch of Fig. 24.17. We measure for the horizontal component of the distance between A and B 21.9 mm and for the vertical component of the same distance again 20.7 mm. The projection of the vector **AB** in the bottom sketch is given by $\mathbf{AB_{yz}}$ = (0, 6.49 cm, − 6.13 cm) with the scale conversion taken into account. Note that it is not a coincidence that we find the same length for the vertical direction in both plots since it is physically the same distance. As long as your two measurements of that length vary within the margin of error for reading data off your ruler, it is fine. Otherwise, this is a built–in self–control and you should go back and check your measurements once more.

From the two projections we now find the vector **AB** and its length:

$$\mathbf{AB} = (3.56\ [cm],\ 6.49\ [cm],\ -6.13\ [cm])$$

$$|\mathbf{AB}| = \sqrt{3.56^2 + 6.49^2 + (-6.13)^2} \qquad \textbf{(29)}$$

$$|\mathbf{AB}| = 9.6\ cm$$

Solution part (b): For convenience we assume that the skull is left–right symmetric, i.e., we have only to determine the position of one of the two last maxilla molars. That point coincides with point B in Fig. 24.17. Let us define the point between the two central maxilla incisor teeth as point C. Using the same approach as in part (a) and measuring on the top sketch a horizontal distance of 12.5 mm, a vertical distance of 2.0 mm and, on the bottom sketch, a depth displacement of 20 mm we find for the vector **CB** = (3.70 cm, 0.60 cm, 5.93 cm). Due to the

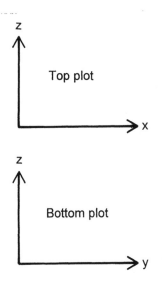

Fig. 24.26: Coordinate system used to analyze Fig. 24.17.

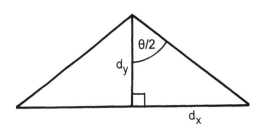

Fig. 24.27: Sketch of the vectors locating the last maxilla molars.

symmetry the vector to the other last maxilla molar (called point B') is $\mathbf{CB'} = (-3.70 \text{ cm}, 0.60 \text{ cm}, 5.93 \text{ cm})$. The angle between these two vectors follows from Eq. (24.39):

$$\cos\phi = \frac{\mathbf{CB} \cdot \mathbf{CB'}}{|\mathbf{CB}| \cdot |\mathbf{CB'}|} = \frac{\mathbf{CB} \cdot \mathbf{CB'}}{|\mathbf{CB}|^2} =$$

$$= \frac{(3.7, 0.6, 5.93) \cdot (-3.7, 0.6, 5.93)}{3.7^2 + 0.6^2 + 5.93^2} = \quad (30)$$

$$= \frac{-13.69 + 0.36 + 35.16}{13.69 + 0.36 + 35.16} = 0.44$$

Thus, we find $\phi \approx 64^0$.

Solution part (c): There are two ways to confirm this angle using Fig. 24.18. Either you read the angle between the two straight line segments off the figure directly using a protractor, or you use a ruler and Fig. 24.27. The figure shows how the distance between the two last maxilla molars, which is given as $|\mathbf{BB'}| = 2\,d_x$, and the distance from that line to point C, d_y, are related to the angle θ we seek. Measuring the distance between the centers of the two last molars as $d_x = 42.5$ mm and measuring the distance perpendicular as $d_y = 31.5$ mm we find:

$$\tan\left(\frac{\theta}{2}\right) = \frac{d_x}{d_y} = \frac{\frac{1}{2}\,42.5[mm]}{31.5[mm]} = 0.675$$

$$\Rightarrow \quad \theta = 68^0 \qquad (31)$$

This value agrees with $\phi = 64^0$ within the precision of the analysis. The skull in Fig. 24.17 and the top view of the dentition in Fig. 24.18 are obtained from different sources, thus, minor anatomic differences may contribute to the variation of value (systematic error).

Note that we did not convert the measurements in part (c) using a scale for Fig. 24.17. This is due to the fact that obtaining angles is based on the division of lengths, like in Eq. (31), where such a scale factor cancel anyway.

Appendix: Error propagation calculation

In your future work, you will often encounter cases where you need to draw quantitative conclusions from experimental data. Since all experimental data are subject to uncertainty, any values you calculate from experimental data carry a margin of error. For example, when you want to calculate the area of a given square, you measure the length of a side of the square, l, then calculate the area as $A = l^2$. But how precise is your value for A if you judge your measurement of the side length to carry an error Δl? The answer follows from a mathematical calculation of the error on A, ΔA, as a function of the error on l, Δl. This calculation is called an error propagation calculation since, literally, the measurement error propagates through your calculation of A.

Error propagation calculations are more general then the case discussed above. Not only can any functional dependence between l and A be considered, but also cases where A depends on more than one variable with an uncertainty. An example is the area of a rectangle with side lengths a and b. In this case, the area is $A = ab$. Assume that both measurements of the side lengths carry an error, e.g., $a \pm \Delta a$ and $b \pm \Delta b$. In this case an error propagation calculation will allow us to express the error on the calculated area, ΔA as a function of the errors Δa and Δb.

The mathematical foundation of such an error propagation calculation is briefly presented here. Let us assume that z is the quantity of interest and depends on two directly measured variables, x and y in the form $z = f(x,y)$. x and y, are measured with a known margin of error, $x \pm \Delta x$ and $y \pm \Delta y$. Then the error of z is given by:

$$\Delta z = \sqrt{\left(\frac{\delta z}{\delta x}\right)^2 \Delta x^2 + \left(\frac{\delta z}{\delta y}\right)^2 \Delta y^2} \qquad (32)$$

In Eq. (32) $\delta z/\delta x$ is the partial derivative. Partial derivatives are a calculus concept not discussed further in this textbook. For typical applications it is sufficient to replace the partial derivative with the regular derivative but then we apply the operation only to any explicitly shown dependence of z on the respective variable. If you do not want to use calculus methods, just look at the examples below as these represent the most common cases.

We consider four examples illustrating how to use Eq. (32) first, then review the solution of problem P–22.4 to confirm the error estimate provided in the previous chapter.

174

Example 1

What is the error of $z = x + y$ if Δx is the error of x and Δy is the error of y?

Solution: We find $\delta z/\delta x = \delta z/\delta y = 1$, and thus, the error of z is given by:

$$\Delta z = \sqrt{\Delta x^2 + \Delta y^2} \qquad (33)$$

i.e., the absolute errors, Δx and Δy, are added quadratically.

Example 2

What is the error of the product $z = xy$ if Δx is the error of x and Δy is the error of y?

Solution: We find $\delta z/\delta x = y$ and $\delta z/\delta y = x$, and thus, the error of z is given by:

$$\Delta z = \sqrt{y^2 \Delta x^2 + x^2 \Delta y^2}$$

$$\frac{\Delta z}{z} = \sqrt{\left(\frac{\Delta x}{x}\right)^2 + \left(\frac{\Delta y}{y}\right)^2} \qquad (34)$$

i.e., the relative errors, $\Delta x/x$ and $\Delta y/y$, have to be added quadratically.

Example 3

What is the error of $z = x/y$ if Δx is the error of x and Δy is the error of y?

Solution: We find $\delta z/\delta x = 1/y$ and $\delta z/\delta y = -x/y^2$, and thus, the error of z is given by:

$$\Delta z = \sqrt{\left(\frac{1}{y}\right)^2 \Delta x^2 + \left(-\frac{x}{y^2}\right)^2 \Delta y^2}$$

$$\frac{\Delta z}{z} = \sqrt{\left(\frac{\Delta x}{x}\right)^2 + \left(\frac{\Delta y}{y}\right)^2} \qquad (35)$$

i.e., multiplication and division of two quantities leads to the same error formula.

Example 4

What is the error of $z = (x/y)^2$ if Δx is the error of x and Δy is the error of y?

Solution: We find $\delta z/\delta x = 2x/y^2$ and $\delta z/\delta y = -2x^2/y^3$, and thus, the error of z is given by:

$$\Delta z = \sqrt{\left(\frac{2x}{y^2}\right)^2 \Delta x^2 + \left(-\frac{2x^2}{y^3}\right)^2 \Delta y^2}$$

$$\frac{\Delta z}{z} = 2\sqrt{\left(\frac{\Delta x}{x}\right)^2 + \left(\frac{\Delta y}{y}\right)^2} \qquad (36)$$

i.e., the square exponent leads to a prefactor of 2.

Now we return to the question of the age of the wood found in king Sneferu's grave (problem P–22.4). We found the mathematical formula used to calculate the age of the sample in the solution equation Eq. (21.20). Assuming that the half–life carries no error (which in reality it does), we want to find the error of the calculated time, Δt_{fin}, as a function of the errors given in the problem text. To keep the notations from becoming confusing, we introduce the notation $\hat{A}$ for the activity, i.e., $\hat{A} = (\Delta N/\Delta t)_{tfin}$, and the notation $\hat{A}_0 = (\Delta N/\Delta t)_{t=0}$. Thus, Eq. (21.20) reads:

$$t_{fin} = -k \ln\frac{\hat{A}}{\hat{A}_0}$$

$$\text{with:} \quad k = \frac{T_{1/2}}{\ln 2} \qquad (37)$$

Both $\hat{A}$ and $\hat{A}_0$ carry error margins, which we label $\Delta\hat{A}$ and $\Delta\hat{A}_0$. To find the error margin on the calculated time, we apply Eq. (32) which reads specifically:

$$\Delta t_{fin} = \sqrt{\left(\frac{\delta t_{fin}}{\delta\hat{A}}\right)^2 \Delta\hat{A}^2 + \left(\frac{\delta t_{fin}}{\delta\hat{A}_0}\right)^2 \Delta\hat{A}_0^2} \qquad (38)$$

We calculate the two partial derivatives in the brackets on the right hand side of Eq. (38) first. Using Eq. (37) we find:

$$\frac{\delta t_{fin}}{\delta \hat{A}} = -\frac{k}{\hat{A}}$$

$$\frac{\delta t_{fin}}{\delta \hat{A}_0} = -k\left(-\frac{1}{\hat{A}_0}\right) = \frac{k}{\hat{A}_0} \qquad \textbf{(39)}$$

(Here we used the chain rule to find the derivative of the ln–function). Substituting Eq. (39) into Eq. (38), we obtain:

$$\Delta t_{fin} = k\sqrt{\left(\frac{\Delta \hat{A}}{\hat{A}}\right)^2 + \left(\frac{\Delta \hat{A}_0}{\hat{A}_0}\right)^2} \qquad \textbf{(40)}$$

We could substitute all values in Eq. (40), or, which is often useful as a method to judge whether a result makes much sense in the first place, calculate the relative error, i.e., $\Delta t_{fin}/t_{fin}$. This is done by dividing Eq. (40) by Eq. (37):

$$\frac{\Delta t_{fin}}{t_{fin}} = \frac{-1}{\ln\left(\frac{\hat{A}}{\hat{A}_0}\right)}\sqrt{\left(\frac{\Delta \hat{A}}{\hat{A}}\right)^2 + \left(\frac{\Delta \hat{A}_0}{\hat{A}_0}\right)^2} \qquad \textbf{(41)}$$

With the values given in the problem text we find for the wood sample discussed in problem P–22.4:

$$\frac{\Delta t_{fin}}{t_{fin}} = \frac{-1}{\ln\left(\frac{8.5}{16.1}\right)}\sqrt{\left(\frac{0.2}{8.5}\right)^2 + \left(\frac{0.1}{16.1}\right)^2}$$

$$\qquad \qquad \qquad \qquad \qquad \qquad \textbf{(42)}$$

$$\Rightarrow \quad \frac{\Delta t_{fin}}{t_{fin}} = 0.038$$

which is the result given in the solution equation Eq. (21.22).